DISCARD

THE OVERT HOMOSEXUAL

THE OVERT HOMOSEXUAL

charles w. socarides, m.d.

GRUNE & STRATTON

New York and London

Library of Congress Catalog Card No. 68–20807

R C
558
S64

Copyright © 1968
Grune & Stratton, Inc.
381 Park Avenue South
New York, New York

Grateful acknowledgment is made to the following
sources for permission to use material contained herein:
Sigmund Freud Copyrights Ltd., Mrs. Alix Strachey,
The Institute of Psycho-Analysis, The Hogarth Press
Ltd., The Psychoanalytic Study of the Child, International Universities Press, International Journal of
Psycho-Analysis, the Journal of the American Psychoanalytic Association. Appropriate bibliographic
reference is to be found in the text.

Printed in the U.S.A.
PC-B

for

Richard Charles

and

Daphne Diane

1199-67

CONTENTS

Section One: Background

Section Two: Theory

Section Three: Clinical

Section Four: Therapy

Section One

BACKGROUND

Chapter I

INTRODUCTION

UNDOUBTEDLY THIS BOOK evolved from the beginning of my training in psychoanalysis. Homosexuality had still to be comprehended and in those days it was unusual for clinics to accept homosexual patients. They were "too difficult" and the prognosis too uncertain. Little information was offered the neophyte by his teachers, many practitioners being unwilling to take on homosexual patients for psychoanalysis because it was generally believed unrewarding to treat someone who was "satisfied" with his illness, albeit a perversion.

If little were known about the male homosexual even less was known about the female. Several senior analysts informed me that they had seen only one or two female homosexual patients in their entire practice and then for only short periods of time. Except for the works of Helene Deutsch, Marjorie Brierley and Ernest Jones (the latter two in England), some case reports by Sandor Lorand and other scattered data in the literature, the presentation of detailed material was meager. There were only two monographs in the psychoanalytic literature on homosexuality, one in German, the other in French. The first was by Hanns Sachs, "On the Genesis of Sexual Perversions" (1923); the other, "Homosexual Fixations in Neurotic Women" (1929), by Raymond de Saussure. These two have recently been translated into English as arranged for by this author.[160,164]

I felt handicapped by the lack of information and the absence of detailed clinical case histories. The scattered bits and fragments of psychoanalytic data I could track down were not sufficiently organized to become a meaningful part of my training. How could it be that a widespread emotional disorder of such striking dimension—a symptom picture which involved such a radical change in human relationship—had not undergone the most rigorous psychoanalytic investigation on a systematized basis?

My own first few homosexual patients seemed to respond well to the psychoanalytic method and I resolved to begin the collection and compilation of all available scientific findings on the subject of male and female homosexuality.

3

In 1958, at my suggestion, the American Psychoanalytic Association conducted its first panel on the clinical and therapeutic aspects of overt male homosexuality, for which I was appointed reporter. This report was published in 1959; the research activities and deliberations connected with it were surpassed only by those required for a companion panel on the overt female homosexual two years later. The conferences whetted my eagerness to pursue the answers to the problem of homosexuality—its origins, manifestations and treatment methods.

In the beginning, as a young analyst, I had become fully cognizant of the formal literature on homosexuality and was perplexed by the uncertainties of causation, treatment and outcome. As my experience deepened and my private practice expanded I began to focus on all aspects of this problem, as well as others in the realm of sexual development and its vicissitudes, informed now by very close scrutiny of and contact with a number of patients. More and more I began to observe recurrent patterns in homosexuality, however apparently different from each other the individual patient's family background, personal endowment and clinical picture were. Certain features became consistently evident and I began to formulate an etiology, developmental theory and treatment techniques which proved effective in alleviating the major difficulties these patients suffered as a result of their sexual deviation. There is no question that at the present time we have sufficient evidence as a profession to demonstrate that homosexuality can be cured or at least, in most cases, its symptoms and suffering greatly alleviated by medical psychoanalysis.

This book, a comprehensive and unified medical work, is not only a compendium of the accumulated psychoanalytic knowledge on the problem as well as a presentation of the author's clinical experience and observations but also presents a definitive theory as to the origin of homosexuality, the mechanisms involved in its development and the procedures most efficacious for its treatment.

Homosexuality has been mislabeled and incorrectly diagnosed as impulse neurosis, psychopathic personality, a form of addiction, a psychosis, a neurosis, a "transitional neurosis." In essence we have been confronted by a condition which baffled clinical investigators in their effort to determine its etiology. Of all the symptoms of emotional origin which serve simultaneously as defenses, homosexuality is unique in its capacity to produce for limited intervals a utilization of profound psychic conflicts and struggles for the purpose of attaining a pseudo-adequate equilibrium and pleasure reward (orgasm), permitting an individual to function however marginally and erratically.

Psychoanalysis found that patients who experience nothing but pain and suffering from their condition are motivated to change. The doctors themselves have been hampered by the lack of a comprehensive work on the background, medical and therapeutic aspects of homosexuality as they cannot search far and wide over the psychoanalytic literature for pertinent and proven points of theory, clinical management and therapy. Persuasion techniques, milieu therapy and drug prescription for the elimination of a symptom so deeply embedded in the psyche cannot possibly alter it; neither can it be successfully treated by suggestion and supportive measures. Since homosexuality is not organic in etiology, hormonal therapy and forms of surgical treatment are obviously contraindicated and would only make the situation worse.

The neutralization of conflict allows for the growth of certain ego-adaptive elements of the personality and so the homosexual may have appeared not ill at all to others except for the masquerade in his sexual life. As a physician and as an individual sharing in the welfare and distress of mankind and as a specialist in behavioral disorders, it is my hope that with publication of this book others will embark on studies of homosexuality, examine these findings and their own, treat their patients always keeping in mind the element of possible discovery, confer with colleagues and amass their own material so that this disturbance can be fully understood and ultimately prevented.

Somewhat over 100 years ago, in 1844, the forerunner of the American Psychiatric Association, then known as the Association for Medical Superintendents of American Institutions for the Insane, was created. It undertook to explore nervous and mental disease on the basic premise that these were medical illnesses with a causation, clinical picture, and probable therapy which could be learned and taught by properly trained physicians. The prejudices, uncertainties, misinformation, claims of vested interests, which beset and cloud over homosexuality are similar to the problems once facing the first practitioners of psychiatry in this country and elsewhere.

The homosexual often asks if there is not some kind of genetic or hormonal factor, innate or inborn, which accounts for his condition. Homosexuality, the choice of an object of the same sex for orgastic satisfaction, is not innate. There is no connection between sexual instinct and the choice of sexual object. Such an object choice is learned, acquired behavior; there is no inevitable genetic or hormonal inborn propensity toward the choice of a partner of either the same or opposite sex. However, the *male-female design* is taught and exemplified to the child from birth and culturally ingrained through the marital order. This design is anatomically determined as it derives from cells which in the evolutionary scale underwent changes into organ systems and finally into individuals reciprocally adapted to each other. This is the evolutionary development of man. The male-female design is perpetually maintained and only overwhelming fear can disturb or divert it.

Homosexuals often express doubt about whether their condition can ever be reversed. The homosexual who attempts to extricate himself from a community of homosexuals is tagged a "traitor," one who threatens to invalidate their claims of having been born that way and that they are "special." There is also a strong defensive attitude that they may appear abnormal in insisting on continuance of their homosexual relationships. It is not uncommon for homosexuals to warn any individual attempting treatment that any change could at best prove only superficial.

A homosexual himself reported:

"I've got to get this homosexual monkey off my back. I just frankly can't live with it. I must either extinguish it, if I can, or maybe by religion to extinguish all sex. And the other thing is to be dead. To have anonymous sex with other sick men, I can't make a life out of that. . . . The homosexuals I know think I'm copping out, and if it's not hereditary they feel at least that it's impossible to change. They say to me 'Once homosexuality is established you can't get out or if you do try to get out you'll go nuts.' They tell you that you will be isolated and they keep telling you you're a traitor trying to leave the group, turning against your own kind, that you're trying to do something and be something that you're not. They say you're self-indulgent and selfish, feeding your ego in a very selfish kind of way in that you're enjoying your neurosis in trying to get well. . . . Homosexuals are destructive people, even in the actual sex act. In homosexuality there's only progressive moral, emotional and physical deterioration."

The widespread nature of homosexuality is due to the necessity for all human beings to undergo the separation-individuation phase of early childhood which is decisive for gender identification as elucidated in this volume. A significant proportion fail to successfully complete this developmental process and therefore to form a healthy sexual identity in accordance with their anatomical and biological capacities.

While this author cannot minimize the hard work and resoluteness which are required of the physician to treat this serious illness and the courage and endurance required of the patient both, in time, may find the challenge and fulfillment are equal in measure.

This is an excerpt from a follow-up interview with a former patient who told me that he now feels completely well as, in fact, he is. His marriage is congenial and in all other areas of life he is functioning well.

"My analysis has also showed me another thing, that is, the value of life. What I am going to do with my life, I'd like to tell people I'm well, that is, the people themselves. I get cured. How can that help anyone else who is homosexual? I hope other homosexuals will realize that they have a chance."

But do homosexuals want "another chance"? I believe that even in those who consciously disavow any such wish and who adamantly defend the nature of their relationship there exists a deep unconscious desire to alter what early environment has so cruelly forced upon them.

For what is the nature of the relationship of homosexuals to each other? Oraison in *Illusions and Anxiety*[155] writes that homosexual passion is the greatest of illusions. In heterosexuality there is an initial passion which perhaps may be very egocentric but often gives way "to a crisis that may well lead to the progressive discovery of a truly objective and sufficiently oblative relation." Homosexual relations do not allow this because homosexual "love" is based on the acute narcissism which is totally enclosed upon oneself. The initial passion may "create an illusion for a certain time but the crisis that follows is fruitless. The other is seen to be both other and identical."

Separation between homosexuals is demeaning and aggressive, more than between heterosexuals. "A pair of homosexuals can sometimes succeed in living together in lasting fashion but in it is a kind of association that is founded more or less consciously on the fear of solitude in which each leads his own sexual life with the radical and unresolvable instability of an infantile emotional state, in an atmosphere of petty quarreling, compromises and sterility that is barely tolerable."

Homosexual circles or clubs consist of a "regrouping of outcasts." Homosexuality means an element of embarrassment and of aggressiveness toward normal human society. There is always a narcissistic element present and a more or less conscious and more or less super-compensated element of inferiority-anxiety.

Although extremely difficult the homosexual person should attempt to try to lead as completely rewarding a social life as possible by developing to the maximum all his extra-sexual capacities for relationships to others. This would tend to compensate him to some degree for the narcissistic inferiority that colors his life beneath whatever rationalizations and facade he tries to project for his homosexuality. His condition is a painful one. It affects not only his feelings of self but his whole concept of the outside world, his feelings of physical integrity and the sensitive roots of his emotionality.

The "solution" of homosexuality is always doomed to failure and even when used for utilitarian purposes, e.g., prestige, power, protection by a more powerful male, the accomplishment is short-lived. Homosexuality is based on the fear of the mother, the aggressive attack against the father, and is filled with aggression, destruction, and self-deceit. It is a masquerade of life in which certain psychic energies are neutralized and held in a somewhat quiescent state. However, the unconscious manifestations of hate, destructiveness, incest and fear are always threatening to break through. Instead of union, cooperation, solace, stimulation, enrichment, healthy challenge and fulfillment, there are only destruction, mutual defeat, exploitation of the partner and the self, oral-sadistic incorporation, aggressive onslaughts, attempts to alleviate anxiety and a pseudo-solution to the aggressive and libidinal urges which dominate and torment the individual.

Chapter II

THE LITERATURE OF HOMOSEXUALITY

HOMOSEXUALITY has most seriously concerned the behavioral scientist in his quest to understand and remedy mankind's most agonizing problems. The etiology and psychodynamics hitherto proposed have often proved misleading, unfounded and contradictory. Fortunately, at times, they have emphasized or shed light on one facet of this multi-dimensional disorder but the phenomenon of homosexuality, in all its complexity, has continued to elude explanation through the use of any one theoretical formulation.

In 1896, Krafft-Ebing[134,135,136] suggested that homosexuality is an inborn characteristic due to large amounts of male and/or female substances in the hereditary composition of the brain. Mantegazza,[148] in 1914, explained homosexuality as a genital malformation caused by the fact that sensory nerves, normally originating in the penis, are displaced to the rectum and the erogenous zone is shifted correspondingly. Hirschfeld[112,113,114] stated that "Homosexuality is always an inborn state, conditioned by specific homosexual constitution of the brain." In 1940, Glass et al.[97] cited hormonal or endocrine factors. Contemporary scientific findings clearly establish that homosexuals can have endocrine dysfunctions just as can any other individuals but the androgen-estrogen ratio among male homosexuals usually falls within normal limits. Large doses of androgens or estrogens influence the overall sexual drive in homosexuals but cannot change the pattern.

Havelock Ellis[41,42] agreed with Krafft-Ebing's fallacy as regards the hereditary composition of male or female substances in the brain. Kallman's studies[123] on the genetic predetermination of homosexuality in identical twins show "concordance as to the overt *practices* of homosexual behavior after adolescence."

However, these statistical studies must always be viewed with considerable caution. The behavior may be due to the temperamental similarity of identical twins and their reacting similarly to environmental influences. More revealing would be studies made on identical twins who have been separated at birth and brought up in divergent environments. Kallman, himself, in the same paper, stated that the

9

"project was extremely difficult. . . . It is fair to admit that the question of the possible significance of a genetic mechanism in the development of overt homosexuality may still be regarded as entirely unsettled." As was definitively set forth by Freud, there is no relationship between sexual drive and sexual object choice.

Ford and Beach[55] have pointed out that the choice of sexual object is determined by learned experience. They prove that even in sub-human creatures psychological experience can determine the subsequent pattern: "Inexperienced males who suffer injury or are badly frightened during the first contact with a receptive female may never develop normal sexual aggression.":

In 1934, Henry[108,109,110,111] studied 250 adult patients grouped according to the predominance of heterosexual or homosexual tendencies. He concluded that: (1) The sexual histories in the heterosexual and homosexual groups are conspicuously different. All patients in the heterosexual group were married and had from one to seven children. Only 25 per cent of the homosexual patients were married; none of them had made a satisfactory heterosexual adjustment. Three-fourths of the marriages were dissolved by separation, divorce or annulment. (2) Prolonged intense emotional reactions to parents and sexual traumata were rare in the sexually adjusted while frequently noted in the early lives of homosexual individuals. Henry felt that when personality disorders occur, heterosexuals tend to develop benign psychoses while homosexuals are prone to have chronic paranoiac and schizophrenic illnesses. (3) Homosexual patients were found to have considerably greater constitutional deviations on a general average than the heterosexually adjusted. (4) A homosexual female has been characterized by a firm adipose tissue, deficient fat at the shoulders and at the girdle, firm muscles, excess hair on the chest, back and lower extremities, a tendency to masculine distribution of the pubic hair and a small uterus and over- or underdevelopment of the labia and clitoris. There is also a tendency toward a shorter trunk, a contracted pelvis, underdevelopment of the breasts, excessive hair on the face, and a low-pitched voice. (5) In general, it seems that the homosexual tends to have a dysplastic constitution in an arrested sexual development at the physiological level of integration. In addition to the incomplete development of other primary and secondary sex characteristics, the reproductive capacity of the pelvic structure remains underdeveloped. This is indicated by the relatively narrow hips in the male (boyish form) and a tendency to a contracted pelvis in the female.

A. Ellis[40] studied 48 cases of hermaphroditism from the medical literature and it was shown that in the great majority of these the hermaphrodite assumes a heterosexual libido and sex role that accords primarily not with his or her internal and external somatic characteristics but rather with his or her masculine or feminine up-bringing. This applied to both pseudo-hermaphrodites and true hermaphrodites. The author concluded that heterosexuality or homosexuality in hermaphrodites is caused primarily by environmental rather than hormonal or physiological factors. Since, however, the hermaphrodite's environment conspicuously includes the somatic anomalies, it is also concluded that the problem of "normal" and "abnormal" sexual behavior among hermaphrodites is importantly a psychosomatic one as is true of the problem of psychosexuality in normal human beings.

It can readily be seen from this review of the literature that homosexuality has undergone investigation of the most infinite variety. The issue appears to stand or fall on the following: "If a person of the opposite sex is available, why should a male choose another male or a female another female . . . or even, sometimes, a lock of hair or a piece of underclothing?"[63] The answer is to be found in the developmental history of the individual.

While Freud's contributions will be dealt with comprehensively elsewhere, certain brief references must be made in the context of this chapter. Sixty years ago he summarized the etiology of homosexuality thus: "The nature of inversion is explained neither by the hypothesis that it is innate nor by the alternative hypothesis that it is acquired. In the former case, we must ask in what respect it is innate, unless we are to accept the crude explanation that everyone is born with a sexual instinct attached to a particular sexual object. In the latter case it may be questioned whether the various accidental influences would be sufficient to explain the acquisition of inversion without the cooperation of something in the subject himself. The existence of this last factor is not to be denied."[63]

Freud felt that ". . . it has been brought to our notice that we have been in the habit of regarding the connection between the sexual instinct and the sexual object as more intimate than it in fact is. Experience with the cases that are considered abnormal has shown us that in them the sexual instinct and the sexual object are merely soldered together . . . a fact which we have been in danger of overlooking in consequence of the uniformity of the normal picture where the object appears to form part and parcel of the instinct. We have thus wanted to loosen the bond that exists in our thoughts between instinct and object. It seems probable that the sexual instinct is in the first instance independent of its object; nor is its origin likely to be due to its object's attraction."[63]

Having introduced the idea of the importance of infantile experience, Freud stated that the libido which at first was polymorphous perverse undergoes development and integration and passes through a "homosexual phase" before reaching the heterosexual level. Therefore, in homosexuals, the libido is fixed on the individual himself because of a congenital predisposition to fixation at that point as a result of psychic trauma which prevents the person from proceeding to heterosexual relationships.[63]

He wrote that the etiology of homosexuality was intimately tied up with constitution. This was due to his belief that the theory of constitutional bisexuality was a valid one. Although embryological observation shows that sexual differentiation proceeds from an identical anlage in the developing foetus, the essential genital organs have homologues in each sex, i.e., penis and clitoris develop from the same embryonic structure, also uterus and uterus-masculina, a tiny cul-de-sac in the male urethra. This theory of bisexuality has received criticism as well as approval from various sources over the years. The theory itself came from Wilhelm Fliess: "The dominant sex of the person, that which is the more strongly developed, has repressed the mental representation of the subordinated sex in the unconscious. Therefore, the nucleus of the unconscious is, in each human being, that side of him which belongs to the opposite sex."[91]

Freud changed Fliess's view to some extent but retained the concept of bisexuality and wrote of the constitution which included a "homosexual component." In each person, he felt, there is a homosexual component which must be successfully repressed or handled to avoid conflict. This idea has been subjected to intense attack on the misleading grounds that the presence of a homosexual component in everyone would negate the concept of pathogenic psychodynamic factors in the causation of homosexuality. Nothing could be further from the truth. All of us inherit the constitutional strength of our sexual instinct. This is what Freud meant by the "constitutional factor."

The principal argument over the years against the psychogenic explanation of homosexuality often centers about the fact that many individuals exposed to a particular set of pressures become homosexual while others in similar circumstances do not. Actually, the important determinant in causation is that the sexual object may have a purely symbolic significance acquired at an extremely early age, usually during the period of the first three or four years of life.

The concept of bisexuality was generally agreed upon although not really understood. Jones stated that although "The assumption of inborn bisexuality seems to me a very probable one, in favor of which many biological facts can be quoted . . . we should not take it for granted."[117]

Bisexuality has erroneously been interpreted to mean the genetic (*inborn*) characteristic of attraction to persons of both sexes, e.g., one is alternately attracted to someone of the same or opposite sex. This was not Freud's meaning at all. He did not believe that any specific genetic (chromosomal) factor was capable of directing the sexual drive into overt homosexuality. He always felt that there were a number of factors which determined sexual integration; of these the psychodynamic ones were the most important. The constitutional factors determine only the strength of the drive.

Gershman's paper[93] provides an example of the type of indecision which grew out of a misunderstood theoretical formulation. He felt that the causation of overt homosexuality was entirely unsettled and that the likelihood was that the genetic mechanism played the more significant role.

Fenichel[47] wrote that everyone is able to develop "sexual feelings indiscriminately and the search for an object is less limited by the sex of the object than is commonly supposed . . . the fact that in a normal person the object choice later becomes more or less limited to the opposite sex is a problem in itself . . . since the homosexual, like any other human being, originally has the capacity to choose objects of either sex, but limits his capacity to objects of his own sex. . . . Analysis of homosexual men regularly shows that they feared female genitals . . . the female genitals, through the connection of castration anxiety with all anxieties, they perceive as the castrating instrument capable of biting or tearing off their penis."

But how does homosexuality come about? In an article by Sherman and Sherman[165] the attachment of the girl for the father is held to account for the development of homosexuality in the female. Jung[122] pointed out that "It frequently happens (in male homosexuality) that at the time of their first love remarkable difficulties develop in the capacity for erotic expression, which may be reduced analytically to disturbances through an aggressive attempt at resuscitation of the father image." In female homosexuality the type of sexual object that alone has the property of invigorating the female sexual functions is so highly specialized by parental attachment that no adequate image or substitute can be had; the individual tends to suffer from the horrors of incest. Passive homosexuality is usually the result of such conditioning.

Ferenczi[50] divided male homosexuals into passive homosexuals or inverts and object-homoerotics; the latter remain masculine in their behavior and merely pursue another man as though he were a female. Thus, he differed from the observation that a reversal of roles can be more the rule than the exception. While he classifies homosexuals into active and passive types, female homosexuals very often are classified either as masculine or feminine. The active male homosexual is defined as one who in sexual relationships with another male takes the active role toward making his partner adopt the female position in intercourse or to submit to, rather than perform, sodomy or other acts. The active physical role is usually accompanied by the social, emotional and psychic activities of seeking, courting and dominating. The same may be said for female homosexuals. The active male and the passive female are frequently of fairly normal physical constitution. The passive male and the active female homosexual are much more likely to show contra-sexual traits of physique and mind and be irreversibly and solely homo-sexually inclined.

Fenichel maintained that "homosexual love is mixed with char-acteristics of identification and it is generally agreed that there is an element of identification with the object in all homosexual love." Homosexuality has proved to be the product of specific mechanisms of *defense* which facilitate the persistence of the repression of both the oedipus and castration complex; at the same time the aim of homo-sexual object choice is the avoidance of emotions around the castration complex which otherwise would disturb the sexual pleasure or at least the attainment of real assurance against them. Another important factor is that a homosexual will reject a part of his personality and that part is externalized onto someone else and becomes a sexual object. What the homosexual is seeking in someone else is an image of himself.[47] Therefore the results are complementariness in the relationship. These views were expounded by Anna Freud in considerable detail in the early 1950's.[59]

The idea that homosexuality is really a disguised form of psychosis has not been borne out. Homosexuality has occurred during psychotic episodes in a large number of people although previously there had been no indication of its presence. In many others, however, homo-sexuality occurs without psychosis or disappears during a psychosis.

As early as 1926, Boehm[21] established the importance of guilt feelings arising from hostility to the father as the genesis of homosexuality.

The Melanie Klein[130] school holds that homosexuality is fundamentally concerned with the earliest phases of libidinal development. The chief factors, therefore, in the production of homosexuality are anxieties around the oral and anal phases. These anxieties produce insatiable need which binds the libido to oral and anal forms. Such binding leads to profound disturbances of the genital function. One of course must not overlook the fact that positive contributions can be made from the oral phase to genital feelings.

One's happy experiences at the breast exert a favorable influence in promoting genitality. Only where there is undue oral stimulation and frustration does the organism undergo an intense fixation to the oral phase and produce an undue degree of fear because of the rejection of its oral hunger. The object relationship of the last or genital phase becomes filled with a pattern acquired at the oral zone including the unconscious fantasies and feelings of desire and fear. In many men this may be interpreted, for example, as a fear of being devoured by the vagina. This is probably the most important factor responsible for psychosexual impotence in men. Similar unconscious fantasies may be responsible for fear of the penis and for frigidity in women and likewise for the development of homosexuality. In the Kleinian theoretical framework there is an emphasis on the preoedipal and oral cannibalistic fantasies as the basic psychological factors in the development of homosexuality. The oedipus complex is a later development and the emotional patterns elaborated in object relationships during this period enter into the defenses against both heterosexuality and homosexuality. However, the emotional nature and intensity of the oedipus fantasies are determined by the earlier repressed oral fantasies with their anxieties in the unconscious.

Sachs's paper[160] clearly demonstrates that we are not dealing simply with a fixation of a component drive of sexuality as the dictum about neurosis being the negative of a perversion would let us assume. Sachs's theory will be taken up in greater detail elsewhere as it directly pertains to the author's concept of the psychodynamics and therapy of homosexuality.

Alexander,[3] in 1930, considered perversions in terms of partial failures of defense, a disturbance of the process of desexualization of intinctual energy, acceptance of aggressive impulses by the ego and their expression in relation to the sexual object. The cannibalistic wish to bite off the partner's penis as an attempt to incorporate the penis as well as the partner in order to regain an endangered masculinity, an identification with the male being impossible due to the destructive impulses, was a formulation of Nunberg's[153] in 1938. The anal-sadistic impulses in homosexuality can be equated with stool = penis = baby = money. Sadger[161] had earlier stated that the impulse to eat the father's testicles was the motivating force in homosexuality.

It was Bibring's conclusion[17] that the homosexual tries to regain his endangered or lost masculinity by an oral attack on the partner's penis in order to acquire it.

Premature activation of libidinal zones may produce a precocious but particularly vulnerable development according to Greenacre.[103] Excessive stimulation results in premature erotization long before the phallic phase. Traumatic stimulation in the first year or two of life increases narcissism and bisexual identification. She thereby emphasized the neurogenic-psychogenic aspects of homosexuality. Despite the intense interest in the anus in most homosexual activity Loewenstein[141] described, in 1935, a type of passive homosexuality which is expressed exclusively in the form of genital gratification in which no anal wish seems to be present.

The role of parental sanctioning of the homosexual was highlighted by Litton, Giffin and Johnson,[140] the mother's behavior being overseductive and frustrating, at the same time sanctioning the boy's homosexuality. In addition the parents' own unstable bisexual identification as well as their defective superego contribute to the development of homosexuality.

Bychowski[30] delineated features of the ego in the homosexual including such primitive defense mechanisms as splitting, introjection, denial, turning against the self, narcissistic withdrawal, and considered them of paramount importance in the genesis of homosexuality. The ego is weakened in these cases because of the necessity of maintaining various identifications which have become not only unconscious but dissociated from each other, therefore allowing less of the libido to be available for object cathexis. Sudden releases of undifferentiated aggressive-libidinal impulses lead to brief attempts at establishing contact with objects because the poorly structured ego of the homosexual does not succeed in binding the instinctual energies of the primary process.

It was E. Weiss's assertion[170,177,178] that most perversions center around the oedipus complex. Childhood misunderstandings and misinterpretations of the anatomy, functions and the role of the other sex, distorted attitudes toward family members, guilts and fears concerning the father's and mother's sexual activity and one's own are inevitable. While the ultimate choice of a sexual partner of the same sex may be due to a number of factors, one has always to bear in mind that every individual is to a certain extent constitutionally bisexual. To Weiss, homosexuality has a different connotation from the usual. He does not mean that there is an *innate object choice* of the same or opposite sex. He means that without elements within oneself of the opposite sex well integrated, rapport based on understanding of the heterosexual love partner is impossible. In a majority of individuals the homosexual trends are sublimated, that is, *desexualized*, but individuals in whom the bisexual constitution is over-accentuated often fail to sublimate this component sufficiently. The reflexive form of narcissms finds satisfaction by "proxy" where it cannot be directly gratified. In other words, *one loves onself in another person of the same sex in homosexuality* (my italics). This is a form of "love choice" according to the narcissistic type. In a strong bisexual constitution, homosexuality may be an outlet or an escape from a severe oedipal conflict. A girl may withdraw from oedipal competition with her mother through masculine identification. Homosexuality reveals more complex mechanisms, however. By projecting his femininity onto the loved woman the heterosexual man can thus vicariously enjoy his own femininity. Weiss adds that the male does not become the female; he simply enjoys the female's functioning in the loved woman, the loved object outside of himself. These comments are a significant contribution to understanding the love relationship between adult heterosexual pairs.

Bergler estimated[10,11,12,13,15,16] that female homosexuality is nearly double that of male homosexuality.[126] Many female homosexuals live the lives of married women because they are driven to find social and economic security, permitting heterosexual intercourse without pleasure to themselves. He believed that female homosexuality was a pathological elaboration of the unsolved masochistic attachment to the pre-oedipal mother. So far as the congruity with male homosexuality exists there are in both male and female homosexuals identical childhood fears and the same defense measures. However, in the female it is primarily her preoedipal unsolved oral masochistic conflict with the mother which is involved. Therefore, in Bergler's opinion, the basic conflict in the female is not of a libidinal but of an aggressive content. Beneath female homosexuality lies a savage, defensive hatred for the mother which is warded off by a libidinous defense of denying hate and superimposing a feeling of love toward a woman expressed sexually. This defense is unconscious and these patients have great difficulty in admitting the aggression beneath their "love" for their woman partners. The female homosexual attempts to repeat the baby-mother relationship with occasional reversal of roles.

In male homosexual relationships, according to Bergler, the male is not aware that what he is repeating is an oedipal and incestuous tie with his mother. For example, he does not have the slightest conception that he is substituting the penis of his partner for the breast of his mother.

A classification system based on the theoretical and clinical material espoused in this book will be found in Chapter X. Several historically important investigations of typology began in 1905, when Freud[63] designated three categorizations.

(1) Absolute inverts, whose sexual objects are exclusively of their own sex and who are incapable of carrying out the sexual act with a person of the opposite sex or derive any enjoyment from it.

(2) In amphigenic inverts the sexual object may equally well be one of their own or of the opposite sex since this kind of inversion lacks the characteristic of exclusiveness.

(3) In contingent inverts inaccessibility of the normal sexual object may lead to their taking as their sexual object someone of their own sex and deriving satisfaction from sexual intercourse.

Ferenczi[49] essayed classification in 1920 with division of homosexuality into active and passive types. Homosexual behavior was classified by Nunberg[153] on the basis of the expression and/or fate of the aggressive impulses, feeling that homosexuality represents a compromise between aggressive and libidinal impulses. In the 1960's, Anna Freud classified homosexuality depending upon the underlying unconscious fantasy.

The classification by Rado[158] bears a striking similarity to Freud's earlier formulations; he divided homosexuality into situational, variational and reparative types. Reparative homosexuality is "ushered in by the inhibition of standard performance through early fear"; it arises from processes of repair which are in the main unconscious and is marked by a high degree of inflexibility. The individual depends on homosexuality for full orgastic gratification in all circumstances. Though he may force himself to go through the motions of heterosexuality (the union of male and female genitals leading to sexual orgastic satisfaction and/or performance) he cannot thereby obtain satisfaction.

Situational homosexuality occurs where the lack of opportunity for heterosexual contact may push a healthy individual to seek homosexual orgastic outlet. This may occur in institutions which enforce segregation such as prison communities. The homosexuality practiced in ancient Greece was in all probability situational in type. Its motivation consisted of the social, economic, cultural and prestige advantages which accrued to the young boys who attached themselves to a powerful patron. The motivation of the latter could have been any of the three types here described. Such expedient acts "are the products of conscious deliberation rather than of an unconscious process and as a rule are dropped as soon as the situation changes."

Variational patterns may occur in the individual who yields to the desire for an alteration of sexual excitation. In some cultures such surplus activity was a part of the established social order, e.g., ancient Greece; in others, entirely an individual departure contrary to the social order.

Reparative homosexuality initiated by early unconscious fears and characterized, by inflexibility and sterotypy is the only type that can be considered true (obligatory) homosexuality.

In 1951, Karl Menninger[150] felt that all formulations as to the genesis of male homosexuality were too general and failed to elucidate the different kinds of homosexuality one encounters clinically. He found it inconceivable that any one simplified formula could apply in all instances and maintained that aggressive hostile feelings toward the homosexual partner play a much more important role than indicated in the literature.

The difference between the pervert and neurotic, according to the American Psychoanalytic Association's 1951 panel on perversions,[4] does not lie in the fact that one approves and the other rejects the component instinct. Difference resides, rather, in the different attitude of the ego toward the *result* of the defensive conflict and the defensive transformations and masking of the component impulse. Therefore, one must not be content with certain formulations such as: (1) the pathogenesis of perversions depends upon the fact that persons react to sexual frustration with regression toward infantile sexuality; (2) homosexuality is the result of castration anxiety related to the oedipal period alone; (3) fixation at a pregenital sexual level without including subsequent vicissitudes of development is the total etiology; (4) frustration and regression to previous levels of fixation are the entire explanation; were this so one could, by therapeutic techniques, simply by-pass the systematic sexual development in infancy and concentrate mainly on the cause and effects of such frustration. The classical theory which explains perversions as caused by early accidental fixating experiences including seductions followed by a traumatic oedipal period characterized by excessive anxiety, although important, according to the Panel, requires careful clinical validation in each case.

Freud's early theory that perversions were simply a breakthrough of id impulses unopposed by the ego or the superego has been clinically disproven. The introduction of the topographic approach[79,80,81] into psychoanalysis made it possible to clarify the fact that not only the instinctual drives but the defenses against them as well are unconscious. Numerous analysts[4] observed that what appeared to be gratification of a perverse instinctual drive actually constituted the end product of a defensive compromise in which elements of inhibition as well as gratification were present. The approval by the patient of a perverted action, however, is not equivalent to approval of the component instinct which is warded off in neurosis. In a perversion the component instinct must undergo extensive transformation and disguise in order to be gratified in the perverse action. This masking is conditioned by the defense of the homosexual's ego which resists the gratification of the component instinct as energetically as does the ego of a neurotic. Thus the perverted action, like the neurotic symptom, results from the conflicts between the ego and the id and represents a compromise formation which at the same time must be acceptable to the demands of the superego. In perversion, as in neurotic symptoms, the instinctual gratification takes place in a *disguised form* while its real content remains unconscious. Furthermore the perverted action differs from the neurotic symptom by the form of gratification of the impulse: orgasm.

Bergler's[11,13,14,15,16] contribution emphasized that the homosexual solution consists of a specific elaboration of psychic masochistic vicissitudes stemming from the first months of life. During these earliest phases the aggression of the child recoils because of guilt and this guilt is secondarily libidinized. The masochism is further disguised and repressed through the illusion of aggression ("pseudo-aggression"). The dynamically decisive masochistic substructure does not become conscious except by analysis. Homosexuality is a "way out" for one's imperious needs for masochistic suffering. He pointed out that the oral-masochistic, rather than a sadistic hate-filled, basis of female homosexuality works on a multi-layered structure.

The psychodynamic motivations of each variety of homosexual perversion in the female were examined by Benedek.[9] She found after prolonged physiological and psychological studies that correlations of psychodynamic constellations with bodily and hormonal indicators of the sexual aberrrations are lacking. In some cases—but not in all and not in simple relation to the severity of the perversion—certain aspects of body build, hair growth, gait and gesture revealed that homosexuality is deeply ingrained, not only in the emotional but also in the physical make-up. All attempts to discover and identify an endocrine imbalance for the purpose of proving that a reverse androgen-estrogen ratio is the basis of female homosexuality failed, since hormonal variations are great in all individuals. Hormone therapy to treat homosexuality failed due to the fact that the resultant increased hormonal tension required discharge in a homosexual way.

Female homosexuality has a strong connection with an aggressive conflict. This aggression boomerangs because of guilt and is secondarily libidinized. Under the guise of a husband-wife relationship an erotically charged mother-child relationship is hidden. Female homosexuality may be an intermediary stage between a break with reality due to a very intense "bisexual conflict." The heterosexual position has first been completely abandoned so that the homosexual position provides the only bridge to the outside world. Should the latter be given up under the impact of intolerable anxiety this may lead to a complete break with reality and to psychosis.

Chapter III

FREUD'S CONTRIBUTIONS

FREUD'S DEEP PENETRATION of the research problems involved in the elucidation of homosexuality in "Three Essays on the Theory of Sexuality"[63] still remains the departure point for all subsequent explorations.

In Part I, "The Sexual Aberrations," Freud first coined the term "contrary sexual feelings," the word "invert" and designated the practice of homosexuality as "inversion." He wrote that homosexuals are considerable in number and that there are many difficulties attendant upon establishing the number precisely. (Hirschfeld had attempted this in 1904.) His proposed classification of homosexuality was based on variance in behavior (see Chapter II).

He noted that many homosexuals feel their inversion is in the natural course of things; others rebel against it and feel it is pathological. It may persist throughout life, go into temporary remission or be an episode on the way toward normal development. It may appear late in life after a long period of normal sexual activity. Periodic oscillations between heterosexual and inverted sexual objects are known. Of special interest are those individuals in whom the libido changes over to an inverted sexual object after a distressing experience with a normal one.

Freud clearly saw through the inverts' assertion that they could never remember any attachment to the opposite sex as untrustworthy, his having realized that they had only repressed their positive heterosexual feelings. He reviewed the two suppositions which had surrounded homosexuality for centuries. One, that it was innate and, two, that it was degenerate, having believed them untrue and of no value whatsoever. Many homosexuals may be otherwise unimpaired, it would appear, and may even distinguish themselves by especially high intellectual development and cultural level.

Were homosexuality innate (inborn), the contingent homosexual would be much more difficult to explain. Freud's assumption was that inversion is an acquired character of the sexual instinct and tested this hypothesis by removing inversion by hypnotic suggestion, an event he felt would be "astonishing" in an innate characteristic. He hypothesized that some experience of early childhood had a determining effect upon the direction taken by the invert's libido. He inferred that the nature of inversion "is explained neither by the hypothesis that it is innate nor by the alternative hypothesis that it is acquired."

He investigated inversion in all its varieties as the expression of a psychical hermaphroditism. He felt that all that was required to settle the question was that inversion should be regularly accompanied by the mental and somatic signs of hermaphroditism; this expectation was not realized. It is impossible to demonstrate a connection between hypothetical psychical hermaphroditism and the established anatomical one. The truth, according to Freud, was that inversion and somatic hermaphroditism were, on the whole, independent of each other. Psychical hermaphroditism would gain substance, in his opinion, if the inversion of the sexual object were at least accompanied by a parallel change of the subject's other mental qualities, instincts and character traits into those marking the opposite sex but it is only in invert women that character inversion of this kind can be looked for with any regularity.

Freud's numerous ideas, discussions and penetrating insights into bisexuality in the earliest history of this phenomenon are also presented in his masterful work, the "Three Essays," as well as in "A Child Is Being Beaten."[74]

In an addendum to the latter, Freud stated that psychoanalysis had not yet produced a complete explanation of the origin of inversion. Nevertheless, it has discovered the psychical mechanism of its development and had made essential contributions to the statement of the problems involved. In the earliest phase of their childhood future inverts passed through a period of very intense but short-lived fixation to a woman, usually their mother; after leaving this behind they identify themselves with the woman and take themselves as a sexual object. They proceed from a narcissistic basis and look for a man who resembles themselves and whom they may love as their mother loved them. In the 1910 edition of the "Three Essays," he again underscored his stand that the problem of inversion is a highly complex one and in the case of women is less ambiguous because among them the active inverts exhibit masculine characteristics, both physical and mental, with peculiar frequency and look for femininity in their sexual object. But here again he poses the idea that a closer knowledge of the facts might reveal greater variety.

In a 1915 note also, he alludes to a most important issue, that is that psychoanalytic research has decidedly opposed any attempt at segregating homosexuals from the rest of mankind as a group of special character. By studying special excitations over those that are manifestly displayed it is found that *all* human beings are capable of making a homosexual object choice and have, in fact, made one in their unconscious. Libidinal attachments to persons of the same sex play no less a part as factors in normal mental life and a greater part of the motive force for illness than do similar attachments to the opposite sex. On the contrary, Freud believed that a choice of an object independently of its sex—freedom to range equally among male and female objects as is found in childhood and primitive states of society in the early phases of history—is the original basis from which has resulted a restriction in one direction or another, and from which both the normal and inverted types developed.

In 1905, Freud was of the opinion that we were in no position to base a satisfactory explanation of the origin of inversion upon clinical material so far available. He emphasized a fact of sweeping importance: "the connection between the sexual instinct and the sexual object" is not as intimate as one would surmise. Both are merely "soldered together." He warned that we must loosen the conceptual bonds which exist between instinct and object. "It seems probable that the sexual instinct is in the first instance independent of its object nor is its origin likely to be due to the object's attraction." These last remarks have been largely ignored by research investigators. Freud's observation as regards the independence between the sexual instinct and the sexual object further clarifies the nature of homosexuality.

He penetrated the interconnections between infantile sexuality, perversions and neurosis, arriving at the conclusion that the neurosis represents the negative of a perversion. In the next five years, Freud, along with Sadger[162,163] and Ferenczi,[49,51,52] developed a formulation of the essential developmental factors in homosexuality.

(1) In the earliest stages of development, homosexuals experience a very strong mother fixation. Upon leaving this attachment they continue to identify with the mother, taking themselves narcissistically as their sexual object. Consequently, they search for a man resembling themselves, whom they may love as their mother loved them ("Three Essays").

(2) The different types of narcissistic object choice were outlined: a person he has loved; what he himself is; what he himself was; what he himself would like to be; someone reminiscent of another who was once part of himself. Combinations and permutations of these possibilities indicate that numerous varieties of sexual object choice.

(3) Clinical investigation of the genetic constellations responsible for this developmental inhibition—an over-strong mother fixation with resultant running away from the mother and transferring of excitation from women to men in a narcissistic fashion—led to an early positive oedipus complex of great intensity.

Freud had, in fact, anticipated the explorations of ego psychology which emerged in 1923.[80] At that time the problem of homosexuality was investigated from the points of view of ego development and the interaction of the ego, superego and id. He had remarked long before the advent of ego psychology that (1) (ego) functions of identification and repression play an important part in homosexuality (1905), and (2) in homosexuals one finds a "predominance of archaic and primitive psychical mechanisms."[63]

The lack of a systematic study of ego psychology and the absence of a concept of ego development comparable to the phases of libidinal development presented difficulties for many years in the application of structural concepts to homosexuality.

Freud saw that the late determinants toward homosexuality came during adolescence when a "revolution of the mental economy" takes place. The adolescent in exchanging his mother for some other sexual object may make a choice of an object of the same sex.[77] In his work on Leonardo da Vinci,[66] he pointed out that the absence of the father and growing up in a feminine environment or the presence of a weak father who is dominated by the mother furthers feminine identification and homosexuality. Likewise the presence of a cruel father may lead to a disturbance in male identification.

Fetishism and transvestitism[85] reflect different compromises between the simultaneous identification with the phallic and penisless mother. Often in masochistic men a feminine identification may exist without homosexual object choice.[74] In this way the masochistic perversion may preserve the individual from overt homosexuality; the "Wolf Man"[72] serves as a good example.

By 1910, Freud had already recognized the defensive function of certain perversions. This was seen in his study on da Vinci where he speaks of a fetish as constituting a substitute for the missed penis of the woman and male homosexuality as due to repression of attachment to the mother, colored by identification with her and the choice of object on a narcissistic basis. He said some homosexuals are fleeing other women so that they are not unfaithful to their mother.

The fact that homosexuality is a complex psychic formation was adequately seen by Freud's work in "A Child Is Being Beaten."[74] It is both defense and id impulse and is related to the oedipus complex and to other perversions. Homosexual behavior in action is not a simple expression of pregenital component instinct but may be compared to the classic analogy of a light ray passing through a lens and being subjected to considerable distortion and refraction. The perversion itself is seen, therefore, as only a small conscious part of a large unconscious system. The perversion is ego-syntonic and pleasurable.

In 1922, Freud described homosexuality occurring as a means of defense against persecutory paranoia[171] and, conversely, that the actual expression of homosexuality was a mechanism of repression and transformation in cases where there is intense jealousy and hostility toward rival siblings. In "A Child Is Being Beaten"[74] the emphasis was on castration anxiety and homosexuality as a defense against the threat of losing one's penis. In 1925, Freud introduced the theoretical background of ego psychology to perversions but this work largely concerns fetishism. The important mechanism of negation[83] in which the ego is able to extend its boundaries by accepting what would otherwise remain repressed with the proviso that it be consciously denied was elucidated. This also plays an important part in homosexuality. In his *Outline of Psychoanalysis*[90] and in the "Splitting of the Ego in the Defensive Process"[89] he showed that the defensive processes are important in all perversion formation including homosexuality.

The various mechanisms, defenses, superego problems, as exposited by Freud and added to by many contributors, will be found in Section Two (Chapter IV) which deals with these particular aspects.

Perversions came to be understood by Freud as not simply the negative of neurosis or the persistence of the infantile components but complex formations involving the defensive functions, expression of id drives, superego conflict, and ego adaptive moves. The role of the oedipus complex as described by Freud achieved tremendous popularity in an attempt to understand homosexuality. Freud himself, however, felt that to understand this condition would require a full understanding of its etiology, not merely an explanation of its structure or how that structure came into being, but the mechanisms responsible for it and an explanation of what determines this particular outcome rather than another.[95]

It is quite clear, however, that there is a great similarity between a neurotic symptom and homosexuality. They are not simply residues of the developmental process of infantile sexuality or the conscious representatives of unconscious instinct. There is often an alternation between phobia and perverse gratification.[95,160] Much study was needed on the relationship between perversion and the superego. Freud's work on the relationship of perversion to psychosis approached the matter from the point of view of the ego.[89] In his paper "Negation"[83] he showed that the ego is capable of extending its boundaries so that it may accept what it would otherwise repress with the proviso that this particular thing is consciously denied. In *An Outline of Psychoanalysis*[90] and in the "Splitting of the Ego in the Defensive Processes,"[89] the splitting of the ego was brilliantly defined as was the splitting of the object.

The concept of a premature fixation of the libido playing a role in the genesis of homosexuality appeared in "Some Neurotic Mechanisms in Jealousy, Paranoia and Homosexuality."[78] We must remember in all these matters to return to the "Three Essays"[63] wherein Freud said the end products may not be of a qualitative nature but may be of a quantitative nature for even if "we had complete knowledge of the etiological factors we would know only their quality but not their relative strength (quantity) in determining the end result." In a reference to Freud, Wiedeman[179] writes: "The qualitative factor, namely, the presence of certain neurotic or perverse formations is less important than the quantitative factor, which is the amount of cathexis that these structures are able to attract to themselves."

The literature is replete with many allusions to Freud and to his remarkable insights, viz., every active perversion is accompanied by a passive counterpart.[63] Concerning therapy, he stated that homosexuality could be treated by hypnotic suggestion.[63,64] Analysis can be applied to the treatment of perversions[63,77]; he was very cautious, however, about the possibility of curing homosexuality through analysis. "The goal of analytic treatment of homosexuality goes beyond the establishment of heterosexual potency, which frequently remains a pseudo-potency, it has to be helped along by perverse fantasies. Analytically speaking, the criterion of a cure is the detachment of the cathexis from the homosexual object and the ability to cathect the opposite sex as well as the ability to love a woman." At other times Freud mentioned that analytic treatment may help the homosexual with his neurotic problems even if there is no change in the direction of his object choice.[88]

It became clear that Freud ultimately felt that homosexuality represents an inhibition and dissociation of the psychosexual development, one of the pathological outcomes of the oedipal period. Analytic literature had not dislcosed any single genetic or structural pattern that would apply to all or even a major part of the cases of inversion.

It would be the task of future investigators, Freud wrote, to attempt to determine what genetic factors are essential for the production of homosexuality, to elucidate a structural theory for the understanding of homosexuality, to examine therapeutic problems inherent in the treatment of homosexuals and to shed light on the connection between the sexual instinct and the choice of object in homosexual behavior. To do all of this, of course, the psychical mechanisms used in the choice of a sexual object of the same sex for orgastic satisfaction, the purpose of such choice (beyond the orgastic purpose), and its infantile origin must finally be discovered.

At various times Freud referred to homosexuality as inhibited development, arrested development, or developmental inhibition. He found difficulty in drawing a sharp line between normal and pathological behavior and stated that in cases where exclusiveness of fixation was present we are justified in calling homosexuality a pathological symptom. He maintained that constitutional factors played a part in sexual perversions but that they played a similar role in all mental disorders. This in no way indicated any repudiation of psychological factors which are responsible for a predisposition to homosexuality. In actuality he was thereby emphasizing precisely these developmental factors which remained. Freud was always of the opinion that the nature of inversion was explained neither by the hypothesis that it is innate nor by the alternative hypothesis that it is acquired. He was able to show that even in absolute inverts, for example, one can discover that very early in their lives a sexual impression occurred which left permanent after-effects in the shape of a tendency toward homosexuality; in others it is possible to trace homosexuality to external influences, in their lives whether of a favorable or inhibiting character which led sooner or later to a fixation of their inversion. Later factors included exclusive relationship with persons of their own sex, comradeship in war, dangers of heterosexual intercourse.[63]

Freud believed that in the female there are more severe early inhibitions or reaction formations against sexuality such as shame, disgust, pity—in contrast to the male—and there is greater passivity of the instinct components. Although the development of the two sexes can be outlined as moving in parallel fashion "since the guiding erotogenic zones are of an identical nature, either objectively or in the case of the genital (penis, clitoris) subjectively, . . . at puberty the female face(s) the additional task of exchanging the infantile genital for the adult one whose stimulation coitus will normally cause her to transfer the erotogeneity of the clitoris to the vagina." Among women, as in men, the sexual aims of the invert are varied with a special preference for contact with the mucous membrane of the mouth.[63]

The focal point of Freud's discussion of both male and female inversion became the oedipus complex and castration fear. These were frequently alluded to in the *Collected Papers*[89] as the motivational force for potential or actual inversion. Freud published his first clinical study on female homosexuality in 1920.[75] His patient was a beautiful and clever girl of eighteen who adored a woman about ten years her senior. She adopted the characteristic type of masculine love, e.g., humility, tender lack of pretension, blissfulness. The precipitating event leading her toward her love object was a new pregnancy of her mother and also the birth of a third brother when she was about sixteen. The object choice corresponded not only with her feminine but also with her masculine ideal (a combined gratification of the homosexual tendency with that of the heterosexual one). She unconsciously wished to bear the father's child, and "it was not she who bore the child but the unconsciously hated rival (the mother)." This led to resentment, embitterment, and turning away from father and from men altogether. She repudiated her wish for a child and the love of a man. The patient "changed into a man" and took a woman (her mother) in place of the father as a love object.

Freud carefully considered the implications inherent in the choice of object on the one hand, and of the sexual characteristics and sexual attitude of the subject on the other. The answer to the former necessarily does not involve the answers to the latter. Experience (choice of object vs. sexual characteristics and sexual attitude of the subject) proves that a man with predominantly male characteristics and also masculine in his love life may still be inverted in respect to his object, loving only men instead of women. Freud added that the same is true of women, but here mental sexual characteristics and object choice do not necessarily coincide. Therefore, the problem of the female homosexual is by no means so simple as it is commonly depicted in popular expositions of male homosexuality, that is, "a feminine personality which therefore has to love a man is unhappily attached to a male body."

Freud developed the theme that all sexual perverts, including female homosexuals, alter their sexual object. A female may dispense with the mutual union of the genital organs and substitute for the genitals in one of the two partners another organ or part of the body, mouth or anus in place of the vagina. He felt, in short, that perverted sexuality is representative of infantile sexuality, magnified into its component parts.[70]

He underscored the lack of understanding of the female regarding certain crucial issues[79,81]: inadequate insight into the processes in the little girl concerning incest wishes, the effect of the threat of castration, the internalization of the object, and the formation of the superego to be distinguished from the ego and the id. By 1924[54,81] he contrasted the girl to a certain degree with her brother describing her as (1) accepting castration as an accomplished fact rather than fearing it as a threat; (2) lacking consequently a powerful motive for the erection of a super-ego and breaking up of her infantile female sexuality; (3) relinquishing therefore the oedipus complex more gradually than the boy while retaining a strong conscious wish for a penis and child from the father.

By 1925 Freud published the first of his studies on female sexuality.[84] He described more fully the castration complex of the girl and its effect upon infantile masturbation and the oedipus complex. The second period of infantile masturbation is disturbed by the inferiority of the clitoris. The girl is forced to rebel against phallic masturbation which agrees less well with her than with the boy and develops penis envy with its reaction formation in order finally to accept fully her castration. In addition this acceptance introduces her to the oedipus complex with its wish for the penis = wish for the child and supersedence of a previous attachment to the mother who is the original love object of the infant of either sex. (R. Fliess published an authoritative critique of Freud's changing concepts on female sexuality.[54])

Even more important is the fact that a comparison between the relation of the castration complex and the oedipus complex in the sexes shows that the castration complex *terminates* the oedipus complex for the boy and *initiates* that of the girl. Since the oedipus complex is never completely relinquished by the girl, its heir, the superego, is in the normal female never as inexorable as in the male.

Six years later Freud[86] traced the lines of development that accrue from the acknowledgment of the fact of castration, the superiority of the male, and the inferiority of the girl and her rebellion. The first developmental line leads to her turning her back on sexuality altogether. "The budding woman frightened by the comparison of herself with boys becomes dissatisfied with her clitoris and gives up her phallic activity and therewith her sexuality in general and a considerable part of masculine proclivities in other fields." However, a second line is that she clings in obstinate self-assertion to her masculinity; the hope of acquiring a penis is sometimes cherished to an incredibly late age and becomes the aim of one's life, while the fantasy of really being a man in spite of everything often dominates long periods of a girl's life. This "masculinity complex" may also result in a *manifestly homosexual object choice*. The third circuitous path is one which arrives ultimately at a normal feminine attitude in which the girl takes her father as love object, thus giving rise to the oedipus complex in its feminine form. The oedipus complex in the woman represents the final result of a lengthy process of development whose motive force has been castration fear. It therefore escapes the strong hostile influences which in men tend to its destruction.

Freud postulated that women with strong father fixations show a long period prior to the establishment of the positive oedipus attitude, a period which he called "preoedipal." In this phase the mother figure is the love object, though the relation to her is highly ambivalent in character. Hostility increases with each fresh experience of frustration until the recognition of the absence of a penis, interpreted as punishment by the mother for masturbation, brings the girl's fear to such intensity that she throws over the mother in favor of the father. In other words, it is still the phallic frustration which is really decisive for femininity, and the core of the complaint against the mother was the fact of being born a girl rather than the oedipal rivalry. A strong father fixation implies a strong mother fixation, and the hostility to the mother is complemented by oedipus rivalry but *not* initiated by it. The solutions are therefore: (1) a general retreat from sexuality; (2) a retention of masculinity which may result in *manifest homosexual object choice;* (3) or a transference to the father ushering in the positive oedipal attitude and subsequent feminine development. In other words, the girl must choose between sacrificing her erotic attachment to the father or sacrificing her femininity. Either the father or the vagina, including the pregenital vagina, must be renounced. The bond with the father often is retained, but the object relationship is converted to *identification*, i.e., a penis complex is developed.

As a culmination Freud summarized his thinking on female sexuality and homosexuality in a lecture entitled "The Psychology of Women."[87] He reiterated his belief in the presence of an exclusive mother attachment preceding the oedipus complex of greater intensity and duration than in the male. The preoedipal phase in girls, he felt, extended into the fourth or even fifth year of life and included most of the phallic period. During this phase a girl's sexual aim toward the mother was at first passive and then active and corresponded to the partial libidinal stages through which she had journeyed from infancy, i.e., oral, anal, sadistic and phallic. The girl's giving up of the mother and her acknowledgment of castration, that is, change of zone and change of object, occur in a complementary fashion. It is castration which is conceived of as a denial of the male genital by the mother which forms the nucleus of the reproach and hostility toward her. What follows is a transition from the mother to the father. "This fulfills the biological necessity of transforming the masculine girl into the feminine woman by drawing on her passivity and her remaining positive sexual strivings. . . . Thus the child-penis is also no longer craved from the mother but from the father."[54]

From Freud's important paper one derives that female homosexuality is seldom or never a direct continuation of infantile masculinity. It is characteristic of female homosexuals that they, too, took the father as love object for a while and became implicated in the oedipal situation. With the inevitable disappointments they experience from the father they regress to their early masculinity complex. These disappointments cannot be overestimated. Girls who eventually achieve femininity also experience them, however, without the same results. The preponderance of the constitutional factors is extremely important but the two phases of female homosexuality are well reflected in the behavior of homosexuals who just as often and just as obviously play the parts of mother and child toward each other as those of man and wife.

Finally, Freud stated that if the girl persists in and adheres to her first wish to grow into a boy, in extreme cases she will end as a manifest homosexual or in any event will show markedly masculine traits in the conduct of her later life.[90]

Section Two

THEORY

Chapter IV

DEVELOPMENTAL THEORY—MALE

IN HOMOSEXUALITY, as in all perversions, the manifest activity represents the peak of a broadly based unconscious construction.[101] Reports have indicated that there exists a scatter of fixation points, varying in depth or developmental level of the ego. This is of crucial significance for prognosis in therapy. Because psychic localization is difficult and unconscious content variable, the origin of homosexuality remained uncertain. All theoretical information must therefore proceed from: investigation of fixation points; understanding of the unconscious construction; intimate knowledge of the developmental stages of the ego and the vicissitudes encountered at each stage; study of the currently manifest activity.

Infantile Sexuality and Homosexuality

Freud, in 1905,[63] penetrated the interconnections between infantile sexuality, perversions and neurosis. He concluded that in the neurosis, infantile sexuality is repressed and represents the negative of a perversion. In the perversion the infantile sexuality persists over-cathected. The early theory that perversions were a breakthrough of impulses unopposed by the ego or superego underwent considerable modification. Introduction of the structural approach into psychoanalysis makes it possible to clarify the fact that not only the instinctual drives but also the defenses against them are unconscious. As a result the gratification of a perverse instinctual drive actually constitutes the end product of a defensive compromise in which elements of inhibition as well as gratification are present.

In homosexuality the component instinct which seems to be approved has undergone excessive transformation and disguise in order to be gratified in the perverse act. The perverted action, like the neurotic symptom, results from the conflict between the ego and the id (a concept developed in 1923) and represents a compromise formation which at the same time must be acceptable to the demands of the superego.[80] In both male and female homosexuality, as in the case of neurotic symptoms, the instinctual gratification takes place in disguised form

35

while its real content remains unconscious. For this reason a perversion differs from a neurotic symptom, first by the form of gratification of the impulse, namely, orgasm; second, in the fact that the ego's wishes for omnipotence are satisfied by the arbitrary ego-syntonic action. As a result, certain broader dynamic aspects of sexuality must always be considered. The defensive aspects of homosexuality and warding off guilt-laden fantasies are crucial for the role of object relations as are family constellations and the specific opportunities to make adequate identifications. Freud's dual instinct theory is indispensable in the analysis of homosexuality. The fusion of aggressive and libidinal impulses, the presence of guilt and hostile aggressive drives, the need for punishment, play important roles.[169,170]

Freud disclosed that the sexual aims of homosexuals were identical with those activities in children.[63] Also in homosexuality and other perversions, genital sexuality is replaced by one component of infantile sexuality. These perverse acts are distorted exaggerations and have a quality of uniqueness and stereotypy which does not appear in normal persons except as introductory activities prior to intercourse. Polymorphous perverse activity may be seen in most individuals at times, especially as forepleasure mechanisms. When there are severe obstacles in attaining genital sexual satisfaction there tends to be a regression to earlier perverse formations. Although an individual seems ready to accept perversion as a way of life his condition may prove to be only temporary and lacks the quality of stereotypy.

The tendency to perversion lies in the fact that all of us were once children. In the "Three Essays," Freud applied the formula that people are perverse who react to sexual frustrations with a regression to infantile sexuality secondary to arrested development. Indeed, perversions frequently are seen to make their appearance suddenly after a severe sexual disappointment. This points to the meaningfulness of the regression hypothesis. But not all perversions represent regression to infantile sexuality. As Fenichel stated: ". . . it is not easy to say where stimulation ends and where gratification begins."[47] Most perverse acts are polymorphous and their main emphasis is simply displaced onto the forepleasure often without actual orgastic pleasure being reached (or, as in fetishism, the displacement is onto the fetish).

One must differentiate between the polymorphously perverse sexuality of children or infantile personality and the perverse sexuality of the true homosexual. The true homosexual has only one way of gaining pleasure and his energies are concentrated on one particular partial instinct. It was once thought that it was simply the hypertrophy of this

instinct competing with genital primacy which constituted homosexuality and other perversions. These individuals do not simply "lack
genital primacy."[47] This capacity is blocked by some obstacle and is
more or less overcome by the perverse act. (In the perversion symptom
we have inklings that the perversion itself is warding off other aspects of
infantile sexuality and thus allowing into consciousness an expression, a
part, of sexuality which the ego can tolerate.) Fenichel, as anticipated
in his early writings,[44] gave us important hints as to the direction of
our investigations. He felt that the difference between neurosis and
perversion lies in the fact that the symptom is "de-sexualized" in the
neuroses, but is a component of infantile sexuality in the perversions;
that its discharge is painful in the neuroses but brings genital orgasm
in the perversions.[47]

What disturbs genital primacy? It is, of course, castration anxiety and
guilt feelings directed against the oedipus complex. After genital enjoyment has become impossible because of castration and oedipal fears an
individual regresses to that part of his infantile anxiety to which he is
fixated.

In the first two decades of psychoanalysis castration fear was of
paramount interest to all psychoanalysts in the understanding of
perversions and especially homosexuality. Castration fear resulted in a
regression to that part of infantile sexuality to which one was apparently
already fixated. It was not simply that some infantile component was
substituted. Infantile sexuality was repressed but it was crucial to
apprehend that there was a *hypertrophy* of one's sexual infantile component and this hypertrophy was then used for the purposes of strength-
ening the repression of other aspects of infantile sexuality.[44,47] Sachs
utilized these findings for his important theory as to the mechanism of
perversion formation.[160]

One must not oversimplify the concept of fixation. It is not merely
that sexual excitement was experienced with an attendant accidental
sexual circumstance and sexual response which then produced a
fixation. These are merely screen memories which serve to disguise the
real causes of the fixation which lay around actual pregenital or preoedipal conflicts. Very often our patients will ascribe to these memories
the reason for their fixation to a particular form of enjoyment. A
fetishist will ascribe his interest in silk undergarments to the sexual
excitement engendered by the rustling of the nightgown of his mother
as she put him to bed. A homosexual will attribute his condition to the
excitement induced by the sound of the father's urinating.

The homosexual, disturbed in his genital sexuality by castration fear, regresses to that component of his infantile sexuality which once in childhood gave him security or at least reassurance against his many fears. At the same time he obtained some gratification in the regression. The over-emphasis on the reassuring infantile expression of his sexuality simultaneously serves to maintain a repression of his oedipal difficulties and other warded-off remnants of infantile sexuality. This is partial repression of infantile sexuality wherein other parts are exaggerated.

The work of repression is apparently facilitated in homosexuality through the added dividend of some other aspect of infantile sexuality being consciously stressed. This guarantees, according to Sachs, the repression of the oedipus and castration complexes.[160] Fenichel wrote that the pleasure in perverse activities is not as intense as that in genital heterosexual activities. He felt that the former are possible only after hindrances and through distortions and therefore pleasure is necessarily incomplete.[47] He quotes Freud on homosexuality, stating: "They are . . . poor devils who have to pay a high price for their limited pleasure."[74]

Developmental Factors

Many of the developmental vicissitudes, their attempted solutions, and the resulting conflict are common to both male and female homosexuality. Therefore, where applicable, i.e., where the male is not specifically referred to, these factors also pertain to the female. Essential differences arising out of the more complex and intricate sexual development of the female will be noted separately in Chapter V.

By 1910, Freud,[63] Sadger[161] and Ferenczi[49] had agreed that in the earliest stages of development homosexuals experience a very strong mother fixation[63] and upon leaving this attachment continue to identify with the mother taking themselves narcissistically as their sexual object.[69] Consequently they search for a man resembling themselves whom they could love as their mother loved them. The family of the homosexual is usually a female-dominated environment wherein the father was absent, weak, detached or sadistic. This furthers feminine identification.[66] The father's inaccessibility to the boy contributed to the difficulty in making a masculine identification.

In addition to the boy's negative relationship to the father and his identification with the mother, there was a renunciation of women to avoid all rivalry with the father.[78] Castration fear is of major importance in the development of homosexuality. However, this is a non-specific agent being present as well in normal, neurotic and any perverse psychosexual development. In male homosexuality the hated rival is transformed into the love object in contrast, for instance, to the paranoiac whose male love object becomes the persecutor.[78]

By 1919, perversions were conceived of as precipitates or scars of the oedipus complex[74] and not simply manifestations of the sexual drive itself. This was followed by other important contributions, especially that of Sachs in 1923,[160] on the genesis of perversions in relation to the oedipal period. His discovery has been accorded little attention and limited clinical application.

Besides identifying the factors of narcissistic choice and castration fear of the oedipal period it was deduced that a pathological retention of the erotic significance of the anal zone provides a marked predisposition to homosexuality. The latter was first noted by Freud in the "Three Essays" and then re-emphasized by him in 1913.[68] In this connection, Nunberg[153] made an important clinical observation on the anal-sadistic impulses in homosexuality. He referred to the importance of aggression when he wrote that the homosexual acquires strength by conquering a bigger and stronger man.

In "Some Neurotic Mechanisms . . . ," Freud[78] returned to his original concept that seduction may indeed be responsible for premature fixation of the libido and plays a significant role in the genesis of homosexuality far beyond what had been previously recognized. Jones, in discussing his "protophallic phase," during which the child has no conflict over the possession or loss of the phallus, and "deuterophallic phase," during which a child becomes aware of the possibility of castration, felt that the largely heterosexual allo-erotism of the early phallic phase is transmuted into a substitutive homosexual autoerotism. The latter stage represents a "phallic perversion" and this led Jones to consider homosexuality as essentially a libidinized hostility to the rival parent.[120] Loewenstein[141] felt that passivity in the phallic phase produces potency difficulties and that a certain type of passive homosexuality, which is expressed exclusively in the form of genital gratification, may be present in which there is no anal wish. The fantasy of this type of homosexual consists in having his own small penis touched by the larger penis of the man he loves. There appears to be a special affinity between phallic passivity and the negative oedipus complex.

It remained for Sachs to offer the epoch-making idea that a perversion is the ego-syntonic remnant of infantile sexuality, which becomes the ally of the ego in its repressive efforts to direct it against other component instincts as well as against the positive oedipus complex and castration fear. A small fragment of infantile sexuality survives puberty and becomes the precondition of sexual gratification; all the other components of sexuality become repressed.

He originally conceived the idea that where there is a conflict involving an especially strongly developed component instinct, complete victory may be impossible for the ego and repression may be only partially successful. The ego then has to be content with the compromise of repressing the greater part of infantile libidinal strivings at the expense of sanctioning and taking into itself the smaller part.[160]

Bychowski[4] and Bak[6] also considered homosexuality largely from the point of view of the role of aggression and the inability of the ego of the homosexual to neutralize it. Homosexuality became a regressive adaptation through identification with the mother. This helped to resolve the destructive impulses originally directed toward the mother and at the same time libidinized the aggression against the rival of the same sex. Homosexuality thereby succeeded in defending against retaliation from both sexes. Other significant contributions were made by Freeman[56]; Nacht, Diatkine and Favrow[152]; Rosenfeld[159]; Thorner.[176] All of them stressed the role of aggression and the presence of pregenital mechanisms and infantile primitive aggressive impulses as important factors which promote homosexuality.

In Anna Freud's opinion[58] the crucial factor in homosexual behavior is the identification with the partner of the same sex through sexual contact. Bychowski devoted special study to the affinities between the schizophrenic and the homosexual groups, finding analogies in psychic structure, especially "infantilisms in the libidinal organization and certain primitive features of the ego." The boundaries[29,169] of the homosexual ego lack fixity which makes possible fleeting identifications. A peculiar weakness is based on its narcissistic and pre-narcissistic disposition. It is fixated at a stage preceding the formation of a distinct ego. These dispositions produce clinging relationships to various persons which, in turn, are based either on infantile leaning or on narcissistic object choice. A clinging dependence is indicative of a feeling of weakness; a narcissistic object choice reveals the hyper-cathexis of the self. As a result of the overflow of primary narcissism with hyper-cathexis of the physical and mental self one sees tendencies toward hypochondriasis and an over-evaluation of fantasy and of emotionally loaded object representations. This may account for the low frustration tolerance in homosexuals. Due to the primitive character of the narcissism one frequently uncovers ideas of grandeur paradoxically existing along with a poor image of the self.

Due to its archaic structure the ego is extremely vulnerable to the impact of libidinal stimulation. Renunciation of primitive gratification with original objects becomes impossible. The homosexual's inability to bind the original instinctual energies and to transform them into a potential tonic energy available for secondary process had been cited by Freud. A primitive ego utilizes incorporation to a high degree; the original objects, never really given up, are incorporated in the ego and remain the prototypes of future object choice. However, these objects become incorporated according to their original highly ambivalent cathexis. This contributes to a split and to the ego being filled, as it were, with contradictory contents. To compound the situation, the weakness of the immature ego does not allow for its synthesis of the originally conflicting attitudes. Here the analogy to the psychotic or pre-psychotic ego is apparent. As a result of this split, the ego may function at times with one or another of its segments, i.e., assume the role of one or another of the introjects. An example is the homosexual in whom the introject of a passive, submissive mother is paramount. This individual can be seen to enact this role in his homosexual activities, according to Bychowski.[32]

Orality is intimately related to the mechanism of introjection. The homosexual changes easily from an active to a passive position because of his ambivalence and intense incorporative needs.

Pregenital elements constitute a decisive factor in fashioning the homosexual's object relations. The importance of the object lies in its ability to fulfill certain demands of pregenital partial drives in homosexuality including those of orality and anality. Homosexual object choice can be defined in shifting ego and libidinal constellations which may represent various object choices such as masochistic or sadistic homosexual object choice. In either case, masochistic or sadistic, the object can represent one or both preoedipal and oedipal parents; in many instances it is not the total individual but rather partial object, the maternal breast for instance or the paternal phallus, which is sought. The preoedipal phallic mother as a sexual object may serve to protect the ego against the real incestuous mother and the oedipal castration threat. The homosexual, forced to deny his own phallus, is compelled to seek a substitute in other men whose genitals he desires. In all instances the image of the self, the narcissistic projection, is sought. The homosexual thus strives to become whole and complete.

He combines a number of roles in all his sexual activities. He may be the aggressor-father assaulting the oedipal-mother; at other times he may play the role of the maternal-substitute passively submitting to a homosexual object which may represent his own phallic self. He may play the role of a projected ego ideal. All these have one thing in common: the homosexual strives to fulfill his own masculinity, to identify with a strong male figure to reinvest his penis with male interest, to become whole, complete, satisfied and without fear of the castrating influences of both mother and father.

In normal heterosexual development the masculine needs of the male become to a great extent "ego-invested," i.e., the ego feels the need to discharge personally and directly this masculine tension.[170] The feminine needs become "object invested," which means that the ego feels a need for a feminine sexual partner whose feminine urges it cares to satisfy. "By so doing the ego can obtain vicarious gratification, as it were, of its own feminine needs." The more an ego "egotizes the urges of its own sex and externalizes to a proper object representation the urges of the opposite sex, the more does such an ego feel complete. . . . On the other hand, the more an ego egotizes the biological urges of the opposite sex, for the satisfaction of which it is not anatomically and physiologically equipped, and externalizes instead the urges of its own sex into an object representation, the more it feels mutilated." This latter condition constitutes inversion to Weiss.

Those homosexuals who do egotize masculine urges and externalize the feminine ones into younger males substituted for females have a stronger ego. The most classic example of this type of masculine homosexuality was found in ancient Greece. Ego weakness, as described by Bychowski,[169] is most frequently encountered in male homosexuals with a feminine ego. Weiss has stressed that children of both sexes identify in varying degrees with both father and mother. But in normal sexual maturation only the introject of the parent of the same sex is maintained while that of the parent of the opposite sex is externalized in a modified form ("ego passage").[178]

Weiss has been of the opinion that some of the traits mentioned by Bychowski as regards primitive mechanisms may not be present in all homosexuals and are not specific to male homosexuality. In many cases the answer to the question of narcissistic object love lies in the phenomenon of a boy's identification with his mother and "this identification can be effected only through the mobilization of the feminine urges in the boy's bisexual constitution. Every homosexual remains strongly fixated to his mother."[169] In other words, it is the mother's introject, to use Bychowski's term, "that pushes the original masculine ego outside into the object world." It is of crucial significance, according to Weiss, that a man's identification with a woman, the mother, must lead to many character traits of the ego different from those of a man who has an ego investment in the masculine part of his constitutional bisexuality while "the feminine part becomes object invested."[169]

The complexity of the homosexual object choice has been mentioned by numerous authors. There is a shift in terms of ego and libidinal constellations in all homosexuals resulting in a change from overt to latent homosexuality and in the reverse direction. They may utilize masochistic, heterosexual and, to some extent, homosexual perverse fantasies and fetishism as a defense against homosexuality, a factor first mentioned by Freud. Often homosexuality may be disguised as a heterosexual masochistic perversion or fantasy in which the female is a substitute for a male (a phallic woman) and what is actually practiced in disguised form is a homosexual union.[169]

Other authors, notably Bacon,[169] have emphasized the shift in identification in homosexuals. Identification is needed in the hope of winning love and avoiding greater danger. An example of this is behaving like a passive homosexual son to a "murderous or aggressive father."

It seems that various aspects of pathological development toward homosexuality appear in all phases of development. The pathology in these phases is often a result of disturbances which occurred earlier than is generally assumed, in the so-called "undifferentiated phase,"[169] which in actuality is not undifferentiated but already manifesting important beginnings of structure formation. The fixation to the mother and the characteristically narcissistic object choice of the homosexual may be traced back to the "undifferentiated phase" of the mother-child unity. The preoedipal origin of homosexuality is fully set forth in Chapter VI.

Specific Mechanisms

On close examination most cases of homosexuality reveal a basic structural pyschological pattern. Inasmuch as the earliest libidinal tie is to the mother how does it come about then that in adolescence or in adulthood a male-male relationship displaces the former? It is well known that an over-intense affective relationship to the mother often with conscious incestuous desires and a father who is inaccessible to the child are standard factors in the production of overt male homosexuality.[18,47,149] The sexual wish for the mother leads to anxiety, guilt and a conflicting urge to cling to and simultaneously to avoid intimate contact with her and later all other women.

This intense attachment, fear and guilt in the boy's relationship with his mother brings about certain major psychic transformations which are effected through the mechanism of the repressive compromise. Having developed infantile libidinal strivings of an intense nature toward his mother with resultant guilt, anxiety and savage hostility the child must attempt to repress these strivings. However, through repression he is only partially successful in attaining relief. The ego then has to be content with the compromise of repressing the greater part of his strivings at the expense of sanctioning and taking into himself the smaller part. This solution by division, whereby one piece of infantile anxiety enters the service of repression (that is, is helpful to promoting repression through displacement, substitution and other defense mechanisms) and so carries over pregenital pleasure into the ego while the rest undergoes repression is one of the major mechanisms of the development of the homosexual perversion.[160] The repression of wishes to penetrate the mother's body or the wish to suck and incorporate the mother's breast undergoes repression; in either case a piece of infantile sexuality has entered the service of repression through displacement and substitution. Instead of the mother's body it is the male body and instead of the mother's breast it is the penis. Homosexuality then becomes the choice of the lesser evil. This is the basic mechanism in the production of homosexuality in both male and female.

The Breast-Penis Equation.[10,43,47,63] In order to defend himself against the positive oedipus complex, that is, his attachment to his mother and hatred for his father and punitive aggressive destructive drives toward the body of his mother, the homosexual substitutes the partner's penis for the mother's breast. The female similarly substitutes a fictive penis on her female partner in place of the maternal breast which she hates and abhors. This can be in the form of a masculine attitude on the part of her female partner (or herself), the substitution and introduction of the finger and tongue in sexual contact, or the use of a penis-like device. Simultaneously, she avoids her incestuous wishes toward the father.

Psychic Masochism. The aggressive assaultiveness toward the mother and secondarily toward the father is drained off into a psychic masochistic state. All homosexuals deeply fear the knowledge that their homosexual behavior constitutes an erotized defense against a more threatening masochistic state. Schematically this may be represented as follows: Libidinal and aggressive impulses against the mother and father lead to masochism. This masochism then seeks effective discharge through the homosexual relationship.

Masochism is, of course, not only a way of neutralizing aggression but of keeping the tie to the mother.[167] The homosexual must no longer fear the all-powerful retaliative forces of the mother; he does not dare to cease being her masochistic, thinly-disguised sexual salve.[13,15,16] In the masochistic state, guilt over incestuous feelings for the mother is continually bought off through self-punitive activities. However, the pain in masochism is self-controlled and self-induced from which process the patient derives a feeling of omnipotence.

Masochism adds to the difficulty in treating these patients as conditioning to a particular type of pleasure-in-pain satisfaction does not readily yield. The conditioning which the homosexual presents is *masochistic conditioning*—pleasure in painful and self-damaging experiences—which helps him keep his precarious psychological equilibrium. The homosexual will state that he is not masochistic at all but that this is a conscious and deliberate way of life which he prefers. Nevertheless, in reality he is unconsciously committed to and captured by his need to avoid what he feels would be extinction due to the tremendous threat of maternal engulfment and destructiveness. To fortify himself and to make himself secure against this possibility he aggrandizes, elevates and romanticizes his variant sexual activity. Masochism is not to be defeated as even in the course of his homosexual pleasure masochism prevails.

The masochistic anxiety is also erotized through its homosexual activity.[47,74,82] Orgastic activity and pleasure partially and temporarily relieve the tendence toward an uncontrollable powerful masochistic state which, were it to get out of hand, would threaten his survival. Every homosexual, both male and female, lives this close to the brink of personal disaster and possible annihilation.

Erotization of Anxiety. Anxiety derived from both preoedipal and oedipal conflicts undergoes an erotization or libidinization. Not only is anxiety erotized but orgasm effected. Individuals who are sure of an intense pleasure obviously find it difficult to relinquish. This erotization applies equally to the female.

Isolation and Loneliness. Because the homosexual must forego his striving for gratification of his intense attachment to the mother and consequently to other women and has also been deprived of closeness to the father because of the latter's abdication, he experiences severe feelings of loneliness throughout life. Homosexuality is an attempt to achieve human contact and to break through stark isolation. The homosexual claims that his motivation is to "find a friend" but this is merely a rationalization for the overriding and imperative need for neutralization of his anxiety through homosexual orgastic contact.

The pathological quality of the homosexual's loneliness is in reality an acute tense depression mixed with mounting anxiety which threatens his psychological equilibrium if contact is not made quickly. He is unable to utilize sublimation or diversion which so often forestalls impulsive and self-damaging behavior in normal and some neurotic individuals. Such imperious need arising out of loneliness is striking in both male and female homosexuality.

Identification With the Male Partner. His primary feminine sexual identification, the castration fear resulting from parental intimidation, guilt feelings for incest strivings toward the mother, impel the homosexual to search for masculinity through identification with the maleness of his homosexual partner.[58]

Similarly, the female homosexual may identify with the "maleness" of her female partner and also, through resonance identification,[170] enjoy vicariously the partner's femininity—a femininity self-denied. Both can occur simultaneously but usually one or the other identification is predominant in the course of any specific female homosexual contact.

Chapter V

DEVELOPMENTAL THEORY—FEMALE

IN REPORTS ON changing psychoanalytic concepts of male and female homosexuality it was pointed out that while the literature on male homosexuality has been rather extensive, that on female homosexuality has been sparse.

Many writers prefer to use the term "Lesbianism" to describe the clinical condition of female homosexuality. This is an attempt to romanticize it. Female homosexuality has been pictured as either a psychosis or a case of perverse morality. An alternative depiction is that of an unfortunate woman fighting off her homosexual desires but remaining emotionally unfulfilled. Homosexual relations between women are often regarded as superficial or dismissed as not meaningful in any sexual sense despite the orgastic experiences between the women involved.

In contrast to the frequent interest of the male homosexual in young boys, the female homosexual is seldom attracted to prepuberty girls to the point of actual seduction. There are very few, if any, female homosexual pedophiliacs; occasionally the act may occur during the onset of a disintegrating psychosis.

Homosexual women may try to yield themselves to marriage for the sake of security, to overcome a feeling of inner and social isolation or to satisfy the expectations of their family. Once married, their sexual life with a partner of the same sex may then of necessity become a clandestine one, without the husband's knowledge. Many women accept marriage and the world then accepts them as heterosexual although they may remain completely unsatisfied sexually. It is not an uncommon occurrence for such marriages to terminate although the underlying cause remains obscured.

In general, homosexual men will usually not marry. They do not ordinarily view a heterosexual marriage as a social and economic solution and could not function sexually in marriage. Because the female anatomy permits the woman to engage in heterosexual intercourse passively she may at least be able to endure the intimate contact with the male if only for a brief period or on rare occasions. There are a few instances when a homosexual woman may marry simply to have a child. She will then divorce the husband and thereafter lead an exclusively homosexual life.

The fact that women are anatomically able to have sexual intercourse without desire or even with aversion is of crucial importance. This promotes both conscious and unconscious self-deception as to her homosexual feelings and wishes. She may not know that her resentment of and lack of love for her husband are due to her homosexual conflict. A man, however, requires the preliminary presence of desire; in its absence he must perforce appear inadequate and face the loss of sexual pride and the esteem of the partner. Women may successfully submit to a sexual life which they find bereft of meaning and even distasteful and still manage to hide their narcissistic mortification, humiliation and opposition, living out a masquerade of womanliness.[172]

Developmental Factors

In one of her several studies on the psychology of women Deutsch[33] observed that at the beginning of every new sexual function, for example, puberty, intercourse, pregnancy, childbirth, the phallic phase conflict is reanimated and has to be overcome each time before a feminine attitude can be attained once more. This complicates the development toward adult female sexual functioning and sets up a condition wherein female homosexuality may be activated at any of these periods.

Horney[115] emphasized that the oedipal fantasies and the ensuing dread of the internal vaginal injury, as well as the clitoris, play an important part in the infantile genital organization of women. She thought it of causative importance that the little boy can inspect his genital to see whether any consequences of masturbation are taking place, whereas the little girl is literally in the dark on this point. An inner uncertainty so often met in women is due to this circumstance. Under the pressure of anxiety, the guilt may then take refuge in the production of a fictitious male role. The wish to be a man subserves the repression of feminine wishes and secures the subject against libidinal wishes in connection with the father, the female role having been burdened with guilt and anxiety.

In 1925, Jones analyzed simultaneously five cases of overt female homosexuality and reported on them at the Innsbruck Congress.[119] In the main, he felt that female homosexuality could be traced back to two crucial factors: (1) an intense oral erotism, and (2) an unusually strong sadism. Together with Deutsch's and Freud's clinical studies,

Jones's paper may constitute the most incisive penetration from the theoretical and clinical point of view into this disorder.

In homosexual women the unconscious attitude toward both parents, writes Jones, is always strongly ambivalent; there is evidence of an unusually strong infantile fixation in regard to the mother, definitely connected with the oral stage; this is always succeeded by a strong father fixation whether temporary or permanent in consciousness. He postulated that castration anxiety is only a partial threat and coined the term "aphanisis" as the total threat, that is, threat of total extinction which includes sexual capacity and enjoyment of life as a whole.

The privation experienced by the girl in not being allowed to share the penis in coitus with the father and thereby to obtain a baby is an unendurable situation, the reason being that it is tantamount to the fundamental dread of aphanisis. Jones slightly preceded Freud as to the correspondence of their views on the future outcome. There are only two ways in which the libido can flow for self-expression: the girl must choose, broadly speaking, between sacrificing her erotic attachment to her father and sacrificing her femininity, either the object must be exchanged for another or the wish must be. It is impossible to retain both; either the father or the vagina, including pregenital vagina, must be renounced. A result of this is that the father may be retained but the object relationship is converted into identification, a penis complex is developed. Faced with aphanisis as a result of an inevitable privation she must renounce either her sex or her incest wishes. What cannot be retained is an incestuous object relationship. A girl may choose the solution of homosexuality because it will save her from the dread of aphanisis. In essence, she can surrender the position of her object libido (father) or can surrender the position of her subject libido (sex) which is then followed into the field of homosexuality itself.

Jones distinguished three types of homosexual women. (1) Those who retain their interest in men but who set their hearts on being accepted by men as one of themselves. To this group belongs the familiar type of women who ceaselessly complain of the unfairness of women's lot and their unjust ill-treatment by men. (2) Another group consists of homosexual women who have little or no interest in men but whose libido centers on women. Analysis shows that this interest in women is a vicarious way of enjoying femininity (which correlates with male homosexuals identifying with the maleness of their partners[169]). This second type merely employs other women to exhibit femininity for them. (3) A third group is found in homosexual women who obtain gratification of feminine desires providing two conditions are met: that the penis is replaced by a surrogate, such as the tongue or finger, and that the partner using this organ is a woman instead of a man. Though clinically they may appear in the guise of completely homosexual women, such cases are nearest to the normal compared with both of the other two types described.

In the opinion of Jones identification with the father is thus common to all forms of homosexuality although it proceeds to a more complete degree in the first group than in the second, where in a vicarious way some femininity is after all retained. There is little doubt that identification serves the function of keeping feminine wishes in repression. It proclaims: "I cannot possibly desire a man's penis for my gratification, since I already possess one of my own, or at all events I want nothing else than one of my own."[119] This is surely the most complete defense against the aphanistic danger of privation from the non-gratification of the incest wishes. Jones remarks that this identification may be regarded as universal among young girls, and so we have to seek for motives which heighten this to an extraordinary extent. Those inborn factors which appear decisive are an unusually strong oral erotism and sadism which converge in an "intensification of the oral-sadistic stage." Jones regards this as the "central characteristic" of homosexual development in women.

de Saussure's work, "Homosexual Fixations Among Neurotic Women,"[164] is the only monograph on the subject. He concludes that at the root of homosexual fixations there is always a warped bisexuality which comes from the fact that the woman has not been able to accept her femininity. This refusal is conditioned by the idea of castration and penis envy. In his case material the identification with the woman becomes impossible and the girl identifies herself with her father in order to give a child to the mother. Homosexual fixations correspond to the patient's projections. More often she projects her femininity onto the mother and then onto other women who continue to represent the mother. Almost as often the patient, thwarted at not being able to satisfy her own masculine tendencies, exaggerates her feminine qualities, becomes excessively narcissistic and sees herself mirrored in some way in other women who have a high degree of feminine narcissism. In these cases, the woman projects her femininity onto others and enjoys an identification with herself. Finally, in homosexual fixations, we frequently find certain women refusing themselves to men, giving themselves to other women who have known how to make men suffer. It is their identification with their ideal of aggressiveness, with the superego (after C. Odier).

An aggressive murderous hate against the mother was revealed by Deutsch's analyses. Childhood memories (four to six years) which turned out to be the nucleus of some of her patients' inversions included the inhibition of masturbation by the mother and the inability of the father to aid the daughter in her distress. Homosexual tendencies always included a reproach against the father and a very strong reaction to the castration complex. With puberty the final decision as to choice of object and readiness for the passive attitude takes place. Developmentally, girls show much stronger dependence upon the mother during the latency period than do boys, although the cornerstone for later inversion had already been laid in the first infantile period.[34]

It was proposed by Brierley[26] that masochistic attitudes and fantasies concerning intercourse are a reflection and a fear of repetition of injury already experienced at the hands of the mother. These masochistic ideas have to do with disembowelment according to the internal life injuries of the Kleinian type. "It is these masochistic ideas which make the heterosexual position untenable. In these cases, however, homosexuality is not a way out too often because it is too sadistic." She firmly believes that most of these situations are not peculiar to women in the sense that there is no counterpart in male sexuality. Men have difficulties due to oral conflicts, failures in coordination of heterosexual and homosexual interests, and archaic superego formations. What seems to be specific in women is not any psychic drive as such but the *balance* which has to be achieved or maintained in order to produce an integrated feminine personality. This distribution of cathexis which might be normal in women would be abnormal in men and vice versa. "The only difference which we can register clinically seems to be differences in integration of drives common to both sexes . . . if we ever achieve a psychological definition of femininity it looks as if it might have to be a definition in terms of types of integration."[26]

By 1933 the preoedipal relation and its significance for the girl's later life began to assume more importance. Deutsch emphasized the identification with the active mother (after Freud) which as yet has no relation to the oedipus complex. In such play the child makes others suffer or enjoy what she has suffered or enjoyed in her relationship with the mother. If the libido remains attached to the original active and passive roles of the mother-child relationship, this play will be continued into later life in the guise of homosexuality. In the analysis of homosexual women Deutsch found that the preoedipal libidinal components appear repeatedly. "The situation is independent of the man; and in libidinal relationships only the role of mother and child are taken into account without reference to men."[36]

Brierley's further researches[27] suggested that there is some evidence that female genital impulses do appear even in the suckling period and, if they do, those impulses must be regarded as primary because they arise in the genital system itself. If they are (indeed) primary, they do constitute a specific instinctual determinant in feminine development and from that fact Brierley evolved her own theory of the development of female homosexuality. The occurrence of true vaginal activity in early infancy is associated with oral impulses. The relative weakness of the uro-vaginal system matters less than its establishment under pleasurable or painful conditions, namely, the degree of sadism with which it is invested. While endorsing Jones's view[119] concerning the role of oral sadism in the genesis of female homosexuality, what is significant is not the purely oral sadism but a strong blend of oral and urethral sadism. "Where the primitive oral-urethral system is highly charged relative to the other oral nuclei, it tends to retain its dominance in later life, and to produce overt homosexuality, or a life of sublimated activity without direct gratification."[27] To her mind, the accomplished fact is not frustration, as Freud stated, but separation from the nipple. From this point of view the girl's discovery of the lack of a penis is a painful rediscovery of the desolating fact that the vitally essential nipple is not her own. Brierley feels that what is common in homosexual women is not so much that they feel castrated as that they are convinced that they are the possessor of a bad penis and not a good one.

The recognition grew that the psychic situation of female homosexuals is indeed more complex than in males as was originally suggested by Freud.[63] Homosexual attachment which may be due to early sister rivalry is extremely widespread. In all cases Glover[100] noted that there are two complicating factors to be taken into account. First, the female passes through a negative mother attachment before reaching a positive father oedipus complex, not after, as in the case of the boy. Second, the castration anxiety links up with deeper fantasies of bodily mutilation than in the case of the male. The little girl believes that she has already suffered castration and that she is bound to suffer still further injury. In addition, penis dread is reinforced by earlier breast dread which in its turn was provoked by oral hate of the breast. Furthermore, the girl has had stronger sadistic reactions against the mother's insides, babies and reproductive organs.

Among the first to describe the girl's fantasies of phallic coitus with the mother was Lampl-de Groot.[138] This is a blow aimed at the mother which gratifies the girl's own narcissistic conceit and vindictiveness but which does not gratify her sensual love. Only later after puberty in some women is this fantasy given a sensual meaning and serves as a basis on which to construct a homosexual attitude.

Female homosexuality was traced back to what Rado[157] felt was its masochistic core: masochism derived from castration fear. The central source of danger for the masochistic woman is the man. The line of defense in her neurosis will be toward him. There are three types of defensive means at her disposal: flight, combat, and the choice of the lesser evil. It is the mechanism of flight which, if extreme, will lead to female homosexuality. However, the neurotic disturbance peculiar to female homosexuality is a sense of guilt, the avowed source of which is the perversion itself with its attendant exclusion from the group. This guilt has at its root a tormenting sense of inferiority, an uneasiness that one will be found inadequate, a fear of being exposed as ridiculous. The fear of exposure is a derivative and an expression of the fear of castration.

Fenichel[44,46] returned to the importance of the castration complex in the formation of female homosexuality. The repulsion from heterosexuality originates in the castration complex and the attraction through early fixation on the mother is of vital importance. These factors supplement each other. The fixation on the mother may have a protective and reassuring function balanced against the force of the castration complex.

The thesis that homosexuality and bisexuality are developmental and not constitutional in origin was enlarged upon by Bacon.[5] "Homosexuality and masculine identification may serve as a protection against anxiety. The mechanism by which homosexuality accomplishes so much is inherent in the tendency to reduce triangular relationships to two-way relationships. Giving up the father attachment, the girl goes back to a two-way relationship with the mother (sister) figure in which in fantasy all real love comes from the partner and all real giving goes to the partner. In spite of her disappointments in her father the patient is unable to go to another man because of fear of retaliation on the *father's part*."

The following unconscious psychic constellation, according to Bergler,[13] produces female homosexuality: (1) an aggressive dominating mother is the sole educator of the child and the father has a "weak personality"; (2) the child hates the mother and is incapable of splitting off the preoedipal ambivalent attitude toward her; (3) the oedipus complex therefore never reaches the normal height; (4) self-damaging tendencies predominate under a pseudo-aggressive facade. The decisive point often is that a female may have to handle an overwhelming compensatory hatred of her mother covering deep masochistic attachment and may choose the way of homosexuality.

Ego Psychology Considerations

Certain broader dynamic aspects of female sexuality must be considered in order to comprehend any special aspects of it.[170] The defensive aspects of female homosexuality and warding off guilt-laden fantasies are crucial for the role of object relations as are family constellations and the specific opportunities to make adequate identifications. The importance of Freud's dual instinct theory is therefore indispensable in analyzing female homosexuality. The fusion of aggressive and libidinal impulses, the presence of guilt and hostile aggressive drives, the need for punishment—all play important roles. In female as well as male homosexuality in general the preoedipal period and its subsequent influence on psychic structure and ego functioning are decisive for sexual orientation. The importance of early identifications and their influence on later development of female homosexuality was clearly outlined by Lichtenstein.[139]

Female homosexuality may to a large extent be analogous to male homosexuality except for one factor which complicates the clinical picture. With women the exclusion of heterosexual genitals can be achieved by regression. The first object of every human being is the mother. "All women, in contra-distinction to men, have a primary homosexual attachment which may later be revived if normal heterosexuality is blocked."[34] A man in this situation, Deutsch continues, has the possibility only of regression from object relationship to mother to "identification" with mother; a woman can regress from object relationship to father to object relationship to mother.

Often a young girl will respond to disappointment over her oedipal wishes with an identification with the father and consequently assume an active relation to women who represent mother substitutes. The attitude of these active masculine homosexual women toward their mother-equivalent objects is frequently combined with all the features of a wish-fulfillment type of female castration complex.

Klein[132] states that the goal of masculine women is in opposition to the pregenital aims of incorporation found in the feminine goal in men. In cases where frustration of the wishes for incorporation has led to a sadistic attack of taking by force what was not given, this force, originally often thought of as a penetration of the mother's body, may be remobilized into later masculinity.

Masculinity in women is not necessarily connected with homo-sexuality in Fenichel's view[44] but would depend upon two circum-stances: the intensity of the early fixation to the mother and on an especial configuration of the castration complex. Some active homo-sexual women after having identified themselves with their father choose young girls as love objects to serve as ideal representatives of their own person. They then behave toward these girls as they wished to have been treated by their father.

He goes on to describe another configuration which may be present. An antagonism between sisters becomes overcompensated and a mild homosexual love interwoven with a great deal of identification may develop. Beneath the latter lies the original hatred. In addition, the turning away from heterosexuality is a regression, reviving the memory traces of the earlier relationship to one's mother. Female homo-sexuality, therefore, has a more archaic imprint than male homosexu-ality.[46] It brings back the behavior patterns, aims, pleasures, but also the fear and conflicts, belonging to the earliest years of life. The usual activities of homosexual women consist mainly of the mutual playing of mother and child. Oral erotism is in the foreground as compared to anal erotism in the male.

Homosexuality has proved to be the product of specific mechanisms of defense which facilitate the persistence of the repression of both the oedipus and the castration complex. At the same time the aim of the homosexual object choice is the avoidance of the emotions around the castration complex which otherwise would disturb the sexual pleasure or at least the attainment of reassurances against them.[74,160]

It was observed by Bergler,[13] Glover[100] and Jones[119] that the hatred of the mother may produce an intense sense of guilt which may then lead to transformation of the hate into a masochistic libidinal attitude. Often the fundamental attitude, "I do not hate you, I love you," originally held toward the mother is reflected in not only the form of direct oral satisfaction in homosexual intercourse with a young girl but also in the submissive-passive attitude toward an older love partner. The homosexual woman may transform the hate toward her mother into love while she is giving the mother's breast to her partner. At the same time she can be the active suckling mother and thereby transform the aggression into activity.

The result of direct prohibitions of masturbation and forceful interference with masturbatory activity, Deutsch wrote,[35] may also arouse hostility against the disciplining mother to a high pitch. If, at the same time, the discovery of the anatomic defect is made known, the girl blames the mother for her deprivation. The sadistic impulses of the phallic phase are directed against the mother and become the impetus for the change of object. The change in the direction of a sadistic attitude toward the mother facilitates the passive-masochistic attitude toward the father. This Deutsch calls "the thrust into passivity." Aggression is not entirely conducted, however, into this passive attitude. Much of the aggressive impulse is turned against the disappointing father and much remains attached to the mother who is now regarded as a rival. The intensity in any case is dependent upon the strength of the phallic activity. However, the passive attitude as regards the development of masochism is full of danger; the patient has bloodthirsty and murderous revenge wishes toward the mother, especially the pregnant mother or one who already has another child. This aggression leads to guilt and the new turning to the mother lies in the release from the feeling of guilt together with the protection from the threatened loss of object. "If my father won't have me and my self-respect is undermined, who will love me if not my mother?" In homosexuality free rein is given to masturbation. These are motives held in common by all forms of female homosexuality. This is a new edition of the mother-child relationship bringing along with it the compensation and satisfaction derived from these activities.

In all female homosexuality there is an element of identification with the object. If we apply this to Jones's classification,[119] we find that members of his first group, that is, those interested in men, exchange their own sex but retain their first love object. The object relationship, however, becomes replaced by identification and the aim of the libido is to procure recognition of this identification. Members of the second group, those interested in women, also identify themselves with the love object but then lose further interest in her; the external object relationship to another woman is very imperfect for she merely represents their own femininity through identification, and their aim is vicariously to enjoy the gratification of this at the hand of the unseen man (the father incorporated in themselves). The identification with the father requires emphasis as it is common to all forms of female homosexuality, though it proceeds to a more complete degree in Jones's first group than in the second, wherein in a vicarious way some femininity is after all retained. Identification serves the function of keeping feminine wishes in repression and constitutes the most complete denial imaginable of harboring guilty feminine wishes.

Certain factors lend their imprint to female homosexuality. In protecting herself against aphanisis the girl in late childhood and adolescence erects various barriers, notably penis identification, against her femininity. Prominent among these is a strong sense of guilt and condemnation concerning feminine wishes, most often unconscious. As an aid to this barrier of guilt she develops the idea that her father and other men are strongly opposed to feminine wishes. To ease her self-condemnation she is forced to believe that all men in their hearts disapprove of femininity.[119]

Bonaparte[24] made some correlations between types of homosexual women and prognosis in therapy. There are some women who refuse to abandon their masculinity and will neither give up their first love object nor the phallic predominated erotogenic zone. Others again, though they succeed in passing from the mother to the father as the love object, and though they cannot conceive of a love object so contemptible as to lack a phallus, nonetheless cling tenaciously to the predominating phallic erotogenic zone and with that organ, essentially male and inappropriate to the feminine function, will love and desire love objects that are themselves malelike.

Clitoridal women, whether manifestly homosexual or, having passed from the mother to the father, successful in developing the object relation proper to the female may always unconsciously remain mostly passively fixated, cloacally and phallically, on the mother they knew when a child. If manifest homosexuals, they continually re-enact the primary scene of active-passive alternations of the mother's ministering to the baby. The most active among them, superimposing her identification with the father on the primary identification with the active mother, will become the more specifically active type of homosexual female.[24]

Chapter VI

THEORY OF PREOEDIPAL ORIGIN

THIS PREOEDIPAL THEORY of genesis rests on two pillars. The first is the presence of a fixation in the undifferentiated phase of development.[53] The second is the utilization and application of the Hanns Sachs mechanism[160] of sexual perversions. It is restricted to the origin of overt male homosexuality of the obligatory type, not due to situational or variational motivation, where non-engagement in homosexual practices would, in all cases, induce intolerable anxiety.

Pathological development toward homosexuality has been ascribed to all phases of development. Clinical studies for the most part have considered homosexuality to be largely an outcome of oedipal conflict. We find numerous references which laid the groundwork for this theoretical formulation.

Freud[74] first emphasized that homosexuality arises as a defense against castration anxiety. Three years later, however, he stressed the premature fixation of the libido as a most significant factor in the genesis of homosexuality.[78] In the "Three Essays"[63] he had already seen that homosexuals experience a very strong mother fixation. Upon leaving this attachment they continue to identify with the mother, taking themselves narcissistically as their sexual object by searching for men who resemble themselves whom they then can love as they wish their mother had loved them. Investigations of the genetic constellations responsible for this developmental inhibition showed (a) an overstrong mother fixation with resultant running away from women and a transferring of excitation from women to men in a narcissistic fashion, and (b) an early positive oedipus complex of great intensity. Significantly he commented that one finds in homosexuals "a predominance of archaic and primitive psychical mechanisms."[63]

In *An Outline of Psychoanalysis*,[90] Freud stated: ". . . genital organization will be attained, but will be weakened in respect of those portions of the libido which have not proceeded so far but have remained fixated to pregenital objects and aims. Such weakening shows itself in a tendency, if there is an absence of genital satisfaction or if there are difficulties in the real world, for the libido to return to its earlier pregenital cathexis." Inhibitions of libido in the course of its development produce various disturbances of sexual life—one example of inhibition being manifest homosexuality. "Fixations of the libido to conditions at earlier phases are then found, the trend of which, moving independently of the normal sexual aim, is described as *perversion*." Despite our knowledge of some of the psychical mechanisms involved, psychoanalysis "has not yet produced a complete explanation of the origin of inversion. . . ."[90] Whether the homosexual fixation belongs to the preoedipal or oedipal period has remained problematic as has the extent of the role of regression as a contributing factor.

Significant contributions as to psychical events occurring in the preoedipal period have hinted at the resolution of the problem of genesis. Bychowski[29] studying the affinities between schizophrenic and homosexual groups found in both related if not similar infantilisms of libidinal organizations and primitive features of the ego (its introjects). He contends that the peculiar weakness of the homosexual ego is based on its narcissistic and prenarcissistic disposition. It is fixated in a stage preceding the formation of a distinct ego.[169]

Melanie Klein[130] and her co-workers[107,159] have demonstrated that perversions may be related to the earliest oral sadistic impulses of forcing the self into another object. In this work the import of early excessive aggression and libidinal impulses and their attempted relief through introjective and projective mechanisms was set forth.

The genesis of homosexuality is the result of disturbances which occur earlier than was generally assumed—having taken place in the so-called "undifferentiated phase."[53] This phase is not truly undifferentiated but is already manifesting important beginnings of structure formation.[4,106] Fixation to the mother and the characteristically narcissistic object choice of the homosexual may be traced back to the undifferentiated phase of the mother-child unity. It may be assumed that relations as they develop out of the original unity in the undifferentiated phase are the forerunners of later object relations. Qualitative and quantitative factors, specifically the divergent tendencies in the separation processes beginning at birth—one leading to separateness and differentiation and the other toward retaining the primitive state of the original unity— leave their imprint on the developing modes of instinctual manifestations and on ego formation. They exercise a determining influence in the structuring of the introjects and their subsequent projection onto the external world.

The fantasies and latent dream thoughts of the adult about his earliest experiences are representative of what once was the earliest reality. Thus external situations become internalized in the structure of the ego. Introjection and projection are ego building mechanisms of the infant, becoming, through change of function, defensive devices of the child's developing ego.

The normal child successfully establishes his own identity as a prerequisite to the onset of both true object relations and partial identifications with parents. "The preoedipal child, vacillating between heterosexual and homosexual, between active and passive strivings, still enjoys the freedom to assume, playfully, various roles: in fantasy, in attitudes or actions, on a more or less primitive ego level, he may alternately identify at one time with the father, at another time with the mother, with an older sibling, or with a rival baby. I have also remarked that fantasies of merging with the mother are considered a normal phenomenon up to the age of three; but the child's discovery and establishment of his sexual identity, which reflects his instinctual advancement to the genital level, considerably reduces the freedom to play various roles."[116]

To the homosexual, the mother has, in infancy, been, on the one hand, dangerous and frightening, forcing separation, threatening the infant with loss of love and care; on the other hand, the mother's conscious and unconscious tendencies were felt as working against separation. Anxiety and frustration press for withdrawal of libidinal cathexis from the mother and result in a shift of libido economy toward increased aggression. This image of the introjected mother leads to a rupture (split) in the ego. In his narcissistic object choice, the homosexual not only loves his partner as he himself wished to be loved by the mother, but reacts to him with sadistic aggression as once experienced toward the hostile mother for forcing separation.

The unconscious hostility reinforces the denial of any loving and giving aspects of the mother. The homosexual seeks to rediscover in his object choice—in the most distorted ways—the primary reality of his narcissistic relationship with the different images of the mother (and later of the father) as they were first experienced. The first introjection of the mother image predisposes the pattern of later introjections.

Homosexuality, therefore, can be seen as a resolution of the separation from the mother by running away from all women. In fantasies and actions, in reality, in the compulsive hunting for partners, the homosexual is unconsciously searching for the lost objects, seeking to find the narcissistic realtionships he once experienced in the mother-child symbiosis. The homosexual is trying to undo the separation and also remain close to his mother in a substitutive way, by using the male. He is trying to be one with her and to seek out the reduplication of himself as an object. This is performed through substitution, displacement, and repression. The mounting evidence of preoedipal conflicts as the causative factor in the formation of homosexuality has required the pinpointing of a mechanism by which conflict could be transformed into homosexuality. In 1923, Sachs provided psychoanalysis with the first valid explanation of the mechanism of sexual perversion. This discovery has not been widely applied to clinical material and the paper remained untranslated up to the present time.[160]

The Sachs Mechanism

In homosexuality a particularly suitable portion of the infantile experience or fantasy is preserved through the vicissitudes of childhood and puberty and remains in the conscious mind. The rest of the representatives of the instinctual drives have succumbed to repression instigated by their all too strong need for gratification or stimulation. The pleasurable sensations belonging to infantile sexuality in general are now displaced onto the conscious "suitable portion of infantile experience." This conscious suitable portion is now supported and endowed with a high pleasure reward—so high, indeed, that it competes successfully with the primacy of the genitals. What makes this fragment particularly suitable? The pregenital stage of development upon which the homosexual is especially strongly fixated must be included in it; the extremely powerful partial drive must find its particular form of gratification in it; and it must have some special relationship to the ego which allows this particular fragment to escape repression.

In obsessional neuroses we know it is the split between affect and thought but in homosexuality the conscious is by no means indifferent; on the contrary, a high pleasure reward is experienced. We are therefore dealing with something special, something else, to which the phenomenon of homosexuality is related. One must remember that in the ego itself unconscious elements are present, e.g., guilt and resistance. Instinctual drives themselves are in a continual struggle through the developmental stages of life. The complete subjugation of one which grants much pleasure may not be possible. Very often what we have to resign ourselves to is a compromise, allowing pleasure to remain in a partial complex to be taken up into the ego and to be sanctioned while the remaining components are detached and are repressed more easily. This separation or split "in which the one piece (of infantile sexuality) enters into the service of the repression and thus carries over into the ego the pleasure of a preoedipal stage of development, while the rest falls victim to repression, appears to be the mechanism of perversion."[160]

We know that the most difficult work of repression is almost always the detachment from the infantile object choice, the oedipus complex and the castration complex. The partial drive does not continue directly into a perversion or homosexuality but only after it has passed through the permutations of the oedipal conflict. This is a kind of working over that wipes out traces of the oedipus complex, eliminates for example, the important individuals involved, eliminates one's own self-involvement, and the product becomes the perverse fantasy. It can enter consciousness and can yield pleasure.

It would follow that fantasies which lie outside the circle of infantile sexual gratification present themselves as a "way out." For instance, in male homosexuality there is an extremely strong fixation on the mother which cannot be dealt with. The end result becomes a fixation on one's own sex as a result of narcissism and in the retreat from later castration anxiety. This is incorporated into the ego and is acceptable to it.

In essence there has been taken over into the ego a portion of what would otherwise be repressed. Nonetheless the rest of the repressed portion may still remain strong enough so that in the course of life it may threaten a breakthrough and the homosexual may, at any time, develop neurotic symptoms.

In homosexuality the instinctual gratification takes place in a disguised form while its real content remains unconscious. We must constantly re-emphasize that we are not dealing with an aspect of infantile sexuality which was allowed into consciousness and which the ego could somehow tolerate; the homosexual symptom does not come about simply because the boy, once disturbed in his sexuality by castration fear, regressed to that component of his infantile sexuality which once in chidlhood gave him security or at least reassurance against his fears and at the same time obtained orgastic relief. We must keep in mind that the overemphasis on the infantile expression of his sexuality simultaneously serves to reassure him and to maintain a repression of his oedipal conflicts and other warded-off remnants of infantile sexuality. This is a partial repression of infantile sexuality wherein other parts are exaggerated. Repression itself is facilitated in homosexuality through the added dividend of some other aspects of infantile sexuality being consciously stressed.

To recapitulate: homosexuality is a living relic of the past testifying to the fact that there was once a conflict involving an especially strongly developed component instinct in which complete victory was impossible for the ego and repression was only partially successful. The ego had to be content with the compromise of repressing the greater part of infantile libidinal strivings (primary identification with the mother, intense unneutralized aggression toward her, dread of separation) at the expense of sanctioning and taking into itself the smaller part.

The repression of wishes to penetrate the mother's body or the wish to suck and incorporate and injure the mother's breast undergoes repression. In these instances a piece of the infantile libidinal strivings has entered the service of repression through displacement and substitution. Instead of the mother's body being penetrated, sucked, injured, incorporated, it is the male partner's body which undergoes this fate; instead of the mother's breast, it is the penis with which the patient interacts. Perversion thus becomes the choice of the lesser evil.

Two defense mechanisms, identification and substitution, play a crucial part in the framework of the above structure. The homosexual makes an identification with the masculinity of his partner in the sexual act. In order to defend himself against the positive oedipus complex, that is, his love for his mother and hatred for his father and punitive aggressive destructive drives toward the body of his mother, the homosexual substitutes the partner's body and penis for the mother's breast. Homosexuals desperately need and seek a contact whenever they feel weakened, frightened, depleted, guilty, ashamed or in any way helpless or powerless. In the patients' words, they want their "shot" of masculinity. They then feel miraculously well and strengthened and avoid disintegrative phenomena. They instantaneously feel reintegrated upon achieving orgasm with a male partner. All their pain, fear and weakness disappear for the time being; they feel well and whole again.

The male partners whom they pursue are representatives of their own self in relation to an active phallic mother. There are two parts to this concept. The first is an identification with a partner of the same sex. In this way they thereby achieve masculinity through identification with the partner's penis. The man chosen as a partner represents one's forfeited masculinity regained.

The second part concerns the maternal breast: the penis of the male partner becomes the substitute for the mother's breast. In every homosexual encounter there is a hidden continuation of the close tie to the mother through the breast-penis equation. The reassuring presence of the penis in place of the breast allows the homosexual to feel that he is faithful and loyal to and simultaneously maintaining the tie to the mother but at a safe distance from her. He divests himself of oedipal guilt by demonstrating to her that he could have no possible interest in other females. He is interested only in men. Furthermore, he is protecting the mother against the onslaught of other men's penises, allowing penetration into himself instead.

The homosexual comes to realize in later phases of treatment that he is engaged in an act of major self-deception, having been victimized into sexual activity with individuals of the same sex by certain intricate psychic transformations. He has not given up his maleness at all; he urgently and desperately wants to be a man but is able to do this only by identifying with the masculinity and penis of his partner in the sexual act.

Homosexuality thus serves to protect the personality against regression. If homosexual behavior did not occur the patient would proceed to the extreme of regression which would lead to a reinstating of the undifferentiated phase with loss of ego boundaries and dissolution of self. Overt homosexuality is crucial for the survival of the ego when it is faced with the catastrophic situation of imminent merging with the mother and the pull toward the undifferentiated phase of development.

The Preoedipal Nuclear Conflict

It is my belief that in all homosexuals there has been an inability to make the progression from the mother-child unity of earliest infancy to individuation. As a result there exists in homosexuals a fixation, with the concomitant tendency to regression, to the earliest mother-child relationship. This is manifested as a threat of personal annihilation, loss of ego boundaries and sense of fragmentation.

Child analysts who have studied the data of infant and early child development by direct observation conclude that "in the second year of life the infant gradually changes from an almost completely vegetative being, symbiotically dependent on the mother, into a separate individual . . . he becomes increasingly aware of his own capacities as well as of his own separateness. This apperception is however still a very precarious one at 12 to 13 months of age. During the second year of life it is the maturational growth of locomotion which exposes the infant to the important experience of deliberate and active bodily separation from and reunion with the mother . . . providing he feels his mother's encouragement and availability. . . . This is that second 18 month period of life in which pregenital libidinal phases progress in a rapid and overlapping procession. Yet this same period is no less fateful as far as the infant's ego development and object relationships are concerned."[147] The period from 12/18 to 36 months is termed the "separa-tion-individuation phase of personality development . . . the character-istic fear of which is separation anxiety. If the symbiotic and separation-individuation phases were normal, however, from three-and-a-half on, the child should increasingly be able to respond to the mother as a 'whole mother' . . . one who can both gratify and disturb him."[147]

The homosexual repeatedly demonstrates that he was unable to make these advances. In a child so unsuccessful ". . . the fear of re-engulfment threatens a recently and barely started individual differentiation . . . beyond the 15 to 18 month mark, the primary stage of unity and identity with mother ceases to be constructive for the evolution of the ego in an object world."[147] By this age the father has become an im-portant object which ordinarily has the advantage. ". . . the inner image of the father has never drawn to itself so much of the unneutra-lized drive cathexis as has the mother's and therefore there is less discrepancy between the image of father and the real father. . . . From the very beginning, the infant creates the world in his own image, wherein the symbiotic partner is the indispensable catalyst and beacon of orientation."[147]

During the separation-individuation phase (18 to 36 months) the infant is attempting to evolve and jealously guard his developing self-image "from infringement by the mother and other important figures . . . a quasi-normal negativistic phase . . ." can be observed along with "all the process of disengagement from the mother-child symbiosis." The more parasitic the symbiotic phase "the more prominent and exaggerated will be this negativistic reaction." If there is severe nega-tivism there is a severe fear of re-engulfment ". . . inasmuch as all happenings in the symbiotic phase are dominated by orality, the infant furthermore loses the necessary and normal delusional experience of incorporating and thus having the good mother in himself, restoring the blissful state of omnipotent fusion with the mother. . . . Instead, he struggles in impotent rage and panic, with the catastrophic fear of annihilation, by introjected bad objects, without being able to success-fully invoke the good part object, the soothing breast of the ministering mother."[147]

Often the "symbiotic parasitic mother cannot endure the loss of her hitherto and vegetative appendage. . . ." This is the type of mother-child relationship found in the study of homosexual patients. The father could constitute an important support against the threat of maternal engulfment but this resource is totally absent. It is as if the male partner were the father to whom the son is looking for the salvation from engulfment. . . . He remains entirely faithful to the mother, but his object hunger . . . drives him to seek the penis as a substitute for the breast." In actuality there is a complete lack of the needed support from either parent. Under such conditions "a re-engulfment of the ego into the whirlpool of the primary undifferentiated symbiotic stage becomes a true threat."[147]

Spitz[174] has shown that "when a psychological development which is age adequate for a given critical period cannot take place, it will be difficult, if not impossible, for the individual to acquire it at a later stage. . . ." This is because "at the appropriate critical period a given item of psychological development will find all the maturational conditions favorable for its establishment." He called this "maturational compliance" and its counterpart is "developmental (psychological) compliance." There must be a "synchronicity of maturation and development . . . an absolutely essential feature of normal development." Spitz showed that if a child does not have the wish to walk when the maturation of the innervation of the lower part of the body enables it to walk the child may later be unable to stand or walk with support. Later ". . . as a consequence of a traumatic affect deprivation, he regressed to the stage where he could neither walk nor stand nor sit. . . . If, during the critical period, the appropriate (psychological) developmental item is not forthcoming, then the maturational factors will seize on other (psychological) developmental items available. These developmental items will be modified and distorted until they comply with the maturational needs, an integration will be established which deviates from the norm. . . . As a result when the by-passed (psychological) developmental item finally does become available at a later stage, it will find the maturational positions occupied by compensating, though deviant, structures and unavailable for normal integration." Deficiencies in adaptation are "pivotal points for pathological regression . . . and play a major role in the etiology of psychiatric disease."[174]

Spitz's observations can be applied to the problem of the early development of the homosexual. He has failed to make the separation from the mother at the proper stage of development and as a result there remains a chronic intrapsychic stimulation or fixation point to which he remains fixed despite other developmental maturational phases that he may have in part successfully passed. In these maturational positions there have been compensating and deviant structures formed because of the infantile deficiency, in an attempt to make up for the deficits. These structures are intimately concerned with identification, faulty ego boundaries, introjective and projective anxieties, fears of invasion and engulfment.

Recapitulation

The nuclear conflicts of homosexuals derive from the earliest period of life forcing them into choosing partners of the same sex for ego survival. The homosexual has been unable to pass successfully through the symbiotic and the separation-individuation phases of early childhood. As a result of this maturational (psychological) developmental failure there are severe ego deficits. Homosexuality serves the repression of a pivotal nuclear complex: the drive to regress to a preoedipal fixation in which there is a desire for and dread of merging with mother in order to reinstate the primitive mother-child unity.

In the mother-child unity one can discern (1) a wish for and fear of incorporation; (2) a threatened loss of personal identity and personal dissolution; (3) guilt feelings because of a desire to invade the body of the mother; (4) an intense desire to cling to the mother which later develops in the oedipal period into a wish for and fear of incestuous relations with her; (5) intense aggression of a primitive nature toward the mother.

At a conscious level the patient attempts to compensate for his primary nuclear conflict by certain activities designed to enclose, ward off and encyst the isolated affective state of the mother-child unity. Therefore he does not approach any other woman, especially sexually, as this will activate the fear of the mother-child unity and he does not attempt to "leave" mother because he feels this would only provoke engulfing, incorporative tendencies on her part. Any attempt by him to separate produces an exacerbation of his unconscious ties. He therefore attempts instead to keep the "safest closeness" to her all the while remaining asexual as regards other females. All sexual satisfactions are carried out through substitution, displacement and other defense mechanisms. Having already made a feminine identification he restores strength through transitory male identification with his male partner. Substituting a man for sexual intercourse the homosexual is unconsciously enjoying sexual closeness to both mother and father simultaneously.

The homosexual is fixated on his wish for and dread of the mother-child unity. This connotes a tendency to regress to the undifferentiated phase with a total destruction of self in union with the mother, an event to be avoided at all costs. The homosexual's life and development are designed to forestall and prevent the realization of this powerful affective state. Homosexual behavior is the solution to the intolerable anxiety connected with the pull to return to the amorphous, undifferentiated phase of ego development. The homosexual object choice (achieved through the Sachs mechanism) is crucial to the repression of the basic conflict: the fear and dread of mother-child unity.

Chapter VII

THE ROLE OF AGGRESSION

In the "Three Essays," Freud anticipated the importance of the aggressive impulse in perversions when he stated that in homosexuals one finds a "predominance of archaic and primitive psychical mechanisms."[63]

He described certain cases of homosexuality in a later paper where the homosexual love relationship is based on a defense against earlier intense jealousy of and aggression toward rival brothers.[78] Freud subsequently elucidated the problems of masochism and sadism with special relevance to the death instinct and their connection with homosexuality.[82]

Ferenczi[50] gave his views on the special relationship of aggression to homosexuality. Regarding a male homosexual he stated: "Whenever this man felt himself offended by a man, especially by a superior, immediately he had to go hunt up a male prostitute. Only in this way was he in a position to avoid an outbreak of fury. The alleged love for the male was here essentially the act of violence and revenge." The importance that hostility has in the genesis of homosexuality was stressed by Boehm.[21] "Hostility toward the father induced guilt feelings, a fear of retaliation from men and a wish to disguise the hate into love of men." Sachs[160] observed that repressive efforts are directed not only against libidinal instincts but aggressive instincts as well in an attempt to ward off positive oedipus complex and castration fears.

Describing perversions in terms of partial failure of defense against or a disturbance of the process of desexualization of instinctual energy, Alexander included the instinctual energy of aggression as well as of libido.[3]

In certain types of homosexuals, Nunberg[153] showed that aggression plays an integral part. A boy may become homosexual out of the inhibition or restraint of aggression against the brothers or the father, that is he may flee from aggression. Another type is one in which aggression is not avoided but, on the contrary, makes up an integral part of the subject's homosexual life. (A similar mechanism, i.e., aggression making up an integral part of the subject's homosexual love, is found very often in the female.) In these cases Nunberg felt that the aim of the homosexual represents a compromise—a compromise between aggressive and libidinal impulses. Pure types of homosexuality, according to him, are: those which represent a flight from the woman due to the fear of incest; those representing an identification with the mother; those which result from inhibition or restraint of aggression; those in which aggression is not avoided. Various characteristics of differing types are intermingled. The disguised aggression type is very prevalent and in this type the patient, through contact with a masculine man, believes he himself will become masculine. We note here the similarity to Anna Freud's[58] later concept with stress on the identification with the male partner as a basic mechanism in male homosexuality.

In one of Nunberg's cases the mother stored up hatred for the father so that love assumed the form of the aggression which much earlier must have existed alongside her love. The mother stated, "Your father has deserted you. He doesn't support you any more so you are small and weakly. If you want to become a big, strong man go to your father and get money from him." Money here stood for food and nourishment and, as the patient conceived it, masculinity-virility. In this patient it was as if through some mutual congress with men he himself became masculine.

Nunberg's comments on paranoia yield much fruitful information. For example, the case of a paranoid brought home to him for the first time that anal homosexuality is not only gratification of the libido but gratification of the impulses of aggression as well. This led him to compare in retrospect the non-psychotic homosexual and from this comparison he realized that aggression plays an important part not only in the object choice of the paranoid but in homosexuality in general and is at least to be regarded as characteristic of a certain type of homosexual. All of Nunberg's cases showed certain paranoid tendencies such as marked ideas of reference and of persecution. The patient whom he described in detail had mild delusions of being poisoned. None of these cases, however, exhibited any other paranoid symptoms and none subsequently developed a psychosis. It therefore seems as though this type of homosexuality has a somewhat close relationship to paranoia. It possibly represents some intermediate stage between neurosis and psychosis. The homosexual, having projected his ideal of a handsome, strong, tall man onto the outside world, then searches for him, turning his aggression toward the outside world. In paranoia, however, libido or aggression is turned toward or against the ego. Nunberg cautions that this is not the only difference between paranoia and homosexuality.

Rosenfeld's clinical material[159] demonstrated that paranoid anxieties arising from intense aggression encouraged the development of strong manifest or latent homosexuality as a defense. Clinical paranoia may result when the homosexual defense fails. Furthermore, the idealized good father figure is used to deny the existence of the persecutor, the hated aggressive figure. The mechanism of projective identification in homosexuals can be traced back to infantile impulses of aggressively forcing the self, not just the penis, into the mother.

The role of aggression has received considerable attention, particularly by Bychowski[32] and Bak,[7] who describe the inability of the ego of the homosexual to neutralize aggression. According to Bak this is due to excessive early stimulation of aggression; homosexuality becomes a regressive adaptation through identification with the mother. This helps resolve the destructive impulses originally invested in her and at the same time libidinizes the aggression toward the rival of the same sex. In this paper Bak[7] reported on a clinical example in which danger of destruction of the object led to a perverse defense against it.

In a 1951 panel on perversions,[4] the defense against retaliation from aggressive feelings was stressed. Other contributions have been made by Freeman,[56] Nacht et al.,[152] Rosenfeld,[159] Thorner[176] and Payne.[156]

Emphasis is placed on the sudden release of undifferentiated aggressive-libidinal impulses by Bychowski.[30] These releases constitute brief attempts at establishing contact with objects because the poorly structured ego of the homosexual has not succeeded in binding instinctual energies of the primary process. This facilitates chance encounters with pseudo-objects and leads the homosexual to attempt to incorporate the power of his partner through the homosexual act. However, the ego has never separated itself from the mother and the homosexual perversion is an attempt at a social experience on a regressive level.[29]

Melanie Klein[132] focused on the role of the *earliest* aggressive impulses with their associated anxieties and the defense mechanisms of introjection and projection in the development of homosexuality. It was suggested by Glover[99] that perversions may form a developmental series reflecting stages in the overcoming of anxiety concerning the individual's own body or external objects. They represent attempts at introjection and projection of anxieties by means of excessive libidinization. Certain perversions are the negative of psychotic formations and "have to patch over flaws in the development of reality sense." Jones's paper, "The Phallic Phase,"[120] is also relevant in this regard. These and similar contributions show not only the importance of the aggressive impulse but the close relationship which exists between perversion and psychosis. Perversions may be to a large extent the negative of certain psychotic formations, libidinization and idealization of the object being exploited as a defense against aggression and concomitant paranoid anxieties.

The vacillation between submission and hostility in the homosexual act was underscored by Miller.[151] Simultaneous aggression and submission may be expressed in such acts because these individuals lack a strong masculine identification and have not worked out a submission-aggression pattern. When an aggressive urge is stimulated their identification is forever with the mother and the expression of strong aggression is through the medium of female identification. Obviously the masculine identification with the virile father is inhibited or underdeveloped and the person's hostility and erotization seeks expression based on the identification with the female.

Orality and Aggressive Impulses

Bergler and Eidelberg[10] ascribed the origin of male homosexuality to intensive hate against the mother and the attendant oral character traits. There is an excessive desire to eat, suck, bite, drink the breasts and milk of the mother with reactions of oedipal hate against the father, a simultaneous effort at repressing interest in the breast, a rise in secondary narcissism, and an intensified tendency toward female identification. Since the breast had failed the child he was compelled to bear this deprivation; as a result there arose a quantitative increase in aggression. This oral-sadism and oral-erotism had been previously investigated by Glover[98] and Abraham.[1]

A special feature, according to Jones,[119] was the importance of the tongue in female homosexuals. The identification of tongue with penis showed the former's extraordinary degree of substitution value: "It is evident that the nipple fixation here implies . . . development of homosexuality in two ways: it makes it harder for the girl to pass from the fellatio position to that of vaginal coitus; it also makes it easier to have recourse once more to a woman as the object of libido."

The two factors referred to above, oral-erotism and oral-sadism, appear to correspond very well with two classes of female homosexuals. Where oral-erotism is the more prominent an individual will probably belong to a group in which she (the female homosexual) has an exclusive interest in women but is nevertheless actually the closer of the two types to the path of heterosexuality. If oral-sadism is more prominent, the female homosexual is likely to show manifest interest in men and in masculine activities.[119]

Female homosexuals have a deep dread of being punished for their oral-sadism. While punishment may stem from either parent, in the heterosexual female this dread relates primarily to the mother; in the homosexual it is primarily the dread of paternal punishment. In the heterosexual this fear of punishment seems to be a simple retaliation for the death wishes against the mother who will punish the girl by coming between her and the father. The girl's answer is partly to retain her femininity at the cost of renouncing the father and partly to obtain vicarious gratification of her incest wishes in her imagination through her identification with the mother. When dread of punishment comes from the father it takes the obvious form of his withholding gratification of her wishes and thus rapidly passing over to the idea of his disapproval of them. Consciously this may be expressed as fears of his rebuff and desertion. If this privation takes place on the oral plane the answer is resentment and castrating biting fantasies. If it takes place on the later anal plane then the outcome is rather more favorable. Here the girl manages to combine her erotic wishes with the ideas of punishment in a single act, namely, that of anal-vaginal rape. The familiar fantasies of being beaten are, of course, a derivative of this. This is one way in which incest gets equated with castration so that the fantasy of having a penis is a protection against both.

Superego Factors

Little consideration has been given to the role of the superego in the formation of perversions. Pregenital and archaic superego formations, as well as the oedipal ones, operate in all perversions in order to prevent destructive impulses toward the object which threaten both the self and object. The superego of the homosexual is primitive and does not allow him to approach a woman since he has a primitive sadistic concept of heterosexual relations.[32]

Parental sanctioning of homosexual behavior has been studied by Litin et al.[140] and Kolb and Johnson,[4,133] the mother's behavior being over-seductive and frustrating and sanctioning the boy's homosexuality, as is frequently found in male patients. The parents' own unstable bisexual identification as well as their own defective superego contribute in multiple ways to the development and reinforcement of homosexuality. These parents consider pregenital sexuality as more permissible than genital sexuality due to their own superego difficulties.

A detailed exposition of superego influences and the effect of guilt on the promotion and maintenance of a homosexual adaptation is presented in Chapter VIII (Patient V).

Chapter VIII

PROJECTION AND IDENTIFICATION

The Projective Mechanism

ONE MUST TAKE NOTE here of a most serious complication which often appears in homosexual patients: severe conscious and unconscious paranoid tendencies are frequently found in overt homosexuals who show no other evidence of clinical psychosis. The presence of projective processes in homosexual patients contribute the most challenging complication in therapy. These can be traced back to paranoid anxieties occurring in the earliest years of life. It is wise to assume that homosexual patients, despite the homosexual defense against it, are still subject to onslaughts of paranoid ideation.

Homosexuality is related to the idealization of the good father figure.[159] In the most severe cases this idealization is used to deny the existence of the father-persecutor; in milder cases, to deny the existence of the hostile, cold, antagonistic father. Persecution goes beyond these other modalities of rejection. Through the use of the projection mechanism another man becomes identified with the self. The origin of projective identification can be traced back to its root, namely, the earliest infantile impulses of forcing the self into the mother.[131] M. Klein[130] has termed this the "paranoid position" and it may be responsible for the frequent combination of paranoia and homosexuality. The loss of masculinity and the penis, which is implicit in homosexuality, is willingly accepted by these patients in order to ward off the greater danger of personal annihilation. Homosexuality in these cases is a specific defense where the persecutor is appeased by homosexual intercourse.[159]

The mechanism of projection is seen in the patient who is attracted to a young man representing the patient himself. Freud defined this as a man treating another man as he wished to have been treated in the past by his mother. It may be seen that the mechanism of narcissistic attraction weighs a great deal. "It is frequently the projection of parts of the self, particularly the penis, into another man which causes the narcissistic homosexual attraction."[159]

Anna Freud[58,59] stressed the projection of the good and potent penis onto other men but she relates this specifically to the phallic phase. The origin of this projection mechanism, however, lies in the early oral-sadistic impulses of forcing the self into another object. The impulses to force oneself into the mother, which belong to the earliest phases of infancy, are strongly present in homosexuals and have been reinforced later in life by regression and by the over-powering attitude of the mother who has ruled the patient's life and virtually forced her ideas into him from earliest childhood.

These oral-sadistic impulses may be partially transferred onto the father at an early age and constitute the most important fixation point both of homosexuality and paranoia. They are responsible for the prevalence of projection mechanisms. Clinically, the homosexual fantasies, paranoid attitude and preoccupation gradually begin to disappear only after the whole early and later structure of the relationship to the mother is fully understood and worked through in the transference and the need and desire to project have been considerably diminished.

Mechanism of Identification

The mechanism of identification plays a crucial part in the development of homosexuality.[47] The continued *primary identification* with the mother arises from the inability to make the separation from her during the separation-individuation phase of development. The child continues beyond the preoedipal period to believe that the mother is all-powerful, all-controlling and is the only one to protect his interests and insure survival. The absence of a strong father furthermore predisposes the child to this primary identification and precludes a shift to identification with the father. The boy later becomes painfully aware of this lack of masculine identification and searches for it in his homosexual relations. He seeks partners who represent strong masculine figures and who would give him almost by "transfusion" the missing masculine attributes which diminish and deprive him, make him feel empty and demasculinized.

It is crucial to separate the primary identification with mother from the *secondary identification* with the male as achieved in homosexuality. The latter is completely transitory and must be continually replenished by male love objects. In the female homosexual the identification is with mother and only secondarily is a masculine identification established in order to avoid oedipus complex feelings and conflict and to escape the fearful merging phenomenon with the sadistic, poisonous and malevolent mother.

The homosexual man may also in another sense identify with mother in that he makes an identification with the aggressor. This has an economic aspect in that he need not fear attack from her as long as he remains identified with her. He also avoids oedipal feelings and cannot be frustrated by her as he and she share identification and, furthermore, he cannot be tortured or frightened by her.

Having identified himself with mother he can then behave lovingly toward men as he wishes his mother would have behaved toward him. This reassures him against the depriving mother and affords gratification.

A further outcome of this primary identification is the development of an anal fixation secondary to his oedipal wishes. These wishes to enjoy sexual gratification with the mother have become a wish to experience sexual intercourse with men as his mother experienced sexual intercourse with a man, his father. He strives therefore in fantasy and in practice to vaginalize his anus. He may attempt to turn his defeat into an assumed victory by behaving like a woman, assuming feminine characteristics and "enjoying" the sexual penetration into his anus. At the same time that he is passively submitting to the anal intercourse he is unconsciously robbing the male partner of his masculinity. The homosexual male receiving the penis into his anus may frequently fantasy the gigantic growth of his own penis.

He is controlling other men through his apparent "acquiescence" but he is castrating the male, exerting power over his homosexual partner through presenting his anus, depriving him of his "secrets," and extracting "love and affection." In all of these fantasies or in actual encounters the patient will harbor feelings of mastery, extreme aggression, impulses to cast aside his homosexual partner as he himself once felt cast aside by his father. There are fantasies of killing the father or the father having been killed through the homosexual intercourse, with the patient having become more powerful by having made the father respond sexually. Through this pseudo-submissiveness he is robbing the father of his potency, semen and affection.

On top of his primary identification he then develops a secondary identification with the mother during the oedipal period because of castration anxiety and fears of retaliation by the father for any remaining signs of sexual interest in her.

Secondary identification with the brother,[166] whether older or younger, may arise from envious and hostile feelings toward him and in competition for the mother's favor. Very often hatred toward the brother may be a form of overcompensation, a reaction formation against excessive libidinal feeling. A brother who seems by comparison more successful than oneself may produce feelings of disturbing hostility or hopeless anger, a feeling one cannot compete with the brother due to the danger of one's own murderous rage. If the brother is the "masculine" one in the family the boy cannot then become the masculine one interested in sports, other masculine activities and in sexual contact with girls. All aggression is impounded. If he then becomes homosexual and comes to desire the brother sexually he will avoid all competition with him.

It cannot be emphasized enough that in identification the determinant of homosexuality is in the last analysis intimately related to the degree of primary identification with the mother, that is, the boy's tendency to identify with the mother. All other identifications are secondary and are accretions to this basic problem of identification. The simultaneous identification with the brother, for example, is completely secondary and does not exclude the primary identification by any means or do any subsequent identifications equal or exclude the primary one.

Patient V

Patient V, a 35-year-old engineer showed a pronounced identification with his older brother. His history revealed the typical primary identification with mother and the presence of a weak father who had suffered severe business reverses at the time the child was born and subsequently. The mother, who was the matriarch of the family and had helped her younger siblings to complete college and to launch their careers, was always over-controlling in the relationship with her husband. She appeared masculine in many ways and dominated the family. The father assumed a quiet, benevolent, passive role but was extremely attentive to his older son who became, in time, prominent in athletics of every description and very popular in his home community.

Patient V always felt inferior to his brother but developed a strong affective life and was rich emotionally in his social relationships, especially those with older women, his grandmother and teachers. The father would force him into sports activities and his brother would attempt to teach him games that he, the brother, excelled in. The patient complained that his father had been overly permissive with him in many ways, allowing him undue "free choice" as to beliefs and range of interests because "my father was mostly tied up with my brother."

The patient had been unable to negotiate the separation-individuation phase, developed a faulty identification but struggled against it. He was seduced by a male teacher at approximately age seven and later experienced a number of seductions by older men at his places of summer employment while still attending school. He was pleased with the affection men gave him but would develop severe anxiety on being fondled, caressed or otherwise sexually approached.

When he was 13, his brother was drafted into military service and one-and-a-half years later the patient answered the telephone call advising of the brother's having been killed in action. This tragic event had a strong influence on his subsequent development; he experienced severe trauma over the death and intense guilt. His guilt was due to his unconscious ambivalent wish for his brother's removal as a rival for the affection of the father. Since that time his homosexual activities, except for an interval of two years in the armed forces when none took place, were motivated by the unconscious search for replicas of his brother whom he would love and achieve identification with. Over the years his physical resemblance to his brother had become striking to those who knew them both.

His anxiety during homosexual relations increased as he reached the end of his twenties and for several years he found himself wishing to achieve a heterosexual orientation. It was almost as if he had been doomed to pleasing other men by giving himself sexually to them, doing penance and sacrificing his masculinity because of his guilt over wishing to usurp the older brother's preferred family position. He had been punishing himself for his infantile hostility toward his brother aggravated by the almost magical fulfillment of these wishes by the brother's death. Expiatory attempts were evident in a series of automobile accidents, some of them nearly fatal, and subjecting himself for ten years to the sadistic practices of his homosexual partner.

One year before entering analysis, Patient V unsuccessfully attempted to terminate this homosexual servitude and leave his sadistic partner. During this temporary separation he met a girl for whom he developed considerable affection and was able to establish a sexual relationship with her. In this instance and in other intermittent relationships with women he could become involved only with those of a different race or nationality in no way reminiscent of his mother or other females of his own cultural and familial background. This pattern rendered any lasting or meaningful relationship unlikely.

His homosexual acts were always carried out when partially intoxicated although he was not a chronic alcoholic. In his homosexual activities he assumed a counterphobic attitude in which he sought out heterosexual men, tested them to see if they would have homosexual intercourse with him and was relieved if they would not. On numerous occasions he succeeded in "making heterosexuals homosexual" but only to suffer intense guilt thereafter.

The patient was plagued by the early exciting and frightening childhood memory of his brother masturbating and by the idea that his brother had wanted to have homosexual relations with him. Unconsciously there was guilt that he did not gratify his brother's homosexual wishes as he imagined them to be. It is clear that this is a projection on the part of the patient of his own homosexual desires and a fear of homosexually seducing his brother. The brother's death actively gave him relief from his unconsciously anticipated and dreaded homosexual encounter with the brother upon the latter's return from the service. Therefore, the patient felt relief when he died, which further augmented his guilt, including a need for expiation, a need for punishment, a need to remain homosexual and suffer throughout life.

Furthermore, as a consequence of his guilt, Patient V had been unable to finish important projects which would bring great advancement in his career. He was unable to accept professional offers which would lead to considerable prominence in his field because consciously he feared exposure as a homosexual but unconsciously could not permit himself the exceptional success for which he was eminently endowed and qualified. He wandered for years in a maze of homosexual dread and desire, guilt and atonement, at times initiating experiments with heterosexuality resulting in some pleasure only to be followed quickly by guilt and wishes for self-punishment exemplified by his sadomasochistic submission to a homosexual partner who exploited him mercilessly.

Prior to entering treatment he had undergone a period of about six months of continual drinking, yearning to break away from the bondage of his homosexual life and fulfill himself in meaningful relationships to others and greater vocational attainment. Unfortunately, every time he attempted a successful advance into heterosexuality it was accompanied by tragedy. On several occasions dearest friends died just as he was trying to free himself from his deteriorated life situation. His first heterosexual exploration in adolescence coincided with the sudden fearful news of his brother's death. His homosexual partner for the past decade had threatened to kill himself were the patient to leave him. He was filled with self-loathing and disgust during homosexual contacts all of which were preceded by anxiety and accomplished only by the use of alcohol. There were episodes of homosexual pick-ups in which he endangered himself by inviting police entrapment as well as physical abuse and loss of personal property at the hands of his momentary partner. He came to the realization that homosexuality "is valueless, cheapening, aggressive, asocial, demoralizing and self-destructive. I have never met one happy homosexual."

During analysis he became aware of the primary identification with his mother and fear of separation from her, his incestuous conflicts which inhibited relations with women, and was able to tolerate the infantile unconscious guilt provoked by both situations. To become heterosexual as brother had been was, he had felt, tantamount to the murder of his brother. With this insight he no longer felt he must retain the intense identification with his brother (an effort to keep the brother alive) and began to see himself as a different and independent person who could live a rewarding heterosexual life once freed of his guilt. He urgently desired both parents to recognize him as a strong and mature man rather than a weakened, depreciated homosexual.

Chapter IX

ADOLESCENCE

DURING ADOLESCENCE the boy or girl is afforded a "second chance"[39] to overcome the anxieties and conflicts of childhood and to educate himself for adulthood through an increasing appreciation of reality, control, and appropriate expression of inner drives, especially those belonging to the sphere of sexuality.

Psychosexual conflict is determined during the preoedipal and oedipal phases and occasionally in the latency period. Although these conflicts undergo subsequent alteration the clinical form of their manifestation in the adult is usually not decisive prior to adolescence. The ultimate form of childhood conflict can appear as psychosis, neurosis, delinquency, character syndrome, and perversion. Rarely does it develop unchanged or with only minor alteration throughout late childhood, puberty and into adolescence and, finally adulthood.

The persistent psychopathology of adult years tends to assume its final form during the adolescent phase of development. This has enormous practical importance as the sooner a fixed symptom complex is treated therapeutically the more likelihood there is of therapeutic success and prevention of further maladaptive processes. Adolescence is a highly favorable time to undertake psychotherapeutic measures to combat homosexual behavior despite the serious technical difficulties which adolescence *per se*, with its violent shifts between the various structural components of the psychic apparatus, produces. At this stage we can more readily undo recent overt homosexual behavior, redirect urges toward heterosexuality, reduce fear and guilt as regards heterosexual strivings and thereby begin to establish a firm basis for rewarding sexual maturity. During adolescence a healthy path toward instinctual gratification should be gradually cleared of any pathological obstacles; fears, impulses and fantasies concerning heterosexual substitute gratifications can be resolved. The ego is thereby strengthened and enabled to cope constructively with both the demands of the intrapsychic apparatus and the environment.

Freud succinctly described the adolescent's position at the beginning of puberty: "With the arrival of puberty, changes set in which are destined to give infantile sexual life its final, normal shape. The sexual instinct has hitherto been predominately autoerotic; it now finds a sexual object. Its activity has hitherto been derived from a number of separate instincts and erotogenic zones, which independently of one another, have pursued a certain sort of pleasure as their sole sexual aim. Now, however, a new sexual aim appears, and all the component instincts combine to attain it, while the erotogenic zones become subordinated to the primacy of the genital zone. Since the next sexual aim assigns very different functions to the two sexes, their sexual development now diverges greatly. That of males is the more straight-forward and the more understandable, while that of females actually enters upon a kind of involutional period. A normal sexual life is only assured by an exact convergence of the affectionate current and the sensual current, both being directed toward the sexual object and sexual aim."[63]

An individual's final sexual attitude, according to Freud,[63] is not decided until after puberty and is the result of a number of factors, some unknown. In inverted types there are (1) "a predominance of archaic constitutions and primitive psychical mechanisms"; (2) "a tendency toward narcissistic object choice"; (3) a retention of the erotic significance of the anal zone. Accidental factors may influence object choice; this is a result of frustration produced by fears ensuing from deterrents used to inhibit early sexual activity. Significant contributions to our knowledge on sexuality and adolescence have been published by Deutsch,[37] Eissler,[39] Frieberg,[57] Blos,[20] Lorand and Schneer,[146] Anna Freud,[62] to mention only a few.

Indicators for Therapeutic Intervention

Since adolescence is the pivotal time to treat homosexuality one should bear in mind the indications for psychotherapeutic intervention at this stage. Although all adolescents have difficulty in stabilizing their appropriate sexual identity, there are several specific indications which are of major significance in determining when therapy is needed:

1. One must scrutinize masturbatory practices very closely. Here we are concerned with the total absence or late advent of masturbation, with the initiation of heterosexual activity, if any, and particularly with fantasy content. Fantasies which are primarily or exclusively homo-sexual, especially with a sado-masochistic coloration, are of serious import. The total absence of masturbation or late advent becomes meaningful when there is no manifestation of herosexual interest.

2. Homosexual behavior throughout adolescence in the absence of anxiety, guilt or conflict together with perverted fantasies is an alarming

sign. It is imperative to initiate therapy in order to create a conflict for the patient by driving a wedge between the id representatives and the ego. In many cases the homosexual symptom is ego-syntonic, especially at this stage of life.

By late adolescence some patients already demonstrate a rigid pattern for solving conflicts. The matter is further complicated by the exaggerated and fluctuating relationships between ego, superego and id drives universally present in adolescence. Psychic swings are so swift that modifications of psychoanalytic technique must anticipate them.[39,92]

3. One often finds a lack of true oedipal relationships from a study of the patient's history when a beginning perverse form of activity is taking place in adolescence. For example, a boy with a primary identification with his mother in the context of the absence or abdication of the father, who is filled with sadistic conceptions of sexual intercourse, searches for his male identification in the company of boys and later on of adult men. The alteration of this condition could best be accomplished through a male therapist who attempts to revive the oedipal conflict. The failure to successfully pass through previous maturational phases weakens the genital organization and the boy has very little interest in forming a heterosexual union as he approaches maturity.

Preoedipal and oedipal patterns therefore are dominant rather than those structural organizations typical of adolescence. The heightened genital pressures of puberty cannot be coped with and such individuals later develop a postpubertal full scale perversion. Adolescence is an extremely strategic time to begin the psychoanalysis of such a boy or girl; otherwise a fixed progressive maladaptation may well occur.

4. When an adolescent is subject to homosexual fantasies and displays no interest in heterosexual socializing, against a backdrop of relative quiescent interpersonal attitudes with an absence of age-characteristic emotional fluctuation and liability, therapy is in order. By adolescence the individual must have developed strong enough oedipal strivings so that he may come fully to grips with them. Otherwise he may suffer throughout life with pregenital urges and feelings, retreating into complete abstinence from sexuality or turning to perversion.[106]

In treating an adolescent with a homosexual problem, he must, of course, be assisted in all aspects of his struggle against infantile conflicts and ties and prevented from returning to an earlier structural organization with its narrower, restricting patterns of childhood.

5. Adolescents sometimes suffer from such an intense degree of fear that they never undo the repression of their sexual drives even in adult-

hood. During adolescence they profess and truly have no conscious awareness of any sexual interest whatsoever. Sexual release may occur only during sleep concomitant with sexual dreams.

Often conscious hostility supplants sexual yearning. Both preoedipal and oedipal periods are the source of such overwhelming fear. Where hostility to one's libidinal urges is present and where conscious awareness of sexual feelings is absent, analytic investigation is necessary to determine whether or not this is a result of homosexual conflict.

6. While not all overt homosexual experience during adolescence should be considered pathological it should not be disregarded or overlooked without careful evaluation. It may be a temporary phenomenon of adaptation and may not connote a homosexual fixation. However, when there is some overt homosexual contact together with a resentment of anatomical "growing up" and a strong suppression and repression of instinctual demands, treatment should be instituted. An adolescent should feel that he has begun to be "on good terms with his sexuality."[47] One must keep in mind that choosing a sexual partner of the same sex is not simply a manifestation of an infantile partial instinct. Although we know that to children the sex of the other person is of less importance than it is to adults and this attitude continues in some individuals into latency and into the earliest years of adolescence, beyond this point persistent sexual intimacy with persons of the same sex is to be viewed as a serious sign. Our clinical material does not support the idea that a certain amount of more or less manifest homosexuality "appears regularly" in the adolescent.[104]

7. A homosexual relationship with an adult constitutes for the adolescent "a dangerous regression to the original homosexual object."[57] This dangerous regressive step back toward the parent calls for immediate treatment, especially when, as so often happens, the relationship encompasses deep feelings of love on the part of the youngster. ". . . the absence of conflict between the adolescent and his original love object can be an ominous sign."[57]

8. Whenever an adolescent confides that "I know I'm a homosexual, I just feel it," having thereby "acquired his identity through inner knowledge,"[57] this verbalization constitutes an immediate indicator for therapy.

In summary, these observations should be seen against Eissler's most interesting conclusion.[39] Adolescence is a kind of lease permitting revisions of "solutions formed during latency which had been formed in direct reaction to the oedipal conflict. It behooves us to do everything in our power to allow this second chance for mental health and happiness in the future." With this in mind indications for therapeutic intervention as outlined above should require our most serious consideration.

Theoretical Features of Male Homosexuality During Adolescence

The first of my cases to demonstrate certain hypotheses is that of a 20-year-old male college student, Patient J, who started in treatment at the age of 18 and had been engaged in homosexual practices for one year. This immediately brings us to our first theoretical point.

Family Pattern

Certain preconditions of the family unit contribute to the problem of homosexuality. *The absence of the father or the presence of a weak father combined with a domineering, harsh and phallic mother favors the development of homosexuality.* For example, the anamnesis of this boy disclosed that the parents were cold and indifferent both to him and to each other. The father was almost entirely absent from the home and played no part in his upbringing except during later adolescence when he evinced some interest in his future academic pursuits. The mother was continually in the home and assumed complete control o᷒ the boy. Her cruelty is epitomized by her device of repeatedly "playing dead" in front of him, lying prostrate on the kitchen floor, breathing suspended, and not responding to his entreaties, whenever she felt he had not complied with all of her demands.

From the beginning of therapy it was apparent that the mother was probably psychotic. Parenthetically, the sister also was accorded equally cruel treatment by the mother who, for instance, in order to insure "good" behavior in her absence from the home would consistently slap the girl before going out; were the daughter asleep the mother would awaken her in order to be slapped.

Fixation and Homosexual Feelings

By age six, there was strong evidence of a *fixation on the part of the boy to an intense oral-sadistic relationship with the mother* and *passive homosexual feelings toward the father*—both of these are fundamental theoretical postulates.

The oral-sadistic relationship to the mother and the passive feminine relationship to the father may best be illustrated by recounting some of the patient's fantasy life during late childhood. At the age of six he would continually fantasy kissing the toes of both parents. By the time Patient J was eight, he developed the fantasy of sucking the father's or some other man's toes, a substitute for the penis. The smell of the feet was important and this later became connected with the idea that the feet were stepping on his face. By puberty, age 11, the following fantasy had developed.

"Mother and I were captured by some sort of enemy, taken prisoners. I was tied down with her above me so that if she urinated it would be on my face. Sooner or later she would. She would not do it willingly but she could not control it any more and she would have to 'go' and she would be trying to hold back and it would be coming out little by little—so I say to her not to hold back. She is only making it more uncomfortable for soon it would come out. So then, with regrets and apologies, she would let go."

Despite the patient's attempt at levity, this fantasy portrays the *intense sadism he attributes to his mother* disguised by the situation that they have been "taken prisoners" and she is *forced* to be cruel to him. The oral wish to be fed from her body (breast-fictive penis) is obvious. Simultaneously, he is attributing to her aggressive and destructive wishes against his self-esteem and masculinity. These fantasies represent mostly a fixation upon the part of the patient but there are regressive elements which promote them.

Primitive Psychical Mechanisms

In all homosexual patients there is a predominance of *primitive psychical mechanisms.* For example, in this case, we see: (1) An inability to form an appropriate identification with the anatomic and physiological role in life; he is already beginning to engage in a wholesale denial of his penis and masculinity. (2) Through the use of incorporation, the intake of body substances of his mother, he can compensate for the deprivation in nourishment and love experienced in infancy and early childhood. (3) He demonstrates a most commonly found primitive mechanism—the splitting of the ego. This boy feels at certain times that he is male while at other times, female, e.g., he assumes a feminine attitude toward his father.

Adolescence Forces a Decision

The genital pressures of adolescence force the individual to resolve his oedipal and preoedipal conflicts and to create an equilibrium in his life, at the same time allowing for orgastic satisfaction. If these conflicts remain unresolved sexual expression seeks substitutive outlets such as heterosexual masochistic fantasies or behavior; homosexual fantasies or behavior, either with or without masochistic features; other perverse activities such as fetishism. Instead of these distorted expressions of the sexual drive, one commonly sees psychotic or major neurotic symptoms.

Parenthetically, we cannot overlook the possibility that the conflict may seek disguise and expression in delinquent behavior.

At age 17, Patient J proceeded from homosexual fantasy to overt homosexual acts, especially the practice of fellatio. Increasing anxiety, shame and guilt forced him to give up this overt homosexual behavior. Both shifts were due to changes in the ego defenses and the increasing strength of his sexual drive. He was able to renounce overt homosexual behavior temporarily through experiencing his first meaningful relationship with a girl. However, sexual gratification with her could take only the form of sado-masochistic perverse activities. "All women are at heart cruel." He would experience sexual arousal and ejaculation upon the enactment of "cruel" treatment bestowed upon him by his girl friend at his command. She was asked to place her feet on his face or to burn his palm with a cigarette. She ultimately fled when he asked that he be put in the bathtub and the water run in at which point the girl would step on his face as if to drown him. The pain or punishment which would arouse him sexually was a regressive expression of his passive genital desires.

Upon his entrance to college, following separation from the girl—the one "loving" female in his life—he was suddenly overwhelmed by extreme homosexual feelings for adult men which produced severe anxiety, guilt and panic. It was at this point that he was unable to continue in school, interrupted his studies and sought psychotherapy.

Homosexual "Surrender"

Although not possible for my patient, *some adolescents directly manifest a surrender to their passive childhood homosexual desires for the father by establishing a sexual relationship with an adult male.* This form of homosexuality, in which the adolescent feels fulfilled, in love, and expresses the conviction that"I know I am a homosexual," indicates that a serious, already rigid and highly resistant form of homosexual perversion has been established.

Shifts Intensify Conflict

Shifting constellations of ego, id and superego drives or forces, so normally volatile in adolescence, *intensify the already tremendously excessive conflicts present in those with a weakened sexual organization.* Upon clinical examination it is also these particular adolescents who require psychotherapeutic intervention and help. We can, during adolescence, more easily undo recent overt homosexual behavior, redirect sexual urges toward heterosexuality, reduce fear and guilt as regards heterosexual strivings, and thereby establish a firmer basis for rewarding sexual maturity. To accomplish these goals the under-lying psychopathology and basic conflicts must, of course, be dealt with.

Theoretical Features of Female Homosexuality During Adolescence

Family Pattern

Almost invariably in the study of the female homosexual one un-covers a similar fear and dread of and fixation to the mother as in the male homosexual. However, there is a more *intense aggression directed toward the mother* on the part of the female. In the early history of these girls one commonly finds a dread of being hurt, devoured and destroyed by a malevolent mother. At the same time, the girl has harbored a *secret wish to be loved exclusively by her father*—a wish which she has renounced almost completely because of a conviction that her father refuses to love her and instead hates her—hates her especially for her phallic deficiency. Even when the father does offer care and affection she turns away in "revulsion" and seeks the company, admiration or love of other females. At the same time she is displaying to her mother her guiltlessness as regards her unconscious sexual wishes toward her father through homosexual behavior. She wishes to indicate her apparent lack of any interest whatsoever in the male organ. She thereby hopes to ensure maternal care and love.

The foregoing description aptly fits a professional woman in her mid-thirties whose first actual homosexual experience was in late adolescence, at age 17, but whose intense physical attraction toward girls began at approximately nine years of age, the onset of her puberty. (This case, presented in detail in Chapter XIV as that of Patient E, is here condensed to illustrate specific theoretical formulations pertaining to adolescence.)

Oral-Sadistic Feelings

As in the male, the potentially homosexual female almost always presents a history of *oral deprivation and intense sadistic feelings toward her mother*. Patient E had been told that although breast-fed she never got enough milk and for the first two months of life lost weight and screamed all the time. As far back as she could remember she had felt "My mother did not love me and she really wanted to kill me." She wished that eventually it would be found that she did not belong to this family at all. The oral-sadism was best exemplified in her poisoning fantasies which were most severe from the ages of three to 13. "I often thought my mother would punish me so severely some day that she would kill me. Once she gave me sausages and I was frightened to death that they would be poisoned or something." It was shown later in the analysis that these, of course, were projections of her own sadism toward her mother.

Primitive Psychical Mechanisms

In female homosexuality primitive psychical mechanisms are even more pronounced than in the male. They often take the form of outright denial of the anatomical differences between the sexes. For example, the girl quite often hallucinates a fictive penis or may identify her entire body with the male organ or may substitute some characterological feature, e.g., intellectuality, for the penis. She may then continue to a protracted age to deny feelings of having been castrated and clings to the idea of somehow acquiring a penis.

Another mechanism is the wholesale projection of fear and hatred onto the mother whom she is convinced had denied her the male organ as a punishment—often for masturbatory practices in childhood. The mother and all women, therefore, are evil creatures but they must be placated through a show of affectionate behavior. They thereby become "good." Upon the failure of this belief she develops temporary or permanent delusional fears of poisoning or mistreatment, at least from her female homosexual partner.

By the age of 11 or 12, Patient E actively felt repelled by her mother's body. She could not bear to look at it. Around age 14, she had a vague recollection of an attempt to swallow iodine. Feeling angry at her mother for somehow "duping" her into this act she then developed suicidal thoughts for approximately six months. This was followed by the appearance of obsessional ideas consisting of the touching of the fenders of cars to prevent "something happening to my mother." At 13, upon the onset of menstruation, she had developed a horror and fear of death. She wanted frantically to be a boy.

Later Adolescence Forces a Decision

The genital pressures of adolescence in the female are less direct in their expression than in the boy. At adolescence the girl is forced to make a change of genital which the boy never has to make. If at the same time as the change from clitoris to vagina, the girl feels a lack of interest on the part of the father and hostility from her mother, she is likely to repudiate her vaginal erotism and create a fictive male role.

This might best be expressed: "Nobody wants me in this castrated, mutilated state—not even my father." What ensues is a prolonged and pathological extension of tomboy behavior into middle adolescence. The renunciation of her feminine strivings will create for the adolescent girl an equilibrium, albeit a possibly disastrous one for the future, because this eliminates superego conflict which then does not interfere during this period of life with her ego aspirations. During this phase she may engage in mutual masturbatory or sexual investigative practices with her girl friends but this is accompanied with considerable anxiety and guilt and is soon given up.

It is only *upon reaching late adolescence and early adulthood when the girl* is confronted with society's and her own demands for proper role fulfillment and *is forced to consider sexual intercourse, marriage and children*, i.e., her entire future, that her previous conflict, apparently set to rest, in early adolescence is now reactivated in all its intensity. The shifts, therefore, between ego, id and superego drives instituted by physiological sexual pressures do not usually produce in the female a multiplicity of overt sexual practices or disturbances (as described in male Patient J) although some masochistic masturbatory heterosexual or homosexual fantasies may be entertained for brief periods.

Homosexual "Surrender"

As in the boy, the feeling on the part of the girl of *"having found herself" in pleasurable surrender to homosexuality* is a serious sign. At age 15, Patient E was told by a friend that she was "probably homosexual." Her response was to feel "very close and loving" to this person for explaining some of the thoughts and attitudes which had upset her ever since she could remember especially her complete lack of interest in boys. The friend's comment was greeted as a welcome relief—a bad prognostic sign requiring treatment in adolescence.

The adolescent girl in sexual conflict may appear rather fortunate in that she does not undergo the intense shifts that the boy does. However, the absence of obvious psychopathology during this period only helps to camouflage the fact that she is in need of help. While her tendency to experience conflicts in overt perverse practices during adolescence is much less than for the boy, it is at this time that these tendencies are taking root only to be experienced later in life. Therefore, the condition is no less acute in the girl but takes longer to manifest itself.

Chapter X

THE RELATIONSHIP OF HOMOSEXUALITY TO OTHER CLINICAL STATES

APPROXIMATELY HALF of the patients who engage in homosexual practices have a concomitant schizophrenia, paranoia, are latent or pseudo-neurotic schizophrenics or are in the throes of a manic-depressive reaction. The other half, when neurotic may be of the obsessional or, occasionally, of the phobic type. They may suffer from character disorders, psychopathic personality or some variety of addiction. Bieber et al.,[18] in reporting on over 100 homosexuals, stated that one-third are schizophrenic, one-third, neurotic and one-third, character disorders.

Part of the difficulty in coming to a conclusion as to the clinical status of homosexual patients arises from the confusion which occurs from studying individuals whose symptom is often ego-snytonic and may enable them to maintain their psychic equilibrium relatively intact for varying intervals. Freud[63] referred to homosexuality on several occasions in different ways: as inhibited development, arrested development, developmental inhibition, sexual infantilism, dissociation of development. He concluded that the presence of exclusiveness and fixation are signposts that we are dealing with severe pathology. Various contributions toward clarifying the question of the exact clinical nature of homosexuality have been made by Alexander,[2,3] Gillespie,[94,95,96] Bychowski,[31,32] Glover,[99] Nunberg,[153,154] Ferenczi[48,50] and Boehm.[21,22,23]

Classification

All attempts at classification so far have rested on the type of overt behavior and the provocation for such behavior. But none clarified the nature of the original conflict, at what level of development this conflict occurred (fixation point) and the significance of regression to the conflict and its expression in homosexuality. The classification system which is set forth here is concerned with the issues of developmental conflict, fixation point and the role of regression.

Obligatory (*true*) *homosexuality* is sexual orgastic activity between individuals of the same sex arising from earliest childhood conflict and is a psychological process of repair and prevention against psychic pain. The ensuing homosexual activity is unconsciously motivated, fear-induced, inflexible and stereotyped. The person depends entirely upon homosexuality for orgastic satisfaction. Enforced heterosexual intercourse brings very little or no pleasure even if functioning is possible.

Obligatory homosexuality originates in preoedipal phase conflict and all oedipal period fears are an accretion to the original conflict. The preoedipal phase conflict fixates the individual to this stage and predisposes him to a rapid regression to this first period of development when faced with the vicissitudes of later stages. For example, fears of castration, fears of mutilation (and penetration in women), guilt revolving around both the positive and negative oedipus complex.

The boy's negative oedipus complex consists of a passive feminine masochistic relationship to the father. This condition of sexual passivity and gender role reversal because of fear of the father's power and retaliation should not be confused with the dynamics of true homosexuality which is a consequence of the preceding preoedipal fixation and *primary* feminine identification.

The girl's negative oedipus complex is a passivity and turning to the mother for love and affection in place of her guilt laden jealous hatred of the positive oedipus period. This secondary attachment to the mother accompanied by a feeling of disappointment, rejection and turning away from the father is not to be mistaken as a manifestation of true homosexual inclination.

Preoedipal phase conflict revolves around the inability to separate from the mother with a resultant identification with her, a fear of dissolution, annihilation and merging with her. In this volume we are concerned only with obligatory homosexuality, an outcome of preoedipal phase conflict.

There are certain states which can lead to a choice of a partner of the same sex for sexual intercourse which may give the appearance of being true (obligatory) homosexuality. This choice emanates from conscious and deliberate thought and action and might be designated *utilitarian homosexual behavior*. The motivations for such acts are as varied as the motivations which drive men and women to seek power, gain, protection, security, vengeance or specialized sensations.

In the situational[158] form of utilitarian homosexual behavior the unavailability of a partner of the opposite sex, in institutional settings particularly, such as war camps, prisons and other milieux, may cause an individual to seek temporary orgastic satisfaction with a person of the same sex. This behavior is discontinued as soon as the situation changes. Social imbalance, where severe inequities exist between one's survival needs and the failure of society to insure their adequate satisfaction, has a precipitant effect. Such imbalance brings on a flight from the female on the part of the male, a flight from certain aspects of masculine endeavor and a retreat to a less demanding role.[125]

In certain civilizations and in certain eras, for instance Hellenistic Greece, it was profitable socially, politically and competitively to join those groups who freely announced their homosexual behavior. In other communities and times, and here we refer for an example to the Comanche Indian tribe, there was no homosexual behavior extant with rare exception. From birth boys were trained, idealized and loved by their fathers for their efficiency as warriors and any deviant sexual behavior would have been demonstrably non-utilitarian.[124]

In the variational form of utilitarian homosexual behavior a person may yield to the desire for an alteration in his mode of orgastic release which involves a partner of the same sex. This is usually an individual act but "In some cultures such surplus activity is part of the established sexual order. . . ."[158] This is a conscious and deliberate search for a "thrill," a new sensation or an attempt to stimulate inadequate sexual functioning.

Situational and variational forms of homosexual behavior do not originate out of the homosexual preoedipal phase conflict. Nevertheless we must be sure that beneath these apparently utilitarian forms obligatory homosexuality is not present.

The homosexual behavior of some severely ill schizophrenic patients proves to be neither obligatory nor utilitarian but is an outcome of their confused, chaotic and fragmented psychic organization. The desperate need to make human contact may involve all forms of perverse activities including homosexual acts but, like other spasmodic attempts to experience relatedness, there is no consistency or sustained quality to these episodes.

Relationship to Psychosis

A large number of paranoic schizophrenics, paranoiacs, pseudo-neurotic schizophrenics or latent schizophrenics have a concomitant homosexual conflict and many manifest homosexual behavior. Freud first called attention to the possibility that certain psychotic symptoms were the manifestation of an underlying homosexual conflict.[67] This hitherto unsuspected reason for the development of a psychosis demanded clinical investigation. Homosexual impulses and behavior in the psychotic have been studied mostly in cases of overt male homosexuality.[28,78,102,154]

Freud's paper on Schreber[67] added great stimulus as to a possible etiological connection between homosexuality and psychosis. "It remains for the future to decide whether there is more delusion in my theory than I should like to admit or whether there is more truth in Schreber's delusion than other people in the relationship would like to believe." Brill observed that homosexuality and paranoia are based on narcissistic fixation but where the homosexual reaches the goal of object choice, albeit on an inverted path, the paranoiac finds it impossible of attainment and has to regress to ego libido. He considers paranoia to be the "first cousin of homosexuality."[28]

Freud's hypothesis that paranoid psychotic symptoms develop as a defense against emerging unconscious homosexual wishes has been subject to clinical investigation and statistical studies in an attempt to determine its validity. Klaif and Davis [127] obtained *statistical data* from the records of 150 paranoid schizophrenic female patients and a control group of 150 non-psychotics, all of them examined in relation to this hypothesis. It was believed that since "unconscious homosexual wishes are emerging during the acute illness" they should expect to find patients preoccupied with homosexual thoughts and wishes. They theorized that since a sexual problem is the basis of paranoia, delusions and hallucinations would have a predominantly sexual content. Furthermore, Freud had stated: "The person who is now hated and feared as a persecutor was at one time loved and honored."[67] It is a remarkable fact that the familiar principal forms of paranoia can all be represented as contradictions of a single proposition: "I (a man) love him (a woman)." The persecutor being, of course, the previously desired homosexual love object, one could expect the sex of the persecutor to be the same as that of the patient.

Their findings were that the final delusions and hallucinations of the paranoid group did not have predominantly sexual content. Comparison with the control group was impossible due to the absence of delusions in the controls. The hypothesis that paranoid psychotic symptoms develop as a defense against emerging unconscious homosexual wishes could not be verified by these authors.

In another paper Klaif[128] wrote: "The data obtained from the study of the records of 75 female paranoid schizophrenic patients and a control of 100 female non-psychotic patients was analyzed in relation to Freud's hypothesis concerning the development of paranoid symptoms.

Of the four deduced consequences of Freud's hypothesis two were found to be verified . . . that we should expect the delusions and hallucinations in the female paranoid group to have prominent sexual content and that we should expect religious preoccupations to be expressed by many acutely ill psychotic patients." However, other data from the study cast doubt on the application of Freud's paranoid hypothesis to female paranoid schizophrenia. First, 57.3 per cent of the paranoid group had delusions and hallucinations of sexual content; 83.7 per cent of these 43 members had delusions or hallucinations of heterosexual content. Second, Freud's paranoia hypothesis requires the sex of the persecutor to be the same as that of the patient. In this study the largest percentage, 61.3 per cent, of the female paranoid schizophrenics had male persecutors. These two results suggested that a disturbance in previous heterosexual relations rather than unconscious homosexual wishes were of importance in female paranoid schizophrenia. The findings on female patients by Klein and Horwitz[129] were basically in agreement with those of Klaif.

Nevertheless, in clinical experience the connection between homosexuality and paranoid schizophrenia and paranoia is very striking in a great number of patients and occurs with considerable regularity. Although this material may not be on the surface and therefore cannot be garnered by statistical methods, paranoid content may appear during the therapy of any homosexual patient. It is clear that the homosexual fears persecution and attack on many levels. Some of these seem realistic, for example, social censure, but others involve threatened castration at the hands of either parent or both. He fears anal attack, he fears the use of feces as a destructive powerful weapon against him, he fears poisoning due to his intense oral-sadistic incorporative drives. The presence of archaic mechanisms is highly suggestive of the primitive introjective-projective dilemmas which beset him.

It may be that in the female paranoiac the male is consciously made the persecutor, although the unconscious homosexual conflict is equally present, because the fears she can admit—social sanction and censure of her environment—are attributed to men. To a woman, her censure and punishment would be experienced as coming from male authority figures just as to a man his punishment and degradation would also come from other men.

Relationship to Other Perversions

Fetishism,[85,143,168] transvestitism,[8,45,47,85,95] and homosexuality[78,84] all reflect different compromises between the simultaneous identification with the phallic and penisless mother.[143] In some instances the fetishist has both conscious and unconscious homosexual wishes and dreads but may never engage in overt homosexual practices. It seems that the use of a fetish protects him against what he regards as more catastrophic, that is, homosexual relations. In other instances fetishism may be present in overt homosexuality.

There is an interconnection and interrelationship between erotogenic masochism, sexual sadism and homosexuality. Freud emphasized that in masochistic men a feminine identification may exist without homosexual object choice and that the masochistic perversion can prevent the individual's overt homosexuality.[74,167,169] In the "Wolf Man,"[72] he described how a masochistic attitude toward the father, resulting in neurotic symptoms, serves a defensive function against assuming an overt passive homosexual attitude toward him.

Bychowski[168] described the forms of homosexual object choice which can include the role of a homosexual object in a masochistic or sadistic ego involvement. Individual factors determine whether the object represents one or both preoedipal and oedipal parents but he qualifies it to mean that it is not the total parent but rather the partial object, e.g., the maternal breast, the paternal phallus or both. The rapidly shifting attitude of the homosexual ego makes it possible for the patient to combine the role of the aggressive father assaulting the oedipal mother with the role of a maternal substitute passively submitting to a homosexual object, the latter representing his own phallic self as well as the aggressive father.

In sexual (erotogenic) masochists,[121] men who seek physical injury, pain and suffering as an erotic requirement for orgastic satisfaction, one finds a strong feminine identification may exist without overt homosexual object choice. The "Wolf Man"[72] is a classic example of this. The masochistic perversion is often the alternative chosen by and acceptable to the ego in preference to becoming homosexual.

A number of female homosexuals show fetishistic and transvestite symptomatology. Barahal[8] attributes the transvestitism of his female patient to a wish for overt homosexual relations. However, it is often true that both male and female transvestites have no homosexual interest but feel that they themselves embody both sexes simultaneously. They often respond to homosexual overtures with marked hostility and prefer autoerotic orgastic fulfillment. The pseudotransvestite is an overt homosexual who uses cross-dressing solely for purposes of enticement. Fenichel[45] felt that transvestitism was particularly common in active masculine-type women.

The homosexual content of sexual activities involving more than one heterosexual couple depends upon the motivational state. It may range from the overtly homosexual to unconscious homosexuality and may even appear to be sought after as simply variational heterosexual experience. Brill[28] gives an example of troilism, or ménage à trois, which he analyzed successfully as homosexuality. In his case it involved a male patient and his wife with another male, the wife having had intercourse with the friend. The patient sought to defend himself against his passive homosexual desires which corresponded to his earlier attitude to the father by reacting to them with delusions of persecution. In the reported sexual acts the patient fulfilled both identifications: he enacted both the father and mother roles and felt, therefore, in control. The woman was "his woman," thereby bolstering his masculinity. He felt he loved both the wife and the other man (parents). He was gratified that his wife preferred him and would say to him, "You are the one I really am attached to—I love your friends as long as you love them—my universe is your universe and what you want shall happen." In actuality he was gratifying his passive feminine homosexual desires by identifying with the wife (mother) in sexual relations and also probably was enabled to function sexually with his wife through an identification with the other man's penis (father).

Why is it that the trauma of viewing the female genital in childhood, for example, was overcome in certain cases while in others it may lead to homosexuality or fetishism? For instance, the threat of separation from the mother is experienced, it seems, as an equal if not greater danger than the loss of the penis. Fleeing to the fetish and all it represents serves a simultaneous means of defense against both castration and separation anxiety. Thus each of the triad—fetishism, homosexuality and transvestitism—illustrate different phases of the compromise between the biphasic identification with the mother.[143]

Freud pointed out that "The beating fantasy has its origin in incestuous attachment to the father."[74] Therefore it is closely related to homosexuality; however, he stated that in the case of the boy the situation bears a greater resemblance to the original fantasy with its genital significance "since there is a difference of sex (at the conscious level) between the person beating and the person being beaten." By repressing and remodeling his unconscious fantasy the boy produces a later conscious fantasy which has for its content a *feminine* attitude without an apparent homosexual object choice. The boy who had tried to escape from his homosexual object choice and "who has not changed his sex, nevertheless feels like a woman in his conscious fantasies and endows the women who are beating him with masculine attributes and characteristics." There is a prevalence of pregenital features in the sexuality of all erotogenic masochists.

In masochistic fantasies or in actual gratification men unconsciously identify themselves with the woman in her role in intercourse with the man or in childbirth. In these cases "the pain or punishment which arouses them is a regressive expression of their passive genital desire . . . the punishing or cruel woman possesses phallic attributes which thus indirectly indicates that a woman here stands for a man."[142] These phallic characteristics of the female partner point to another feature of great importance in the life of the masochist, namely, his insistence on denial of the absence of a penis in women and thus a denial of the castration danger. Loewenstein[142] takes this to mean that the crucial problem which human sexuality has to deal with during its development is the fear of the loss of the object and fear of loss of its love together with castration fear and superego anxiety. Therefore, in both fantasy and actual acts of beating, passivity and helplessness have the aim of appealing to the mercy of the "threatening and protective parental figure."

In masochists strong homosexual tendencies are readily observed. All homosexuals suffer from a severe degree of psychic masochism. At its root this is an expression and fulfillment of the original masochistic relationship of the helpless child to the overwhelming, engulfing, overpowering, cruel mother to whom the child must submit in order to survive now continued into the relationship with homosexual partners.[165] Inevitably the sexual masochistic aim continues because of its initial survival value. The sexual object has been changed but the sexual aim remains the same. Thus his hope to escape from his masochistic enslavement to a woman (mother) by choosing a male partner is utterly defeated. The masochism of the homosexual often takes the form of and is experienced as the masochistic pleasure of social and moral censure and loss of personal dignity because of homosexual behavior.

Masochistic heterosexual and sadistic homosexual object choice may alternate. Both object choices represent one or both preoedipal or oedipal parents. The first case presented in Chapter IX (Patient J) emphasizes the shifts which may occur from overt to latent homosexuality and the reverse. The psychopathology of this young patient clearly demonstrated shifting ego and libidinal constellations and the resultant alternation in types of object choice and clinical symptomatology. In his fantasy and activity he quite consciously denied the anatomical fact of his penis and thus the danger of castration. The pain or punishment which would arouse him was a regressive expression of his passive genital desires. His utilization of masochism and foot and toe fetishism as a defense passed within a short period from fantasy to overt homosexuality for approximately one year. At that time the overt homosexuality was repressed and the shift to an apparently heterosexual masochistic relationship began.

As already noted, Freud[74] thought that the beating fantasy has its origin in an incestuous attachment to the father. In the case of the boy, even though there is a difference in sex (at the conscious level) of the person being beaten, it is clear that he, too, was avoiding his overt homosexuality by repressing and remodeling his unconscious fantasy. The remarkable fact about the latter conscious fantasy—to be made to suffer at the hands of a female, to be nearly drowned, to be urinated upon—is that it has for its content a feminine attitude although without an apparent overt homosexual object choice. The fear of castration is lessened by the substitution of a female figure for the father and the indignities, threats and attacks which he contrives are a substitute for a passive genital penetration by the father.

In these outright perverse masochistic fantasies and practices what is actually taking place is a homosexual, albeit disguised, union. One could predict further that with a shift of forces involving drive, defense and ego-adaptive functions that later one might expect the overt homosexual object choice.

Latent Homosexuality

There is much confusion in the use of the term, latent homosexuality. Correctly it means the presence in an individual of the underlying psychic structure of true homosexuality without sexual orgastic activity with a person of the same sex. While the preoedipal origin is the same, these individuals may never engage in homosexual activities. The manifestation of one's conflicts and the homosexual solution depend largely on a number of factors:

(1) The strength of the fixation at the preoedipal level (quantitative

factor), severity of anxiety and the intensity of regression from the later oedipal conflict.

(2) The acceptability of the perversion both to the ego and superego.

(3) The strength of the instinctual drives, i.e., libido and aggression.

The latent homosexual may or may not have any conscious knowledge of his preference for individuals of the same sex for orgastic fulfillment. There may be a high degree of elaboration of unconscious homosexual fantasies and homosexual dream material. He may live his entire life span without realizing his homosexual propensities, functioning marginally on a heterosexual level, sometimes being married and having children.

Another pattern can be that of the individual who, fully aware of his homosexual preference, abstains from all homosexual behavior. Other individuals, equally aware, as a result of severe intolerable stress episodically and transiently engage in overt homosexual behavior, however, living the major portion of their lives as latent homosexuals. In the latent phase they may maintain a limited heterosexual functioning, albeit unrewarding, meager and usually based on homosexual fantasies. Or they may utilize fantasy for masturbatory practices or they may abstain from sexual activity altogether.

These individuals are, of course, truly homosexual at all times; the shift between latent and overt and the reverse constitute an alternating form of latent homosexuality. All types of latent homosexuality are potentially overt.

A 38-year-old professional man with two children had a vivid dream life of homosexual relations, including mutual fellatio and anal penetration. It was only after certain precipitating factors, the wish of his masculine wife to return to work and her rejection of him sexually that he began to engage in homosexual activities. These grew into a "satisfactory" period of sexual relations with another male and for a number of years he lived with the male partner.

While claiming he derived considerable gratification from his "new way of life" he was in great conflict over the failure of his responsibility toward his family. He entered analysis because of progressive depression, episodes of stealing (kleptomania) and his wife's threats of divorce.

To make a comparison with organic medicine, research has revealed a latent form of diabetes. This condition has important effects on all body systems even though it may not express itself as overt diabetes mellitus and the patient may live out his life without ever being aware of this condition, able to tolerate its various negative influences on his general health. Only refined clinical tests may be able to reveal the presence of this condition and its ongoing consequences. Such a latent state can, of course, become overt with its unmistakable clinical signs and symptoms.

It is misleading and incorrect to assume that because an individual, due to regression, has dreams of wishing to be admired, loved and taken care of by older, authoritative and protective men he is suffering from homosexuality in its latent form. This is simply an infantile adaptation of extreme dependency and has no connection with the complex of psychodynamic factors which are responsible for true homosexuality, manifest or latent.

Any neurotic state can produce such infantile dependency patterns. While these have been referred to in the literature as "sublimated homosexuality" they have no relationship to true homosexuality. Sublimated homosexuality correctly refers to activities and behavior whose aim is to ward off the expression of an actual underlying homosexual conflict, these activities and behavior adhering to the concept of sublimation in general.

Many life conflicts involve passivity and a regression to infantile behavior, a flight to the negative oedipus complex with submission to the father and other powerful men, the individual playing the role of the female secondary to his inability to deal with the positive oedipus complex and aggression. To become homosexual requires the three factors cited above which have been a part of the developmental history. The case of Patient T is an example of the confusion that can arise around the diagnosis of latent homosexuality.

Patient T adopted early in life a "preacherlike" attitude which led others to admire his "maturity" while still in high school. Although desiring to make a favorable impression on girls throughout his teens and into his twenties he felt himself to be awkward, lacking in experience and unable to gain acceptance by them. There were no homosexual conflicts or unconscious fantasies during his adolescence or earlier. He was, however, extremely shy and lacked confidence to a severe degree in all relationships with females. He was very fond of his older brother who was killed in an accident when the patient was 19 years of age. He continued through adulthood to mourn this loss and longed for the love and affection of his ego-supporting brother.

While there were no homosexual fantasies as regards his brother, the first twenty years of the patient's life was marked by suppression of all sexual expression.

At the age of 26, he was moved through feelings of guilt and responsibility to a girl friend to marry her but never felt comfortable with her sexually or otherwise because of her different sociocultural background and limited intellectual status. When she decided to leave him after his career required his moving abroad he developed an attack of bronchial asthma, a repetition of a childhood condition which had lasted until he was ten. He felt severely depressed over the separation but ultimately was able to accept the divorce and in the course of treatment the depression lifted.

He suffered from severe castration anxiety and had feelings of guilt upon entering sexual relations, ardently wishing for passive satisfaction, wanting a woman to make seductive maneuvers toward him and show him by her interest that he had a "proud phallus," that he was "masculine and powerful." This sexual passivity was in direct contrast to the aggressive strength that he demonstrated in the vocational area of his life. Because of his difficulties in the heterosexual sphere there were anxiety dreams over the strength of his penis, its size, its effectiveness and its being taken away from him, that is, castration.

He feared rebuff and rejection by all women whom he admired. At times he was unable to have an erection and realized that his guilt about heterosexual desires was the cause. On occasion he would awaken from dreams in which he had been surrounded by Indians or other tribal males about to attack him or dreams of being rejected by women with pains in his rectum of such intensity that they would produce a near shocklike syndrome (Proctalgia fugax*). It was quite clear that at times the patient feared being assaulted and degraded by more powerful men pushing their penises into his rectum. He would awaken in a sweat with agonizing pain and symptoms of shock.

Patient T will not become overtly homosexual and this is not an instance of latent homosexuality. The consequences of his passivity is the fear of more aggressive males whom he knows have uninhibited relations with women. None of the criteria governing the diagnosis of latent homosexuality is to be found in this case illustrative of the kind of symptomatology which gives rise to confusion about the clinical state involved. Here we see a problem in heterosexual performance as a result of oedipal conflict.

Patient T is not limited by this conflict to choose objects of the same sex but has an interest in and freedom to choose objects of the opposite sex handicapped by an inability to enjoy himself because of superego guilt. His conflict is between active-passive and masculine-feminine, not between heterosexual versus homosexual urges which latter imply gross and severe

---

* Proctalgia fugax is a disease of hitherto unknown etiology which consists of massive spasm of the anal canal or rectum, perhaps sigmoid and lower colon. The pain is so severe that it can cause faintness, sweating, increased pulse rate, alterations in consciousness and other signs of a shocklike state. These phenomena are due to a spasm of the lower intestinal tract and represent the defense against anal rape. It usually occurs during sleep when conscious control is absent. The anal rape theory can be verified by the dream material *preceding* the spasm and concomitant with it which clearly reflects the marked fear and dread of anal penetration. This disease is erroneously attributed to an imbalance in the autonomic nervous system involving the lower intestinal tract. Significantly this author has seen several cases of the disorder, none of which has occurred in overt or latent homosexuals but instead in passive individuals in the throes of the negative oedipal relationship with its accompanying intense conflict over taking the less demanding role of the woman in sexual intercourse.

disturbances in all areas of adaptation and the utilization of certain specific psychic mechanisms. He does not have a tendency to identify with his mother but a tendency to identify with more powerful men. He does not suffer from a pregenital fixation and the readiness to substitute identification for object relationships. He does not have a body-ego disturbance. He did not have a weak or absent father and was not frustrated excessively by his mother or made to keep helplessly close to her or radically intimidated by her.

On numerous occasions he was able to function heterosexually with complete competence, orgasm and pleasure and had an affective interest in women. There was no conscious or unconscious fantasy production or conscious desire for persons of the same sex for sexual intercourse. His best sexual functioning was achieved with the diminution of infantile guilt and an alliance with the analyst's more permissive superego. He was also aided in attaining more satisfactory sexual functioning by a woman who admired him and strengthened his otherwise shaky heterosexual position.

Section Three
CLINICAL

Chapter XI

MALE HOMOSEXUALITY (Part 1)

Patient A

PATIENT A entered psychoanalytic treatment at the age of 27, having been referred by a clergyman-uncle to whom the patient had confided that he was a homosexual. The patient was very pleased that his uncle took enough interest, for the first time in his life, to wish to help him. The patient was still a college student preparing for one of the major professions.

At the initial interview he told the analyst he had been a homosexual since age 14, and had led an active homosexual life from the age of 18. He was an attractive young man, vivacious, articulate and generally personable. He sought relief from the futility he felt was ahead of him were his homosexuality to continue. He complained that such a course did not lead anywhere, that his only friends were homosexuals, he wished to enlarge his social life, develop a heterosexual personal life and had become increasingly fearful of exposure and the ensuing legal and social consequences. On one occasion he had been apprehended by the police and permitted to get off with a warning. He realized that his homosexuality could well interfere with his future career were it to be discovered and could court disaster. He was extremely unhappy and suffered intensely because of his inability to desist from homosexual practices.

The patient came from a lower socio-economic background, his parents having migrated from Europe without material resources or vocational skills. He felt it would be "pathetic to fail in the fundamental aspect of living—sexual fulfillment—when other things had turned out successfully" for him through his prodigious effort and persistent application to educational goals. In a somewhat defiant way he had announced to his parents shortly before entering treatment that he was a homosexual and requested their help in obtaining therapy. His uncle had demanded financial assistance for him from the parents and the mother consented to "help for a while." His father received the announcement with alarm and exclaimed that he could not understand how his son "could live in a sewer." The mother apparently accepted the pronouncements of both son and uncle without equivocation but felt that the homosexuality was "only a passing stage."

Throughout his childhood he has been dominated by his tyrannical, overpowering and often cruel mother. She was in complete charge of the family, responsible for all decisions. The husband was a passive and yielding individual, frightened of his moody, irascible, uncontrollable wife. The mother controlled the social and academic life of the patient and his brother, concentrating mainly on the patient, the slightly younger of the two. Until his entrance into analysis every decision had first to be discussed with his mother; every concern, problem, incident at school, were to be submitted to her for approval. All friendships were to be discussed with her and no secrets were allowed.

His childhood was marked by endless parental bickering, violent argument and open physical assault. The mother would harangue and finally provoke her husband into a physical attack against her at which time she would seize a kitchen knife and threaten him. The patient constantly witnessed these scenes. The father was unable to offer any effective resistance to the mother's autocratic, domineering control of the patient and assumed a submissive, completely passive role in the household. The father himself appeared to have been terrorized by his wife's psychotic-like behavior. She threatened the patient with abandonment and divorcing the father if her son did not comply with all her requirements, wishes and desires. The mother's aggression could not be handled by the child and he soon began to identify with her, taunting his father at times, making fun of him, siding with his mother on nearly all occasions. The father rarely intervened to prevent the mother from scratching the child deeply or otherwise abusing him bodily or verbally. The boy, however, learned that he had best remain silent to protect himself as much as possible from the mother's vicious outbursts.

The patient's aggression was continually stimulated throughout early and late childhood. He was teased, provoked, ridiculed, slapped and clawed by his mother. Whenever he would try to defend himself she would beat him to the ground by sitting or lying on top of him, scratching his arms, his face, hitting him in the stomach. Fighting back in self-defense only produced more physical damage.

During infancy he had difficulty eating and recalls that at three and four years of age he was often force-fed when he did not "clean up" his plate. On two or three occasions he vomited his food and was forced to "eat the vomit." Consequently, he vomited frequently upon becoming even slightly upset during adolescence and early adulthood.

Up to the age of 13, his mother would often sleep with him in the same bed. He would enfold his arms around her from the back and feel as if he were merging with the mother and her body warmth. She frequently disrobed in front of him; at other times, half-dressed, she would walk around with her pendulous breasts exposed. In late childhood and early adolescence she continually asked his opinion as regards the shape and size of her breasts and her general physical attractiveness. There was no actual sexual fondling of the mother to the best of the patient's recollection. Occasionally, though, she made fun of his penis, stating that he would never be able to function as a man with a woman in later years.

She criticized all his friends, especially girls, minimizing their good qualities and pointing out their weaknesses, failures, frailties and their unworthiness compared to him thereby managing to isolate him. He was fond of a neighborhood girl at the age of 8, and when her mother became psychotic his mother teased him relentlessly, saying his little girl friend was "crazy like her mother."

The one thing that was allowed him was success in intellectual and academic pursuits. During adolescence the patient was unceasingly jeered at by his mother for failing to rival his brother academically. The brother successfully eluded the mother by staying in his room; her attention was centered on her younger son. The father sided with the older brother and they both teased the patient for his attachment to the mother.

Although he surpassed his brother in college he was not accepted at the graduate school of his choice while the brother was; the brother subsequently married, moved to a different city with his wife, and, so far as is known, showed no signs of homosexuality.

The patient achieved remarkable success in the alternative graduate school he attended. He was somewhat feared by his colleagues there for his angry, aggressive, verbal attacks upon those whom he felt were inferior to him or who tried in any way to take advantage of him, misused him or misunderstood him. He took great delight in his verbal onslaughts (similar to his mother's) and revealed even to people in authority their "falseness and weaknesses." This was no doubt due to the identification with his mother and his wish to reveal to his father his weaknesses and inability to protect him and take care of him as a child.

Patient A determined to make a success of his psychoanalysis because he had no meaningful emotional activity in his life. He participated with vigor, attention to details, including dream material, and application of the analyst's interpretations. He voluntarily resolved to cease homosexual activities by the end of the first year of analysis and did so for approximately six months only to revert to sporadic homosexual episodes. Within the first five months of analysis he had successfully engaged in heterosexual intercourse with orgasm and considerable pleasure. However, later he complained of the difficulty in finding suitable heterosexual partners. He spoke resentfully of the social pressures he felt were put upon a man, including the girl's insistence upon marriage as an almost immediate condition in any sexual relationship. He dwelled on the lack of available women as compared to the vast number of readily available homosexual contacts of every description. Nevertheless, he had several heterosexual relationships during the first two-and-a-half years of analysis, feeling at times quite affectionate toward his female partners and elated because women did not reject him.

Patient A's childhood recollections of the mother's asking him to help her dress or choose a brassiere were tremendously stimulating. During analysis the emergence of sexual material concerning his mother induced marked fear and he realized that he wanted "to have her sexually." A favorite erotic fantasy was of his mother wearing only her brassiere and a skirt. "It was a strapless bra, low-cut, and she had an attractive face, made-up just right." He was afraid to speak of childhood erotic incidents and of the fantasies they later gave rise to but began to realize that when he had "sex with a man perhaps I am having sex with mother. . . . It's fantastic but it's what I want to feel. . . . It's my sexual interest. It has to do with the fact that I want her, to be a part of her, and that she wants me. She's always wanted me to see her that way, as a sexual interest. I guess I've always wanted her body. That sounds supid when I say it. When I used to sleep next to her that's what I wanted and I would put my arms around her and sort of enfold myself right into her and that was terrible. I'd forgotten that since I was a little child. I didn't get an erection but it seemed to me I always went too far. I recall that I used to have fantasies around age 12 and 13, about putting my penis into my mother's vagina with my arms around her. It wasn't like a lover but like mother and son and I'm getting pleasure out of it, it's a terrible sick picture that I get of myself. And she's gloating at me, she's enjoying it, too, and she has control and power over me."

This memory and affect were important to relive as the patient was able to engage in heterosexual relations only when he could see that he had been fearful of domination and the woman's (mother's) great power over him. He discovered that he had to dictate the terms of sexual intercourse if he were to function properly. He had to be more powerful than the woman and therefore not be controlled by his mother as he was in his fantasies of sexual intercourse with her. These recollections brought up further incestuous feelings and memories, including those of the primal scene. On occasion he had seen his mother having intercourse with his father when he entered their bedroom. He always felt that his mother controlled his father as she controlled him but as her son he could do nothing about it.

For a brief period when the patient was age seven or eight he was not permitted to get into bed with his mother and instead "she took my brother." Within a few weeks he was again permitted to sleep with his mother frequently. Sometimes he would hear the noises of sexual intercourse from the parental bedroom, especially his father's grunting and groaning. He would then "stick my head under the pillow—I didn't want to hear it. I remember his climbing on top of her at times. I can picture her submitting to the whole thing." He shows an obvious confusion as to which parent was the aggressor in their sexual relationship. His mother had told him over the years that she was completely uninterested in sexual relations with his father and was truly not interested in any sexual matters. "I would picture my father's penis going into my mother who was lying there very innocent-like and mother not being very instrumental in the whole thing."

When during the course of analysis the patient began to enjoy heterosexual relationships he felt that "bond between my mother and myself—that crappy bond—was being broken. But it's like I'm losing something when I tell you about my interest in women and when I begin to think of having sexual intercourse." His first intercourse with a girl was preceded by an identification with his analyst in which the analyst was on top of him. There was no sexual intercourse but he felt the power and penis of the analyst.

Dream: "You being on top of me. We are not having intercourse but you're telling me, forget my real father and you're my father and not to tell my mother about it. We were clothed. And then you got up and left. It was very nice. But you didn't really leave. You just got up." This dream preceded heterosexual intercourse by a few hours. He stated in association that he was beginning to have a good relationship with his father. He felt more confident of his masculinity. It was like the analyst's telling him to be a man.

After the intercourse he had the following *dream:* My mother is sitting in a car and my father is with her and I'm coming toward her carrying two pieces of luggage and she leans over so that I can see her face which looks very twisted, a very twisted, distorted face. She keeps calling me a bastard. 'Move yourself, bastard. Hurry up, bastard.' I put down the luggage and just look and she keeps saying, 'Hurry up, bastard.' My father has a very relaxed, pleasant false-pleasant look. He's trying to get me to do what my mother wants by his facial and hand expression. He's trying to get me into the car. Instead I push the two bags up. I go off to the right. And the last thing I see is the expression on my mother's face. She is bewildered and shocked like a stupid error of some kind has been committed."

His associations have to do with his protest against his mother's attempt to deprive him of the analysis. She continually plagued him with the financial liabilities of analytic therapy and attempted to attack the analyst at every turn. He was very angry with his father in the dream. He is trying to push the two of them out of his life and obviously wants a strong male figure. It is apparent that he feels his father has threatened him with his mother in order to "get off the hook himself." There is no protection from his father, no love, and he bears considerable hatred and aggression toward him for delivering him as a child into the hands of the mother.

He is protected in reality only by his confidence and trust in the analyst. As a result he can muster enough strength through identification with the analyst to consummate his first heterosexual experience which he feels is a triumph.

A *dream* reported at the subsequent session is as follows: "It's about burying my father and my mother's being her usual bastard self and stating how he was going to be buried. We are both very angry with each other." His associations had to do with his wish to get rid of his father. He was burying him with a shovel. He wanted to do it right. Previous to this dream his father had argued with him about not working in the family business, saying that the mother wanted him to work part-time. He was angry that he was not protected by his father. It was as if he were threatening him with his mother. "I got a little fear in me at that point. I became angry that my mother could control everything. She said 'all that we have given up for you.' He said to his father, 'You know something. I don't know who's worse, you or your fucking wife.' "

Both dreams represent: (1) the patient's fear of his mother and of her retaliation for any sexual activity on his part with a female; (2) his feeling that he has been duped by a weak father who failed to make him secure against his incestuous and murderous aggressive feelings toward his mother and fears of her abandonment of him; (3) his ability despite these fears to defy them both and to initiate heterosexual activity despite their condemnation, indignation, irritation and destructive verbal assaults.

The dream material further shows that for him to have heterosexual intercourse means to give up the quasi-friendly contacts with men, e.g., his father, that he experiences in homosexual relationships. He feels he has to "bury" his father and forget him. It was apparent that in heterosexual intercourse he felt fear and guilt, that he would some-how lose the attention and affection of his mother, the attraction to her and unity with her. "A lonely type of feeling would come over me afterward every time I had intercourse with a girl." The patient realized that his mother not only dismissed his homosexuality but sanctioned it. If he were interested only in men he would never leave her for another woman. The mother accepted homosexual activities in her son as a sop to his instinctual needs.

The patient's homosexual relationships began in early adolescence. They consisted at the beginning of mutual masturbation with boys his own age, occasionally mutual fellatio and, rarely, anal penetration of the partner. Twice he had brief masochistic relationships with an adult male who pinched and slapped him on the buttocks, but rebelled when subjected to a mild beating with a leather strap and had since dis-continued these practices.

He was exclusively homosexual until after entry into psychoanalytic therapy, picking up casual partners in public rest rooms and some-times having intercourse with fellow students. There had been no "love" relationships and no prolonged affectionate contacts with one par-ticular man. It was only later in the analysis that the aggressive and sadistic nature of his homosexual relationships could be perceived by the patient. His homosexual activities constituted a severe sadistic assault upon men (his father and mother) and were highly overdeter-mined. For example, in having intercourse with a male he was forcing his father to give him the affection and love which he could not acquire passively or actively in childhood. In addition he was substituting the penis of the male for the female breast (mother) and was enjoying disguised sexual intercourse with her. Feelings of weakness were dissipated by his active expression of a seizing, destructive, powerful urge. Anxiety which always preceded his homosexual arousal was libidinized and neutralized through homosexual orgastic contact.

Desire for and actual homosexual relations occurred whenever he felt frustrated by life's disappointments or fearful of abandonment by his mother. Simultaneously with quieting his fears of loss of his mother he gratified his sexual wishes toward both his mother and father. Thus he felt assured of their love, acquiring a potent and strong penis from his partner and warded off fears of castration. His homosexual desires, which progressively diminished throughout the analysis, decreased in frequency and intensity. They were revived when: (1) he "felt abandoned by mother" and frightened as regards his dependency needs and security needs; (2) he felt frightened by the omnipotent powerfulness and aggressiveness of other men who might threaten him socially and professionally; (3) he felt tense and anxious depressive loneliness, a state which demanded he search for and gain possession of another male; (4) he experienced an overwhelming aggressive drive due to unsatisfied infantile love needs.

In several instances, following his first successful heterosexual experiences after starting analysis, he would dream of his mother's attempting to pull his testicles or his penis away from his body or he would dream of wanting to run back to and escape by homosexuality. "I should be screwing my mother and not other women. She always wanted to mold me into being a girl and as a result I've always wondered about how I look. I think I look too effeminate. My chest is not big enough." On such occasions he would feel depressed over the loss of his mother and his fear that she "would somehow pay me back" for his interest in girls.

He discovered that his homosexual feelings were filled with violent impulses. "When I get a sexual feeling the man must become extremely submissive and as I say this I get a dizzy feeling as though I'd like to punch these men or strangle them or strangle their genitals rather than do anything else with them. I'd like to remove their genitals by pulling them off, tearing them off, and causing them pain and enjoying the pain. I'd like to strangle them with my legs around them and I'd like to see the pain on their faces. I get a real charge out of this. I have a very lot of angry feelings within me and all this facade of being nice to people, it's all an act. . . . And I hate my mother so. I hate her for all that she did to me, her selfishness and everything being for her. I feel like crying and I feel awful and the hate is getting more and more about all the things that have happened to me and I guess I've wanted to kill her for a long time."

These feelings toward his mother had been both repressed and suppressed. The patient felt that the analyst was creating a "magnificent monster" as he began to be aware of and verbalize the hostility and murderous hatred he had felt for his mother over the years. Simultaneously he began to feel liberated from his hatred toward his mother with the verbalization and the emerging ability to tolerate his aggressive feelings. "It's not a nice feeling to hate somebody but what was there is there still. She was a very sick woman and still is and this is what she did to me. I called my father after I felt these things last time and I told him I was all right. When I spoke to him he suggested I not come home as often as I have in the past because of getting my mother upset."

When Patient A's girl friends would become demanding, his homosexual feelings would recur and occasionally "quite bad ones." This was a reproduction of his reaction to a severe attack from his mother, usually a verbal onslaught about his lack of appreciation about "all we have done for you"; any feelings of disapproval, imagined or real, on the part of the analyst, or fears of the failure of his father's health could rouse homosexual feelings again. The mother constantly expressed to the patient her hatred of his father and poured invective on the latter because of his ill health. Furthermore, she attempted to trick the patient into a feeling of trust in her due to her "great interest" in his welfare. Her unending manipulations and machinations in the service of "making me into her masochistic slave" had to be continually pointed out to the patient who was still vulnerable to her despite his growing insight. On numerous occasions the mother would tease him by saying "I'm going to see your doctor and from what I tell him he's going to throw you out." And she threatened again and again to stop the analysis by withholding funds.

As in other cases of homosexuality, this patient presented a severely distorted body image. "You know, I don't feel I have my own body. I want somebody else's body. My body is flat, I guess because the penis is flat or never gets erect with girls. I keep looking for a body in another man and that's one of the reasons for choosing a man, especially if he's clothed so he looks masculine. It seems I'm reaching for that when I want a man. It has to do with the muscles. I want more muscles. I was never allowed to do anything that would make muscles for me, such as sports. My mother would laugh at me and say to me, "What are you trying to be? A killer?" His mother would make fun of his penis. "I used to think at moments I wouldn't be able to have children. My mother used to say something like that. She'd look at me and say, 'You'll hurt yourself if you ever have sex.' She said if I ever exercised strenuously or lifted heavy things that I might hurt my penis. She'd stop me and have my father or brother do it for me. My brother used to be a fat little boy. She once made me eat the vomit I had vomited up. I'm nauseated now. She made me eat it as she fed me and I'd gag and she'd say 'If you vomit you'll have to eat it again.' I don't feel I have a chest, I'm very narrow, no contour, more of a V-shape. It's like my arms are very thin, like an image of an emaciated person. I'm startled sometimes when I look in the mirror to see that I have muscles and I am a man and other times when I've felt down and out and frightened I see no muscles. It was only after several months of analysis that I began to see that I had these muscles."

The patient's body image changed gradually over the course of treatment and he felt attractive, that his chest size had increased and that he suffered from no physical abnormality. In actuality he had always looked attractive and masculine. As an adolescent he had put his penis and testicles between his legs in order to make them disappear. He would simply see a lot of hair reproducing the image of the mother's pubic region which he had seen quite frequently in childhood when she appeared nude before him. This was, in part, a desire to be a female and thereby avoid incestuous feelings toward his mother and also represented his self-castration.

In this case the patient consciously feared and hated both parents. His identification with the good male figure, the psychoanalyst, allowed him to take steps toward heterosexuality. However, even his identification with the analyst was not equal at times to withstand the fierce intervention by his mother who threatened him with loss of funds, abandonment, and intensified her attempts to diminish him in his own eyes.

The analyst explained to Patient A how to conduct himself in a heterosexual relationship. He showed him by diagrams that there was nothing to fear and that he certainly could have heterosexual intercourse. The analyst constantly exposed the ruthless and irresponsible, fearful and sick, totally negative and destructive behavior of the mother and the patient gained courage through facing up to this reality. He began to emulate the analyst's objective appraisal of the mother's behavior and lift himself out of his unconscious masochistic sexual submissiveness to her. Many times he requested advice, helpful criticism and insightful knowledge from the analyst about handling current life problems and human interactions in his professional and social circles. This was his education by a new, good father who would protect him against his crushing mother and inept, inadequate and weak real father. He became a man and was not afraid to become so through this positive identification. The constancy of the analyst and his benevolence allowed the patient to regain his father, to feel loved and to become first a boy (son) and, in time, an independent man. As his work progressed he ultimately opened his own office and this development give him a further sense of independence and the conviction that he could exist without his mother and be strong enough to stand any of her onslaughts no matter from what avenue of approach they came. He no longer needed to be ashamed of himself. He had a good body, a penis that could function, he could earn money and become self-sufficient, and he could feel kindly and compassionate toward others. In time he would be confident enough not to feel threatened by women and be able to control the "vicious woman" in the environment as epitomized by his image of his mother were he to be confronted with this type of person in reality.

The defensive gratifications of the homosexual act no longer were essential for survival. Affectionate feelings from women with whom he could now relate comfortably freed him gradually from the anxiety of being rejected, "sat upon" and crushed by the female. Occasionally he cried because of the trust he felt for the analyst and wished that his father had somehow shown him feelings of love, affection, caring and protection despite the tyranny and intimidation of his mother.

The patient's homosexual inclinations would recur upon his feeling lonely after having had a quarrel with his girl friend and feeling abandoned by the analyst, especially if the latter were on vacation. "I wanted to screw somebody. I wanted to be with somebody. I felt angry at the thought of being alone, the thought of your not being in your office, and I was alone. This frightened the hell out of me. It made me feel very unhappy and the anger gets me all annoyed now. My father said when I was two years old he thought of divorcing my mother and this was after my brother was born. He had the two of us. He thought of it and he was going to leave my mother. The reason he didn't was because of us children. The fact that he could think of leaving us, when I recall it, makes me feel lonely now." Loneliness led to massive anxiety. The anxiety then became libidinized in the homosexual act. Before engaging in homosexual activity he frequently dreamt of his mother's punishing him or calling him insulting names. In certain dreams he felt that she was about to suddenly jump on him from behind the curtain. She would usually be dressed only in a skirt and brassiere. On one occasion he had a fantasy that his mother walked in with a lighted cigarette, dressed in her brassiere and half-slip. "She bends her head down and presses the lit cigarette down on my penis and I feel a great pain." On other occasions it became clear to him that he engaged in homosexual experiences in order to exasperate and upset his mother. He hoped she would feel sorry for his state that she had produced through her behavior toward him and therefore he would gain her love.

He would develop homosexual feelings if the analyst did not answer a question in the session: "If I feel I love you, and you don't answer, I get scared and I have a lonely feeling. If you don't participate the way I want you to it makes me feel alone and maybe later on I'll have a homosexual desire." On several occasions the patient developed guilt feelings after heterosexual relations. These guilt feelings directly pertained to his doing something against the best interest of his mother and giving his body to another woman. His sexual feelings for a man often preceded severe masochistic attacks of loneliness; at the same time he would almost invariably develop a severe rash of both arms which he scratched incessantly to the point of bleeding. These masochistic dermatological manifestations were part of his homosexuality

and were relieved in the homosexual act through the discharge of unconscious sado-masochistic fantasies always implicit in such acts. The
deep masochistic loneliness ensued from his desire to be caressed,
fondled and touched by his mother. At times his masochism had direct
expression in his involving himself in homosexual episodes under
conditions where he might be apprehended by the police as had occurred
twice.

In the seventh month of the analysis, when the patient voluntarily
attempted to desist from all homosexual contact, he said he "felt strong
enough" to resist it. "I can take a guy or leave a guy now. I have that
strength. This has been built up because of my relationships with girls
and that I now have the ability to go to bed with a girl and the fact
that I realize now how sick my mother is. She's very sick and she
doesn't have the big hold on me and she can't frighten me as much.
I think it also has to do with not wanting her breast and that the
breast is the penis that I wanted in men. I remember that I never used
to look at a guy's genital area because I guess I was afraid that I was
looking at a breast." Following this point in treatment the patient was
able to discontinue homosexual relations completely for two months
without much difficulty. However, this improvement was only short-
lived and on other occasions, whenever lonely, depressed, rejected by a
girl, frightened by his mother or lacking strong masculine figures with
which to identify, homosexual episodes would occur. It was only in the
third year of the analysis that he was successful in completely eliminat-
ing homosexual contacts for long intervals lasting several months. He
began to develop affection and object love toward a particular girl and
although occasionally he experienced homosexual fantasies of mutual
masturbation, during the last year of analysis, his fourth, he was nearly
free of all homosexual fantasies and homosexual episodes. Even though
heterosexual functioning with full orgastic satisfaction was achieved
early in treatment the patient characteristically would develop homosexual wishes when he felt "imprisoned" and constrained by his girl
friend. Here one sees fear of the overpowering female, his mother, and
the consequence of this fear—the turning to men for orgastic satisfaction and the acquiring of a penis and male identity through homosexual fantasies and experiences. In his turning to men he is continuing
his masochistic relationship toward his mother utilizing a substitute
figure, the male, who evokes less conscious conflict. He felt that women
only weakened him if they came "too close" and became too possessive,
invaded his life, demanded services from him or attempted to control
him in any fashion.

At times the patient's omnipresent conscious and unconscious masochistic suffering became especially vivid during homosexual intercourse. He cried and whimpered during acts of mutual fellatio. "I relate it to my mother. I feel like I don't trust her and I am leaving myself open to a blast by calling her or doing anything for her and I feel dizzy as I am talking about it. If I do call her I am giving in to her and I have a guilty feeling when my father tells me how she was ill the other day and my not calling her. I'm still not calling her and I'm a terrible son as she is so ill. Everyone says she's ill and that I'm being terrible. My father tells me the same thing, too. He wants me to go all out and give myself to my mother in order to protect him. He also took the promise of money away from me that he was going to give me."

In this material is clearly seen: (1) the patient's abandonment by both mother and father; (2) his attempt to secure mother's love in homosexual intercourse (penis = breast) and his crying bitterly because of her maltreatment of him; (3) his suffering during homosexual relationships, whimpering and crying during intercourse.

Homosexual intercourse also afforded discharge for his murderous aggression toward his mother. Described elsewhere is his mother's continual provocation of him in childhood to severe aggressive outbursts and temper tantrums. She would scratch him with her fingernails and he would hit at her hands violently up to the age of 13. He would also strike her on the arms and enjoy seeing her cry. At times she so enraged and provoked him that he would attempt to choke her and on many occasions she would mockingly offer her throat inviting him to choke her to death. "I became frightened that I would kill her and then suddenly I would be overwhelmed with an awful sense of guilt and then I would stop." He therefore became the guilty captive of his mother through her provocation.

During analysis he realized: "I want to choke my partner with my legs around him or my hands around his neck just the way I wanted to choke my mother. However, I guess I substitute a man for a woman. I want to choke her by shoving my penis so far down the man's throat that he is choking and gasping for breath. I get pleasure out of that."

Homosexual relations were usually followed by an increase in the patient's feeling of strength as reflected in the following *dream:* "My cousin and myself going to the basement of the house and we crept into a peculiar kind of position with our legs wrapped around each other and leaning backwards as if we were pulling something out of each other and we hear somebody coming and we stop it." His associations were that this person was the cousin with whom he first had homosexual relations when he was very young. "There is a certain strength in the position. I wanted to pull away and still keep contact. I was pulling something out of him. He is my penis and that's why I feel so strong."

As treatment progressed the patient became aware that when he was attracted to men he would concentrate on parts of the body, especially the genitals or the buttocks. With women it was quite different and he began to notice for the first time that when he became attracted to them it was to a "pleasant over-all picture—their total appearance, dress, manner and gestures. In homosexual feelings there are always lonely feelings and also the wish to be a man. At the same time there is an angry component. I'm angry with myself and angry with all these guys, angry with wanting homosexual sex and angry with my parents. This has come through quite clearly recently to the point where I grit my teeth hard. When I can turn off the homosexual feelings I feel pleasant and thankful toward you and a determination not to do it again, thinking about you at the same time, a determination to be a person, a good person, and a realization that heterosexuality is there, it's there to be taken and it means being a good person, not being an angry, destructive one."

Whenever the patient's mother was effective in hurting him through her verbal attacks he became weakened and frightened and masochistic. Following one such incident, which was brought up in the analytic session immediately afterward, he went to the subway toilet and engaged in mutual masturbation with a casual pick-up. Simultaneously he observed two other men: "This one guy went over to the other one, went down on his knees and started sucking him. The second guy was dirty-looking, a positively dirty guy. It showed extreme masochism. It looked so terrible. This first guy dressed splendidly in a business suit, clean-cut and good-looking. I've seen guys suck other guys but it was never like this. He was on his knees on the dirty subway floor and he was feeling this guy, running his hand up and down his arms and legs and taking him all in and with his other hand he was masturbating himself. I was watching. I know why I was. I was punishing and hurting myself, too. I *was* the guy on his knees and I wanted the disgust to go all over me. I was watching his degradation and enjoying it. Every time I engage in homosexuality I'm sure that I am enjoying a degradation with men. Also I feel that I only degrade myself in front of my mother and I really want to eat her up, eat her breasts, eat her, eat all of her. Other girls are out. Her breasts are to be eaten and they are substituted for by the penis of men."

This incident was followed by a *dream* that night: "My mother and I walk into a place like a restaurant and we see a girl sitting there and she is a pleasant girl. I keep saying that my mother is crazy, that I don't want to hurt her. My mother doesn't hear. She is with me and, of course, she hears what she wants to hear, you know that. Somehow or other this girl is involved, perhaps it's being the girl I am having intercourse with but getting involved with her further will hurt my mother. I yell over to this girl, 'I know my mother is crazy but I don't want to hurt her.' "

His associations were that if he becomes progressively involved with a girl it will hurt his mother in the long run as he'll wish to marry the girl someday. He retreats from heterosexuality to submitting himself to a "crazy mother" who will only hurt him. He feels that his mother "probably is crazy" but this further ties him to her because then she needs him even more. "I feel sorry for her. I remember her cold, hard self and how she used to treat me but it seemed at least she loved me. In my homosexuality I think I'm giving in to her, too. I do not take another woman; I take a man. I subject myself to such humiliation and torture in these subway things."

The patient's conviction that he would hurt his mother by going with girls and having intercourse with them had a double meaning. If he had intercourse with girls he felt he was much more directly having intercourse with his mother than when men are substituted; if he penetrated another woman he felt he was penetrating into his mother, a dire event to be avoided at all cost. The importance and meaning of this penetration into the mother and its deep implications as regards the basic conflict of this patient became apparent a few months later. He reported a significant *dream*, the unraveling of which demonstrates the basic conflict of this homosexual man and, in the author's opinion, of all homosexuals. The understanding of this dream and the affective discharge together with the associations was one of the major turning points of the analysis.

Dream: "It's only a short dream. It's of my mother bleeding right down the middle and I'm rolling over on top of her." His associations were: "I am hurting mother by talking against her, by going out with girls. You recall the last dream I had of importance, it seems to me, was the dream that I was hurting my mother when I approached other girls. Every time I feel I've hurt my mother I then begin to have homosexual desires. In the dream the blood was all over me. It strikes me as odd that I'm telling this all to you, that I have to force myself to talk. Last night I tried to masturbate with this girl's image in mind but I couldn't. I could only masturbate with a man's penis in my thoughts. . . . I find I look at certain guys depending on what I feel I'm missing or needing at the time. If I feel loneliness I need a gentle guy. If I need strength I get a fierce-looking, wise type, hate-look-in-the-eyes kind of man. In the dream my mother was bleeding from the heart but it was in the midline and it was a slash, a long cut, deepest at the heart and some sort of conflict in the dream. She deserved it but I didn't want her to have it. She deserved to die. I was almost choking in the dream myself, like almost it was my death, like Siamese twins together, the blood. I got almost vicious in the dream, pushing away and yet not pushing away, holding tight to her, the way I hold tight to homosexuals. It makes me feel very nauseous, very upset, and my heart is going very rapidly and I'm frightened like I wish it was over and I didn't have to keep going back to it. . . . Suddenly I feel shame about wanting to have intercourse with my mother. I know I've wanted to for years. It brings tears to my eyes when I say that and I'm crying now. I'm loving her all over that way but I wish my mother could have my father and my father her and that I could just let it go at that, the two of them, I just can't blame one of them if I separate myself from them."

The patient felt shame and guilt at his incestuous feelings and his desire to unite with the mother and then suddenly substitutes a man to alleviate his deep anxiety. The patient was asked if he could now see why he had not tried intercourse with women instead of men. He said that he wanted to be a child with his mother but that if he approached a woman he would not get rid of his incestuous wishes and his guilt of joining with his mother. He would also not be able to control his aggression as vividly depicted by the slashing of her body in the dream. By not approaching a woman he shows he has no interest in mother and therefore denies his aggressive, murderous and libidinal wishes toward her: "In the dream I am loving her all over and she is holding me even though she's bleeding and it's mostly her holding me and my clinging and all those things make me feel ashamed. I hated myself and my feelings and my mother but more I felt ashamed and now I feel relief as I tell you and it brings tears to my eyes . . . relief from guilt. I didn't feel I did anything wrong as a child but I see now that in loving her I'm killing her and destroying her. The killing of her and below that is the intercourse with her but I feel there is a good reason to kill her, to kill our relationship, to get her out of my life, to let my father have her. . . . There is an expression, 'Go in health and peace,' if it could happen that way my mother could have my father and my father her."

This session was marked by great affective release expressed by the patient's tears, grief, sorrow, thrashing on the couch, despair and depression. He left the session only to call the analyst a few hours later, saying that he "never felt so happy" in his life.

This last session demonstrates clearly the nuclear conflict of the homosexual. The isolated affective state which he attempts to ward off is the mother-child unity which is so frightening and upsetting to him. This wish and dread which have come out of an intense fear of the mother and the lack of a strong father are what had been repressed during the infantile sexuality phase of life. The homosexuality acts in the service of this repression. In the mother-child unity complex are: (1) A wish for and fear of incorporation. (2) A threatened loss of personal identity and personal dissolution. (3) Guilt over any attempt to heal the bond through invasion of the mother. (3) Intense desire to cling to the mother which later develops into a wish for and fear of incestuous relations with her. (5) Intense aggression of a primitive nature toward the mother. The patient through being "forced" by the analysis into heterosexual relationships and being stimulated into aggressive attacks because of the devouring nature of his mother who would deny him his independence and masculinity touched off the underlying nuclear fear of the union with the mother and as a result, in the previous session, experienced her death, destruction, merging and his own death as a result of their clinging together and joining in an everlasting union.

It is important here to state that out of the nuclear conflict of this patient certain secondary conflicts developed in early childhood: (1) aggression against the father and men who do not protect him from the female; (2) a sense of inferiority; (3) confusion as to body image; (4) an avoidance of anxiety-producing situations, especially being left alone without the mother. There is almost invariably a report of protracted screaming in the early childhood of homosexual patients whenever they were separated from the mother (screaming phenomenon).*

---

* Almost invariably in all homosexual men there is a history of protracted screaming, lasting for hours, whenever, as a small child, they were separated from the mother. This even occurs in the presence of the father or a satisfactory maternal surrogate should the mother not be available. Screaming will stop abruptly with the mother's return. This phenomenon probably starts at around two years of age and may last up to age seven. Probably this screaming is tantamount to a scream for survival as the child fears for its life when the mother is not present due to feelings of being threatened with ego dissolution and the inability to achieve individuation, i.e., the sense of individual ego.

Its distinctive characteristics are its great intensity and prolongation. Often the screaming phenomenon cannot be remembered by the patient but is confirmed by relatives who observed it after the analyst has asked the patient to find out if he had been a "screamer."

In the normal child screaming is usually a reaction to frustration and is not protracted; the child's attention and interest can be diverted and he can accept another adult to whom he can draw near. The normal child can invest other objects with interest and can allow them to substitute their care and affection for that of the mother. The child who develops into a homosexual is not interested in acquiring care and affection but the survival of his ego.

Viewed schematically Patient A's nuclear conflict can be designated as the centrum or nidus around which secondary conflicts and a tertiary layer of action and behavior formed. These tertiary patterns and attitudes are designed to enclose, ward off and encyst the isolated affective state of the mother-child unity. As a result: (1) He does not approach any other woman, especially sexually, as this will touch off the isolated affective state of the fearful mother-child unity. (2) He does not attempt to leave his mother or else she would by her actions provoke the isolated affective state. He attempts to keep the "status quo," being asexual as regards other females. (3) He carries out sexual activities with the mother but only through substitution and displacement and other defense mechanisms. He therefore gratifies his sexual desires through a masquerade. (4) He solidifies his female identification but to gain strength must seek his transitory male identification through the penis of his partner. (5) He substitutes for mother a man for sexual intercourse but is in essence enjoying sexual intercourse and closeness with the mother in a disguised state. This helps him overcome his loneliness, depression, loss, fear of abandonment and helps deny his primary conflict.

To summarize, the homosexual is fixated on the wish for the mother-child unity. This, however, signals an attempt to regress to the undifferentiated phase and a total destruction of the self in a union with the mother. It is to be avoided at any cost. All further activities of his life are designed to ward off the realization of this situation. Homosexual behavior appears to be the solution for forestalling a powerful affective state which threatens to destroy the individual both by anxiety and the loss of personal identity with a return to the amorphous, undifferentiated stage of the ego. The choice of partner of the same sex, a phenomenon of the polymorphous-perverseness of infantile sexuality, is pressed into service for repression of the basic conflict: the mother-child unity accompanied by the dire fear of loss of self. This is in accordance with the Sachs's theory of the mechanism of sexual perversion.

To recapitulate: The infantile libidinal wishes which are repressed are the desire to merge with the mother and protect the original mother-child unity. This is fraught with personal disaster and terror. As a result libidinal activity with all females is prohibited in the unconscious and therefore in conscious life. Homosexual activity is a way out of this dilemma and at the same time keeps the original tie with the mother. In later life the avoidance of the female precludes the activation of the primary nuclear conflict of the patient. Depending upon the basic ego organization and psychic structure of the individual, defensive mechanisms will come into play whose aim is to ward off the activation of this nuclear conflict and to afford some degree of satisfaction in life. Therefore some individuals will use projective techniques; others, obsessional; others, phobic; others, hypochondriacal mechanisms of defense, thereby giving each homosexual patient's clinical picture a particular coloration. Homosexuality can occur concomitantly with all forms of emotional disturbances including character disorder, sociopathic personality, neurosis, psychosis. The nuclear conflict, however, is the same in all cases: the mother-child unity.

During the course of treatment, Patient A discovered that his guilt feelings came from a number of sources. They arose from his wish to penetrate into his mother, destroy her and produce her death and at the same time join with her in the mother-child unity. This aggressive destructive murderous urge increased his guilt (preoedipal guilt). He felt guilty for his incestuous wishes toward his mother and his desire to replace the father in intercourse with her (oedipal guilt). His attraction to men caused feelings of disloyalty to his mother which were expressed as "I give myself to men and I feel guilty toward my mother." Whenever he attempted to break the mother-child bondage and become a mature and independent man he felt guilty because he felt beholden to his mother for his very life and security and therefore believed he would be punished for this "rebellion and renunciation."

Referring to his attitude toward the female the patient remembers the fear of the mother's breast and his fear of looking at breasts of other women since childhood. "When I think of breasts I get a little nervous. It has to do with my mother's breasts and how she would walk around and show them to me. I can remember seeing a scar on one breast of my mother. She used to blame the operation on her breast on the breast-feeding she gave me." Whenever he approached women he remembered that at times he had hurt his mother's breasts through breast-feeding although he does not believe his mother's assertion that he was the cause of a scar. He compares homosexual intercourse to heterosexual intercourse by saying that he has had the feeling that in heterosexual intercourse women would use him while in homosexual intercourse he was not under anyone's control but his own.

The patient became increasingly aware during analysis that many of his fears, whether having to do with work or social engagements, had been libidinized into homosexual activity (erotization of anxiety*). "At several points I stop thinking of what causes my fear, it takes over.

Even if I think at work I'm not doing enough of what I'm supposed to be doing I develop a quick fear and this is immediately replaced by homosexual desire and then when I do this I feel well again." Homosexual activity is here seen to be generalized from its initial and primary use to ward off fears of the mother-child unity.

When the mother threatens to engulf him the patient develops fears which lead to sensations of "weakness." These sensations then develop into homosexual desire and terminate in the homosexual act. "It's like an automatic response, first caused by my mother in childhood and she does it now, too. If I show her in any way I have a problem or bring it to her and instead of showing her I could handle it the only thing I can do is have her handle it for me. To get away from my mother I then look for a man to protect me from her, to help me, guide me, to show me how I can work without my feeling weak. To help me develop, to teach me. I didn't just want that only. I wanted somebody continually there as my mother is so strong and so overwhelming I need a fulltime man. My homosexuality defends me against these fears, the problems of life, the reality of life. On another level it's a defense against being able to help myself, against the thoughts about my lack of ability to help myself . . . my very helplessness with my mother. But when I act homosexually I strengthen myself with masculine strength to do all the things I have to in everyday life. I sneak in a shot of masculinity between encounters with my mother. It's also a way of postponing the challenging things of life until the last moment."

As treatment progressed the patient commented on certain difficulties

---

* *Erotization of anxiety*—That anxiety or mental pain can be neutralized or diminished through sexual stimulation and orgasm is quite obvious. There are three possibilities by which this could be effected. One is a regression to infantile modes of adaptation through the exaggeration of infantile components of sexuality. This is the regressive hypothesis. Another is that under certain circumstances anxiety can be transmuted into libido, such as in the anxiety neurosis. The third "where unconscious libidinal fantasy contrary to the demands of the superego (ego-dystonic) may provoke anxiety in the ego as in a psychoneurosis where unconscious incestuous impulses provoke the fear of sexual punishment or castration anxiety."[47] The last, stated simply, involves unconscious sexual fantasy which leads to superego anxiety.

Upon reflection it seems that in the first instance anxiety leads to erotization but the latter two instances consist of the opposite, namely, libido or sexual excitation is transmuted into anxiety. Particularly in the second hypothesis it is the damming up of libido and in the last instance it is superego guilt which dams up libido and provokes anxiety in the *ego*.

in turning to heterosexuality. In his resistance to heterosexuality he brought up many objections to it. Homosexuality was "much easier. . . . Homosexuality itself has a wildness about it, an urgency and a mystery. It's true you can have that with a female but in heterosexuality there's a slowness about things and no wildness. You can't just go and lay a girl on the street. Everything that I noticed in heterosexuality is in moderation; there are no extremes. If it were, of course, I guess it would be so sick. So to become heterosexual in a way means a much more boring existence. I was also wishing this week-end that it would be different if I had been stopped before expressing my homosexual life so completely." In his sexual intercourse with men not only is there a wildness but he does whatever he wants to do to the man. He claims he is "truly free" as he cannot be with a woman. "Fucked him and he did everything I wanted him to do. I had temptations to hit him and I was very rough. I don't like talking about this aggressive side as it is one step removed from my mother and the way she was so sadistic to me. It makes me feel that I'm acting the way she does. I never got a good feeling from being beaten once or twice but I do get a wild feeling from subjugating other men and making them love me and think highly of me the way my father did not."

It was not until an advanced stage of treatment that the patient remembered his first homosexual feelings. They occurred at about 7 or 8 years of age. "The children used to take a nap in the afternoon in a nursery where my mother left me and there was something about a bigger boy. . . . I wished to have him as a substitute for my father and for a friend and he'd do something in bed with me. He was 12 years old and he'd lay on top of me and I liked that. Before that time I was a sexless kind of kid. I don't remember any sexual feelings. All the other boys in the nursery seemed weak except for that one."

He recalled that at the age of 15, "We used to play with each other's penis and I remember I had an ejaculation but didn't know what was happening." He recalled significantly that in the earliest years of life "my father always loved me a lot" and "that he loved me most and that's why my mother took it out on me." He began to grant that his father did try, for a short while in the boy's mid-childhood years, to fight against the mother's undue attentions and torture of the patient but the mother turned on the father in rage and the father left the boy to her mercy. This recall is meaningful in that the patient had an early period in his life in which he felt that the father was not completely helpless and weak, as he had always characterized him to the analyst and did indeed care for his younger son and loved him but eventually "sold out" to the overwhelming mother. This maternal domination intimidated not only the child but the father. Yielding to the female was a means of survival for the father as well as the son. The patient began, however, very early to show an identification with the aggressor. "I began to make my father feel like shit. He was a skunk and a shit and I would hurt him and embarrass him and it would give me satisfaction and my mother satisfaction. I would gang up with her on him. If I couldn't fight my mother it seems to me I would join with her. I would fight and hurt my father and this would please her. I feel terrible and ashamed in realizing what I did."

The patient's heterosexual activities were made possible by his comprehension of a crucial factor. This factor involved controlling the sexual situation. Whenever he would lose an erection it was "because the girl was trying to control things and I feared her the way I feared my mother when she would control me." He also feared that the woman's sadism would take over and therefore stimulate his own sadistic assault againt her (his mother). Gradually, however, he began to allow a more active sexual participation on the part of the female and to enjoy her sexual excitement. His heterosexual desires became progressively more intense and some feelings of warmth and affection showed themselves. Occasionally the glance of a girl passing him on the street could produce genital excitement and genital sensation. He saw the difference between relationships with men and with women partners and that you could "have a good feeling" in heterosexual relations. However, he was always upset by the fact that in homosexual desire the motivational state which would overcome him would be extremely powerful while with women it had to be slowly built up. He recognized that such a state is best "as it led up to something" while all homosexual activities were transitory, vicious and aggressive, lasting only for the moment and yielding no satisfaction comparable to the relationship between man and woman.

He was much more able to suppress homosexual desires when he felt it inopportune to act on them. He was never asked in the sessions to desist from homosexual activities; he first suggested this course. On numerous occasions near the end of treatment, upon having initiated a homosexual contact, he would, on the slightest pretext, end it without proceeding to any sexual activity. These momentary lapses were attempts to be reassured that he could capture the affection of men; at the same time he would punish them by abruptly leaving them. He found he no longer desperately needed his "shot of masculinity." He found homosexual relations uninteresting and even boring in direct contrast to his earlier evaluation of their being "wild" and "exciting." His deep feelings of loneliness could very well be alleviated by calling a girl and spending the evening with her. Above all he came to recognize the truth of the analyst's position that there was no innate desire for sexual intercourse with men. This had been a compromise form of sexual behavior. He contrasted his sexual feelings toward girls with that toward men. "There's a relaxed pressure in my sexual feelings with girls . . . toward homosexuals there is an angry feeling, a big force behind the genital feelings and a pushing forward. It's not a pleasant, relaxed genital feeling and I would rather have that with a girl."

He saw that sex with men aroused aggression while with women aggression is not what creates desire. He began to see that his sexual intercourse with men was really a repetition of an incident in childhood which he had transformed into a childhood fantasy. After having been threatened, tortured, subdued, harrassed by his mother and not protected by his father, he would lie on his bed face down and move his body and say, "Fuck you, Father." He expanded on this by adding "I had similar things happen to me with my mother and when I was younger and angry at her I might lie down on the bed face down and I'd get a genital feeling and I'd say 'Fuck you, too, shit-ass, Mother.' It was always translated into sex, this angry feeling, and finally I would masturbate and it would take out some of the hate and I'd have a feeling of relaxation." Clearly the substitution here of the man instead of the mother and his incestuous feelings with the resultant relaxation, dissolution of anxiety and quieting of hate was an essential factor in retaining the mental equilibrium of this patient.

Whenever he had intercourse with a girl his dreams would show that he felt "unfaithful to my mother. . . . There's a big conflict between my interest in girls and my relationship with my mother which has been so satisfying in so many ways all these years and on a certain level I want to keep this mother relationship, I want to keep it subconsciously and therefore when I dream that I spray a girl with my ejaculation I send her away angrily. Even after I was with this girl and had intercourse and left her apartment I felt alone, there was no continuity. Like I'm sometimes glad it's all over. I don't have a feeling I want to talk to these girls or get a good feeling out of telling them any of my problems or the good things that happen to me. I don't get that certain feeling that I get with my mother, that secure feeling. Why is that? Why is it so strong with my mother that it can't be with other girls? I derive a *strength* from my mother. This contrasts so much with the way she treated my father. She was just so destructive it frightened me. It was no help just swearing at him. If he ever had a problem she made him feel very bad. I even have the feeling most of the time that she wants him to die." This quotation from the patient aptly demonstrates the mother-child bondage. He wants her close but, of course, not merged with him which is the frightening aspect of the mother-child unity. The loneliness he experiences at times when he has been with a girl comes from jeopardizing the mother-child relationship and closeness.

His next association following the remark about deriving "strength" from his mother has to do with her destructiveness. In essence it was her destructiveness which induced such fear in him that he could not make the separation process from his mother a reality in his early years of development in the preoedipal period. He also feels that if he attempts to go against his mother her full destructiveness, now in part visited upon his father, will certainly be turned against him in its entirety.

When the patient did not engage in homosexual intercourse he would occasionally have homosexual impulses which were abated through masturbation with a homosexual image in mind. "I would be able to get my shot of masculinity this way in the morning on waking up and also before I went to sleep occasionally." It would be a homosexual image that would come to mind, "somebody that I knew, that they want me and that they would be close to me, touching my penis, masturbating me, putting their penis in my anus or vice versa. All of this would *strengthen me*, combining with another guy." Again part of the meaning of the homosexual behavior is emphasized by the patient himself, i.e., the gaining of strength through identification with the potent penis of his partner, and overcoming feelings of weakness due to separation from the mother.

Following an episode when his mother threatened to stop paying for the analysis he sobbed in the session, "My lousy mother and my lousy father, too." He got angry at his mother, felt terribly weakened and between bursts of anger had intense homosexual desires. At the same time "I hated the whole mess and then I wanted to hit her." Mixed with these desires was a rebellion against having homosexual feelings and a frantic attempt to deny them to himself and to rise above them. That night he had the following *dream:* "A woman in a fur coat and her breasts hanging out. She is holding her coat open so the breasts can hang out to be seen. There are four or five fellows nearby and she's walking away from them and these fellows are happy, as if they had had intercourse with her. She's looking back as if she's pulled a sneaky one and holding her coat out as if showing the breasts to me. The guys are happy and have a pleasurable look. As a matter of fact, they begin to imitate the lilt-like walk, a bounce, as she starts running from them when half-way down the block. She is no longer holding her coat open. She has pulled a fast one and she's getting away and one of the fellows is now looking as if something has been stolen from him. Some of the others discover that something has been stolen from them and they get a hate look on them. They are very angry and they make a motion as if to chase the woman and maybe kill her. I then awaken."

The patient's associations to this dream had to do with his fight with his mother on that day. "I think I am the boys and this is the kind of, sort of, helpless feeling I have. I guess I have intercourse with my mother and then I want to kill her. I guess they feel helpless as I do. When I went to our store and helped my mother this equals looking for my mother's breast then realizing that you have your own masculinity taken away from you by her, your own identity. These men are not themselves either. They have a bounce but they are not really feeling themselves. The bounce is a phony, a fake, they are not really themselves. It's like all those guys who walk around with a bounce and pretend they are masculine. It's not normal to walk around that way. Then they realize they've been robbed and she looks like a dirty woman. The breasts hang like a blob, like an old woman's breasts. These young men, they just had the old woman. Yesterday my father wanted to get mother off his back and on to me. The breasts upset me. In describing these breasts I feel terribly anxious. I can't appreciate the breasts with women. My mother's breast, it is always threatening, it was always a threat. I get now a very angry feeling thinking about her breast, a hateful feeling, like I'd like to hit the breast and pound at it. Why? Because I don't like my mother. If my mother's breast represents her bad treatment of me, too, it's like I must have taken poison milk in me. I remember once I ate anchovies and one day I got a terrible taste from them and it took a long time before I could enjoy anchovies again. My mother's breasts are like this. I can't enjoy women's breasts because of this. It has to do with the controlling factor, like doing something for a woman is giving in to her the way my mother wanted me to give in to her. It's why I feel uncomfortable when I touch or lick these breasts, always the same feeling of loss of control. I feel the same way about the vagina, that is, when I try to suck the vagina. It means being passive and commanded by my mother. She is offering herself to me, teasing me and stopping me from going with other women by saying that I don't need other women. Other women are just like her. This is it. Big deal! Nothing more to it. Don't get aroused by women. Not making it pleasant and she makes it something not to be aroused by."

The above dream stresses the following points: (1) The patient's feeling that the mother is very powerful and can command men and control them and also rob them of their masculinity through sexual intercourse. (2) The severe aggression toward his mother. (3) The sexual interest in her and jealousy of other men. (4) His sense of defeat at her hands and castration. (5) The mother's interdiction against sexual interest through her showing of herself to the patient. (6) The strong emphasis placed on the breasts of the mother which were in fact a tremendous stimulant to the patient when he was a child.

The patient's motivational state during sexual intercourse with a man was shown to be that of severe aggression. For example, while having intercourse per anum with his homosexual partner he realizes that "I have my fist clenched and I have a killing fantasy, like I wrap my arms around the guy and strangulate him by grabbing him around the waist or around the neck with my feet or my hands. I want to get a better grip on him to jab harder into his rectum with all my might, a lot of force behind it. I become angry even as I describe this. I'd like to punch and kick him at the same time and maybe even kill him." In actuality whenever a homosexual partner-to-be became gentle and began to talk pleasantly and like him, the patient might lose his sexual interest.

"I often have fantasies about hitting a man, hurting him. I thought about the guy the other night, screwing him in his office, and sometimes it even changes from sexual to pure aggression, like just jabbing him. After I talk of these feelings I feel somewhat kindlier to men. When I started my homosexuality with the boy across the street it used to start out as a fight and it always starts with people who appear aggressive or I start fights with women, not sex, with women who are aggressive and might hurt me, just like my mother. And even though I know it's my aggression there's suffering involved in it. In my search for my partner with whom to be aggressive I can stay up all night and not get enough sleep and not establish any relationship with anyone, either male or female, and in case the man is stronger than me it goes the other way, too, a wish on my part that the guy become more aggressive than me and does all these things to me. There's my masochism."

In the above session the patient clearly expresses the severe aggression underlying all homosexual intercourse. The homosexual while behaving as a sadist to his partner can at any moment switch into masochistic behavior if the strength of the partner overwhelms his. In both cases he plays a dual role, vicariously enjoying the other partner's role. There is a continuous oscillation, therefore, if not in actual act then in fantasy, between sadism and masochism in homosexual intercourse. The aggression serves multiple functions: To protect the breasts of the mother as the aggression is vented upon the substituted penis. To have intercourse with the father and force his love and affection. To punish the father for his denial to the son of masculinity and protection against the crushing mother and relief from the mother-child unity which the boy fears.

Patient A struggles mightily to rid himself of all traces of homosexual urges. There were certain characteristics of homosexual stimulation which seemed to him to be stronger than those of heterosexual although he felt both. In the homosexual it was an instantaneous reaction. This continually surprised him and at times disappointed and depressed him by its strength. He clearly saw, however, that the sexual reaction to a man was due to a number of forces, not least of all the severe aggression and aggressive discharge which accelerated his excitement and orgastic release. The "visual thing" in homosexuality was important although he acknowledged that it also occurred with the female. "The acceptance that the look is saying, the immediate acceptance of wanting me, and you don't get that with a girl. The look of the homosexual goes immediately to the genitals compared to a girl where it would go to the face or to the body in general. (The homosexual deals in part objects.) It was like having a mouthful of penises—that goes along with the look at the genitals and the nauseous feeling that comes after it. I get slightly nauseous now when I look at a guy's genitals." This last statement clearly indicates the oral incorporative mechanism present, the primitive introjection that comes into immediate play in homosexuality.

The response in the homosexual is so immediate that Patient A experienced considerable difficulty in dampening it through the knowledge of the aggression and the multiple functions that homosexual intercourse and homosexual "acceptance" signified. "There is a childish desire, it's like becoming a child and wanting a father, wanting a man. You become small. Your facial expression becomes sort of simple. It's really like you want to look for a daddy. Maybe it's what we have said, that the man is substituting for a girl. In actuality I don't really like the feel of a beard and the man has to be soft and have some feminine qualities it seems. I seem to have both my mother and my father in a love relationship and it's true happiness, like I'm reunited with both of them in my homosexual relations." At other times he stated "that the great pleasure of the homosexual urge is the release of these primitive feelings without concern for the demands of reaility."

He became aware as the analysis progressed that sexual intercourse with a girl involved more sublimation and less aggressive output. The homosexual look itself satisfies a desire in him to be wanted but he thinks he could get that satisfaction from a woman who wants him if he is not frightened by her. But he also suspects and distrusts a woman who might readily give him friendship and love. He would feel closed-in and trapped as if he were trapped by his mother. "With a woman you have to cater to her, that's because she's the all-powerful woman like my mother. You might just become a complete masochistic slave and then I might become engulfed and lose my identity, become a girl or become like my cruel mother."

In the late phases of analysis he again contrasts the two situations. "In homosexuality it's a wild type, groping thing. In heterosexuality I'm left with nice feelings, there's something intangible there, an overall feeling of warmth, sometimes some of the girls I find I become dependent on and I'm not frightened. It doesn't leave me guilty and dissatisfied and cold. I have something that I want. I'm left 'me,' I don't feel torn apart."

The connections between breast and penis had become adequately clear to the patient. "The realization right along that this had something to do with my becoming homosexual . . . it is very important . . . has helped me a great deal. My mother's breast and the penis of these men is quite the same. I don't have the same kind of homosexual feelings now. I realize they're wrong for me and when I think of sucking a man's penis or his sucking mine my homosexual feelings vanish. The penis is the breast. This is the feeling that I've had since I discovered that penis and breast are the same. It has something to do with talking about it to you. It gives me a masculine feeling rather than a homosexual one to realize this. It's very sick. This is not really a part of my life and should not be. The attraction of the penis seems to be fading away like the homosexuality is fading away but as I say this I'm frightened and I begin to feel a terrible lonely feeling so I give up the penis and the breast, it has something to do with feeling alone, a lonely feeling. What is it due to? It's leaving the security of the home which to me *represents my mother*. It is also a sexual orientation, something to do with the sexual orientation. As long as I know that the breasts of women are not my mother's breasts I can approach them and enjoy them. I realize to give up my homosexuality seems to be to give up my mother. It is sex with my mother's breast, that is what I do when I have homosexual intercourse."

The insight that masochism is an integral feature of homosexuality is often strenuously resisted. This was the case with Patient A. While masturbating to ejaculation he would fantasy that he was being jabbed in the "rear end" and "it hurt like hell. . . . I jumped up and I was shouting, I remember, when this really happened. I associate masturbation with homosexual fantasies, with hurting myself, and it's pleasurable. This is my masochism that you have been talking about. I do this and I think all the time that it will basically hurt me. I was angry with my mother today and I had a sudden homosexual feeling. It was obvious to me that I do not have a father to stand between me and my mother and the only way I can get one is through homosexuality and the only way I can enjoy her is through homosexuality and there's always an urgency in it. My homosexual thoughts have to do with my need for my father, too, wanting the father and hating the father and hating the mother and loving the mother. Why do I have to contend with these things? In actuality I no longer need a mother and a father, I'm an adult, I no longer need them to take care of me."

The patient had been expressing a set of feelings about both parents. (1) Punishing himself for hating his father. (2) Punishing his father through punishing other men for not being his father. (3) Taking the partner's (father's) penis so that he becomes a man by force. (4) "I know I get anxious when I think of my mother, what she'll do to me, leave me, and then I change it into sex and I feel better. I get rid of anxiety. The whole thing starts with anxiety and it's gotten rid of by orgasm" (erotization of anxiety). (5) "Look, Mother, I love only you. I have no interest at all in other women. I only like men and I only *love* you." (6) Making up for the deprivation suffered at the hands of both parents. There is a sado-masochistic pleasurable core throughout. "I want everything and I get everything although I suffer for it."

During analytic treatment the patient became aware that:

(1) His basic problem entailed his inability to separate from his mother. Whenever he tried, he developed anxiety despite the constant and obvious understanding that she was a false, malevolent and inimical person to him in every way.

(2) His unconscious incestuous desires for his mother which for the first time began to appear in dreams.

(3) His incorporation of his mother which he attempts to remove from his body through nausea and vomiting.

(4) The necessity to finally and ultimately detach himself from his mother if he wants to become heterosexual. The fact that in his dreams he can enjoy sexual intercourse with women is, of course, a major step forward. He states: "The worst thing that my mother can say to me and

the worst thing that she can do—which makes me homosexual—is when she tells me 'You are just like your father.' First she tears him down and then by saying this with a terrible smile on her face she makes me feel awful.''

The patient had just finished reading the story of a homosexual boy who, realizing he cannot escape his mother, wants to travel to a distant city, fabricates an allegiance to and heterosexual interest in a local girl. The mother, first desiring him not to go away, then allows him to travel to this city in order to separate him from the girl. The terrible malevolence and destructiveness of the mother in the story was similar to that, Patient A said, of his own mother. He wished to finally and ultimately "get rid of her," to purge himself of this terrible need for her. He then developed anxiety and nausea. He could not go to sleep that night and did not want to. He was afraid he might "think or dream something terrible."

Finally, upon going to sleep, he had the following *dream:*

"I was with a woman and we had intercourse twice. During the process of these two times I was sucking and kissing her ears. I've found women's ears to be very sensitive and I've used this with women when I have intercourse now. It gets them excited. I was screwing her very well. The third time instead of this woman it was my mother and she lets me do it a little bit and then she says, 'Oh, no, you don't!' She prevents me so that she won't let me fuck her. This is what she does to me in real life, of course. She stimulates me just enough and then stops with everything she does. I pretend I have an ejaculation anyway to hurt her and I pretend that my ejaculum comes on my pajama pants . . . my pajama pants . . . often I have laid down in my pajama pants and had homosexual fantasies and ejaculated on these pants. I usually had a penis fantasy in the past and I masturbated. . . . To return to the dream I pretend I come on my pajama pants and I pant as if I had obviously 'come.' She is very much annoyed at what I've done. It's as if I had said to her 'Screw you, Mother. I am going to have my fun anyway. I am going to be a man.' She goes out to buy the newspaper. When she came back another woman is in the room and she throws my things at me and she says I should get out and take my things with me and she says 'Don't take the paper.'

"In actuality this is what she has been doing now. She threatens to make out another will and all the money she has will no longer go to me because I'm changing. She's threatening me with taking all the money in the bank that she has in my name. She is going to leave nothing for me and this has upset me but this is a pain in the ass and that's all. I smile at this now. Let her do it. What is more important—my life or this money? To be a man or this money? Then she chases me around the room and we are both deriving pleasure from it. It is a pleasure but it is mostly sadistic now in my mind as I'm going to *leave anyway*, no matter what she says or does, and in a way I'm torturing her for the first time because she has to chase me. She always says no money for analysis and no seeing her. Well, all right, we'll put up with that. That's what we'll do. One of the reasons she's chasing me is that she really wants to see if I've 'come.' I think maybe I can spit on myself but I don't have a chance to do it. She comes into a small room and just before she's going to look at me I wake up." (The patient is committed to being a man and defiantly shows his mother that he can have an ejaculation despite her wishes that he identify with her and be like her and not be a man. He awakens in anxiety.)

In his associations to this dream he recalls that the analyst stated at the last session that an older woman who paid some attention to him was not necessarily someone whom he could not have a personal relationship with. He was "annoyed" at the analyst. He was also very upset about the short story of the homosexual boy and his mother. "This was so true, a typical engulfing, dominating, castrating mother who had no concern for her child but simply to use him in her way and no other woman should ever get him. Only for her own benefit. When I read that story was when I developed the nausea and confusion and after that came my dream which means I'm going to get away."

This session clearly indicates the patient's stabilization toward heterosexuality. He no longer fears the mother in the same sense as he had in the past. He wants a heterosexual life and he will defy his mother to have it. He is able to express himself heterosexually and even is able to tolerate the ideas of incest and to make peace with his infantile wishes and impulses and not be frightened by them. He realizes that his mother has had a tremendous effect in promoting this incestuous conflict by her provocative behavior and possessively seductive attitude. He feels unsure of himself at times and experiences loneliness and fear when confronted with the necessity to finally separate himself from the mother but he fully realizes this must be done and he will do it.

The Homosexual Encounter

There is no empathic affective reciprocity in the male homosexual relationship. Each partner is playing his part as if in isolation with no cognizance of the complementariness of a sexual union, as if the act were consummated in "splendid isolation" with the other person merely a device for the enactment of a unilateral emotional conflict. There is a rudimentary reciprocal affective situation between female homosexual partners where either may play mother or child and alternate role designation.

The imagery accompanying the homosexual act between males is total fantasy without relevance of the other except as a device. This is a masturbatory equivalent and highly narcissistic. The act permits discharge and expression only of individual dynamic forces. There is no reality awareness of the partner or his feelings; the contact is simply epidermal, mucous and anatomic. There is no psychic relatedness which involves reciprocal recognition of the affective needs of the partner. He is seen as a vehicle for the expression of one's own conscious tension and unconscious feelings. These are the "emergency emotions," fear, rage, hatred, guilt, envy, bitterness and revenge, all arising from psychic pain. The "welfare emotions," those arising from pleasure, are conspicuously absent: joy, love, tenderness and pride.

Multiple homosexual contacts between a variety of partners assembled in a group and one-to-one contacts have as their aim the immediate gratification and alleviation of urgent destructive feelings threatening extinction to the self were they to be contained. Other individuals are the instruments through which the homosexual seeks expression of and release from oppressive and importunate anxieties, guilts, incestual feelings and aggression.

Every homosexual encounter first concerns itself with disarming the partner through one's seductiveness, appeal, power, prestige, effeminacy or "masculinity" and then taking one's satisfaction from the vanquished. To disarm in order to defeat is the motif and if one submits in defeat gratification is nevertheless obtained by the victim vicariously through identification with the victor. Despite any surface mianifestations to the contrary, *to disarm and defeat* invariably characterizes all encounters between homosexuals.

The homosexual act is purely egocentric; any tender affective reciprocity is pretense. Some homosexuals prefer to achieve contact through the aperture in a toilet stall door, extend and/or grasp the penis without face-to-face encounter. This is the enactment of the fundamental nature of their object relationships: relating to part objects, not whole objects.

Along with the totally narcissistic attitude of the homosexual there is a supercasual air and a preoccupation with appearance and adornment which is meant to produce a show of perfection and imperturbability in order to "conquer" men and deny a deep sense of inferiority. This exterior hauteur serves to keep in repression the homosexual's knowledge that he is "held together only by his clothes." Ego boundaries must be carefully preserved through dress and studied action, a seeming casualness most calculated. The posturing of this self-presentation serves as a defense against deficient ego boundaries which cannot withstand any stress or unexpected circumstances.

Homosexuals rarely participate in athletics or competitive sports because of childhood fears of being different from other boys, the fear of their own aggression, the fluidity of body ego boundaries. They must control their body lineaments in an attempt to form concrete or static body ego boundaries through external measures. Their deep distress on this count is seen in dreams where once the clothing is removed there is no person underneath or part of tne body is missing.

Chapter XII

MALE HOMOSEXUALITY (Part 2)

Patient B

AT THE AGE OF 26, this patient dropped out of graduate school because he experienced periods of "confusion," depression and a progressive build-up of homosexual desire which produced intense anxiety. He greatly feared the imminent return of his mother from abroad and concurrently he was troubled by a relationship with a girl, intended by him to remain quite superficial, which was now leading to insistence on her part for sexual intimacy, even the idea of which he dreaded, and marriage.

The "pressure" on him was so intense he would develop fits of crying, despondency, with "rolling on the floor in agony." These attacks culminated in his first homosexual relationship on the evening before his mother's return. The partner, an older man, was a street corner pick-up. Since that time, two years prior to the beginning of treatment, he had engaged in several isolated episodes of homosexuality with older partners, most of them occurring while in Europe the summer before entering treatment.

Patient B was an attractive, personable, charming young man, winning in manner, with many cultural talents and extremely intelligent. He was born and brought up in a large metropolitan area where he lived for most of his life. He attended private schools during childhood, entered preparatory school, was admitted to a large university and had a Master's degree. He was employed at a professional level in an organization dealing with social and economic issues. An only child, his parents were of mixed West European extraction, the mother highly cultivated and intellectual, the father a rugged explorer contemptuous of what he deemed his wife's ultra-refined tastes. He became an alcoholic, at times openly abusive and hostile, and left the home without legal separation but continued to reside nearby. He contributed intermittently to the support of his wife and son. The mother, an attractive woman, worked in a sales position for many years, amplifying the father's reluctant and unwilling financial contributions. She had instigated the separation after years of dissension, rejection of her

138

husband's sexual advances, consistent condescension toward him mixed with convictions of her social, esthetic and moral superiority. The husband, goaded, resentful and defensive, exaggerated any objectionable traits in order to provoke his wife in futile retaliation. In effect, the mother controlled the father through her depreciation of him and forced his withdrawal from the family. He remained an insubstantial and weak figure to his son.

The father had habitually thrown up his athletic proficiency to his son as he had always considered the boy a "sissy."

In the chaotic year prior to entering therapy, as Patient B became more and more caught up in and troubled by his homosexuality, he decided to send a letter "of explanation and self-exposure" to his mother whom, he felt, he dearly loved. Although the letter was not sent to her the patient brought it to the analyst early in treatment:

"The fact that I write it at all is a tribute to the utter closeness of our relationship. As you read it I ask only that you think about what I say calmly and soberly. Don't let maternal pride cloud the facts and offer some easy solution for, believe me, there is none. . . . Not all of what I have to say is pleasant but I think it should be told if only in deference to the frankness which has been a unique and noble part of our friendship.

"As you know, my personality has grown and developed over the years, I feel honestly that I have progressed in more senses than just growing up. For this progress I hold you chiefly responsible and for it I will always be deeply grateful. But along with this progress, constantly co-existent with it, has grown the 'flaw' in my nature. Now, the pure question of my sexual orientation is compounded of biological and psychological factors in great part beyond my control. Unfortunately, the ramifications of any deviation extend into every phase of my life and development. No one knows better than you how the 'sissy' problem hurt and tortured my childhood, it was always with me, and although it didn't keep me from a happy youth it was the ever present problem and bogey man.

"As I have grown older the direct brutality of childhood has worn off and the luck of having a personable face and personality has aided me. Too, the greater sophistication and education of the environment in which I live has all kept the problem from the brutal urgency of childhood. Nevertheless it is still with me. I've known since childhood that there was something confused in my 'boy-girl' balance, i.e., dressing up as a girl, etc. As I came into adolescence the 'divergences' in my reactions startled me. Instead of the one fairly directed urge mine was diffuse and confused. My own solution of the problem was a tremendous repression of it. So long as the other avenues of life were free and clear I could keep under full sail.

"The Navy experience broke into the problem. I was thrown with rough people, the screen of breeding and education was off, I was back in the 'jungle' of early childhood. The fact that I nearly died that winter can I'm sure be traced to the mind as well as the body. . . . The problem still torments me. The full blast of college learning in the social sciences also only increased my fears by showing for facts what I had hoped were fears but along at the same time it freed me from the sense of a unique affliction.

"Last December came the great struggle which nearly snapped me. . . . As far as men go I haven't had any contact at all. I do know that I have always wanted a man to love me. I think because I always felt Daddy didn't. I've had crushes on boys just as I have had on girls. I always desperately want them to like me. . . . Nothing seems more horrible to me than the 'fairy' life, flitting from one affair to another in a world where all values are changed, no love permanent.

"I think I would kill myself rather than partake of it. . . . How it will work out I can't venture to say. I only ask for your help and patience. I cannot marry under false colors. As sad and terrible as it is I am not looking at it with a hopeless attitude. If it can be worked out it will be. If not I will do whatever is most graceful. It is a pity that with so much talent and real worth I should be afflicted with something that Conrad said 'is really a terrible cross.' In any case I'm sure I will have to go away for about a year to work it out by myself. By its very nature it must be done away from home, away from any environment where it might prove fatal. In many ways this is the deciding year of my life and it will cast the frame in which my future will be set."

Ever since late childhood the patient had daydreams in which he planned to "eradicate" his father. These occurred frequently as it always seemed his father was a "nuisance." One form the daydream took was to find his father drunk and with an unlit gas jet turned on, which he, the patient, would leave on. He might daydream of dropping a "potion" in his father's drink or equally "attractive" was the daydream of saying, when his father telephoned, "I really don't need you any more, so go to hell." These fantasies obviously indicate vast aggression against the father along with the great need to be loved by him. The father upset the patient by frequently talking provocatively about his wish "to go out and punch some fairies." At other times the father would become salacious in the course of a telephone conversation, attempting to shock his son by crude and obscene language.

For years after the father lived away from the mother he would take Patient B out one morning a week, from 10:30 to noon. Punctually at that time he would send the boy home in a taxi and the patient would feel depressed. "I would be sure he had promised to stay together longer so we could go to a movie." An early homosexual fantasy was to have someone older than himself be proud of him: "Give me a job and then say 'You did that so well,' to have an older man love me, put his arm around me, who would be interested in me. But he would have to be a person and a real man." He felt throughout his childhood that boys didn't like him but after his experiences in the Navy he felt better, realizing that young men his own age did "care" about him.

Early in treatment the patient felt that his homosexual problem must be tied up with his mother and his feelings toward her. "There's a big 'voltage' toward my mother but not so much with father. There's a strong resentment against her and a tremendous dependency." As a small boy he hated sports and felt awkward. His mother used to push him into going to dances, tell him where to stand, tell him whom to dance with. He would do everything he could to stay away from girls. In preparatory school he was poor in mathematics, did not do his assignments and almost failed. Taking a great risk he once cheated by sneaking into the teacher's room to steal examination questions from his desk.

In late childhood he and his mother enjoyed uninterrupted "closeness." She would undress in front of him, nearly to complete nudity. As an adult he found it "terribly irritating whenever she is in a state of undress in front of me. I kid with her about it and say, 'Mother, aren't you the provocative one.'" He tried to make it a rule that she not walk into the bathroom when he was there. He could not imagine "that I would ever want to go to bed with my own mother." He feels she "got a bad deal, an alcoholic husband to whom she had to act the mother. Always the mother to her younger sisters and brothers. Then she became engaged first to someone who was brutal to her. Then she married my father which proved to be a disaster."

Patient B was born within ten months of the marriage. It was a difficult birth with extensive surgery required for his mother in order to repair a third degree perineal tear. She had a long convalescence, suffering a series of complications while at the same time taking care of her infant son.

"Father was a very powerful man physically who gave Mother a raw deal. I feel that the homosexual business may be my mother's fault, something she didn't do consciously." He screamed a great deal (see "screaming phenomenon," Chapter XI) when she left him as a child for frequent vacations. He stayed behind with a Scotch maid, a strict disciplinarian, obsessional to a severe degree and upset by the boy's masturbation, continually punishing him for it.

In early childhood he would often dress up in his mother's clothes. He liked dolls and had a family of Teddy bears he played with to the age of nine. He had always had a marked interest in clothes and could remember over many years a particular costume that any friends of his mother wore. He always felt that his mother wanted to "keep me at home."

When he was 13, his mother "fell in love with another man." The man's wife would not agree to a divorce and the patient's mother became "a part-time mistress" although herself still married to his father though living apart from him. At first Patient B was proud of this relationship and wished his mother would marry her lover because of his wealth and position. In retrospect he professed to being neutral about the arrangement but suspects that he had been jealous of her affection for the man.

His father, passive, drunk at times, and other times angry and demanding, confused his own mother with his wife. He sometimes called his wife "mother" on the telephone.

In adolescence the patient developed a strong desire to dye his hair. "I bought a bottle of peroxide and dumped it on my hair but washed it out immediately." The following day he cut his hair shorter and shorter in order to get away from the "exquisite torture" which he had heaped on his head. This hair-dyeing practice began at boarding school and continued into graduate school. He felt that with dyed hair he became much more attractive, resembling a boy whom he had met a few years before entering treatment, a blond, attractive boy, whom he felt "love" for. With blond hair, he would be "terribly successful and terribly popular and exercise power." This was one aspect of the patient's identification with the mother.

He became increasingly unable to adapt adequately to environmental demands and conditions, felt that he was "not enough of a man." He had just failed his last examination in graduate school and would soon be asked to leave. He was extremely unhappy and "sorry" for the girl who said she was in love with him but was engaged to marry another student. Because of his academic failure he faced imminent military service. Frightened and weakened by these reality stresses his homosexual urges became more conscious and terrifying.

His fear of the female was profound. "I can't even think of looking at the sexual image of a woman. I'm scared of kissing, too. Even the thought of the female form scares me. I look away when I think of it now." He obviously suffered severe castration anxiety. At school he never liked "dirty jokes, they disgusted me." As a child he felt he was treated like a girl. His mother would always take him into women's restrooms and into ladies' bathhouses when they went swimming. "She would keep me on the women's side." He recalls seeing women putting on their girdles. His mother excused all this later on by saying that she had thought of him then as only a baby.

"I've always been so scared of men, too, but if a man wants me I have a hold on him." Since becoming active homosexually he would have the thought "If you go home without some sexual escapade you are not wanted." This was a defense against having sexual feelings toward his mother. Even in his earliest homosexual activities the patient had been aware that during the sexual act he would have sadistic ideas. "I had an awful urge to beat these men." Several homosexual partners had told him, "Don't bite me," or "Stop pinching me." He wished to penetrate men partners anally and on many occasions had engaged in sado-masochistic activities. On two occasions he was tied up and beaten. He had not taken the sadistic role in these situations. Most of the time he fled the sado-masochistic scene as soon as it began.

Patient B's sexual practice was fellatio or anal intercourse. On rare occasions when his masochism was intense he allowed anal penetration which ordinarily occurred only when he was intoxicated. His homosexual bouts often took place when he had been drinking and terminated by awakening in his own or some strange bed, possibly robbed and amnesic for the preceding events. His contacts were of a transient nature except in one instance when a relationship lasted approximately a year with an "attractive, intelligent artist" who, however, mistreated him and stole money from him.

During the first year-and-a-half of analysis his homosexual activities were mostly confined to the setting of a Turkish bath where he would have multiple contacts. He was always reluctant to discuss the details of his homosexual encounters in the analysis, feeling embarrassed and humiliated. The incidents were usually precipitated when he felt threatened by his mother or weakened by any job difficulties or by authority figures at work. He frequently would force himself to abstain from homosexual contacts for two or three months.

He came to many conclusions concerning his homosexual behavior: That perhaps it was a way of controlling men so that they did not attack him, especially when he felt vulnerable; that a homosexual act sometimes saved him from "some sort of chaotic, mysterious fragmentation. "I will fall apart if I don't have it." Suddenly, after homosexual intercourse he felt relieved, whole again and strong. He often experienced a "split" in himself, like two selves existed, that he did not know who he was. On the one hand, he believed himself to be benevolent, gentle, kind, attractive, interesting, powerful and heterosexual. On the other, he was homosexual, defeated, frightened and "belonged to Mommie." He noticed that homosexual feelings came on whenever he was afraid of his mother "turning around and engulfing me." He felt a weird excitement when his mother approached him suddenly if he were half-asleep at home or if she suddenly sat on the bed or walked into his bathroom when he was there. This "excitement" had in several instances proceeded to a conscious sexual feeling and he was "terribly afraid" of this. At the same time the erotic sensation was mixed with aggression. "I don't know quite what I would do to her." He came to see that his homosexuality was directly related to incestuous and aggressive feelings toward his mother. He feared he would either have intercourse with her or perhaps "murder" her. The meaning of the following *dream* is evident:

"In a room looking out there are two seals walking by, a white and a black one. The baby seal is with children. I fear the children will hurt the seals who are lovable. Then there is a large bed, big enough to hold Mommie. A black man tries to kiss me. I am bent in an arc and his comment is 'I guess you only do this for Mommie.' "

In this dream the patient clearly substitutes himself as the object of desire of the man to protect his mother. Simultaneously he is vicariously enjoying the seduction of his mother. In this connection he remembered that at age nine or ten, when his father was violent toward his mother, he got between them declaring to his mother that he would save her. He recalled at that time he specifically meant that he would save her from the father's sexual attack, bearing the force of this assault on his own body.

He used to be fascinated by pornographic pictures which involved men and women. He would "look at the woman and go through the woman to the man." He felt that this meant he would perhaps become the woman. This would result in a considerable confusion in his mind. Why should he be more interested in what happened to the woman? He had always been with mother too much, engulfed by her and had assumed her outlook, he felt.

Whenever the patient attempted to concentrate on women and sexual intercourse with them, the picture of mother would "flip into my mind" and his interest would abruptly cease. On several occasions, however, it didn't "flip out of my mind and it seems I had an erection at these times." He was unable to have sexual intercourse with men toward whom he felt friendly as he found that homosexual intercourse was really a "hostile and aggressive act," in which he felt superior, that he had a weapon on his side and was able thereby to disarm the partner. All homosexuals are engaged in a continuous struggle to disarm the partner. He didn't like to touch other men's penises and at the beginning of analysis hadn't liked to look at his own; it made him feel uneasy. He yearned for power over other men because he wished he had power over his father. As a child the only power he had was by irritating him. Father would always resent "that I'd read a lot. I'd deliberately curl up with a book in front of him."

Not only did he fear castration, he equally feared penetration of his body. Anything coming toward his eyes—a pencil, a gesture or some article—would cause severe fright. "It unnerves me." He had an irrational fear of children being run over, "it almost makes me jump out of my skin." This was a reaction to feelings of murderous rage and to his own masochistic desires of being penetrated, being castrated and being destroyed.

He was aware of his "terrible fear" of normal men but he felt superior with homosexuals. He felt "terribly vulnerable" with boys who made fun of him for being effeminate although, in fact, he did not appear feminine. "I can vividly remember every remark about my being effeminate or unmasculine. All the remarks in prep school tortured me terribly and the awful guilty feeling that I might give myself away."

Fears of effeminacy seemed to vanish when he was required to enter the Navy after his failure in graduate school. But he had a "year of decline" in the Navy where he worked in a mess kitchen, experiencing homosexual wishes, extremely afraid of his effeminacy and of his homosexuality. He then went into a "calculated career" of homosexuality. He was away from home, had lost all his social status and wanted revenge on the Navy. He could now be quite coldly effective and "felt unusually happy, although I still had to work in a scullery."

In the evenings he drank a great deal and became "completely animal." In actuality he felt "it saved my sanity. Before, at college, I had reached the end of the world, awful fear. Then I suddenly failed my exams. Then the underlayer of fear, uncertainty, came, that I was going to be at the mercy of people once I got into the Service and would have no way to protect myself."

Patient B's adaptive mechanisms were not sufficient to maintain him while in the Navy. He regressed and became ill, suffering a severe pneumonia which kept him hospitalized for three months in a critical state. Then came an intense outbreak of homosexual behavior which he no longer fought against. In the homosexuality he felt his sanity was preserved. By interrupting some paranoid-like symptomatology involving generalized distrust and extreme aggression it served as a defensive mechanism against a probable psychosis. He had not, on any occasion, become overtly psychotic but he did exhibit profound regressive phenomena which belonged to the undifferentiated phase of development.

During the first year of analysis a series of dreams on the same night indicated his intense distress, confusion and aggression. The series of dreams were captioned. The first caption was "What Have I Done Wrong?" In this dream there were Negro and white men engaged in various forms of sexual perversion. Parts of bodies were visible and there were suggestions of sadistic practices taking place. There were black and pink "behinds" which were aimed in his direction and men approaching him sexually with erect penises from which he looked away in fright mixed with anticipation and pleasure.

The second sequence was captioned "See Her Finally Deceived and Humiliated." There was a picture of a man with long pants, a man he had met in a Turkish bath, who approaches him and who "desperately wants to make a pass at me." He ejaculates as the man approaches. He felt that this connoted his mother's humiliation if she were to discover the full extent of his homosexual activities. However, he got a strange pleasure out of her embarrassment and severe disappointment in him. It was as if he were "taking out some kind of resentment on her."

The third sequence was "See the Last Agony of this Man." Under this caption he sees a man who apparently is Hitler being hung by the neck. His head is in the noose "broken—he has been hanged. The only reason he is there, it seems to me in the dream, is a device to show some sexual sadism. I guess my sexual sadism and my anger." The hanging man also signified the hanging penis.

The most terrifying aspect about these dreams to Patient B, however, was not their content but the fact that they were blurred, they came in and out of focus and they consisted of partial images or superimposed images, one upon the other. At times there were parts of bodies which had been mutilated and a conglomeration of black and white bodies. He did not see how he possibly could get well or improve but had to go deeper and deeper into the quagmire of his homosexual relations "and the underworld of homosexuality." He felt "justifiably depressed" at this point in therapy and could see no hope for the future.

Throughout his life, the patient had been "convinced by my mother that I have no sexuality at all." He was terrified of his mother's touching him as it stimulated sexual feelings. He used to tell her not to kiss him goodnight beginning at the age of 14. Before boarding school, at 14 or 15, she told him to come to bed with her, that is, to sleep in the same bed with her the one night before leaving for school. His mother had always come into the bathroom while he was occupying it. "Mother was always very stupid about that. I was rather offended that I didn't seem to have any sex at all to her." It was shortly after he went to boarding school that his father left home permanently to live a few blocks away. His recollection, from age 9 on, is that his father did not sleep in the same room with his mother.

Since age 18, Patient B had had the "compulsion" to shave the hair off his chest and other parts of his body with the exception of the pubic region. "I realize now that this was a kind of self-destruction, an obliteration of myself. I did not like the hair, did not like having it. It was very dark and ridiculous. I wanted to do it but I did not want anyone to realize it. Both the peroxiding of my hair and shaving the hair off my body were done compulsively. . . . I have to do it. It's such a temptation. It's irresistible." In actuality, this was a sign of defeat of his masculinity and protected him against the anxiety of not being loved by a man. If he could only become a woman he would get love from men. The first hair shaving was associated with the first peroxide incident begun after the blond-haired boy rejected him for touching his body, saying to him angrily: "What's matter with you? Are you a queer?"

"It was my reaction to all this, to the personal cut, a kind of defiance, this would make me considerably more appealing. Peroxiding my hair was certainly a feminine thing, filled me with pleasure and with fright, wondering whether people would notice it. A wet, warm fright, something to do with increasing my physical allure, and that a miracle would occur." These episodes of hair dyeing and hair shaving would result in a "kind of hysterics" in which the patient would sob, cry, feel intensely confused and occasionally wish for death; he certainly could not become a female in fact.

He had numerous childhood fears. One of them was that if he left his hands outside the covers when he went to sleep someone would cut them off. Another was that there was someone, especially his father, at the foot of the bed who had come to murder him. Often during childhood upon going to sleep he would suddenly awaken with a terrifying sensation that his legs were going to drop off. All these fears derived from a fear of castration and a fear of attack by the father because of his superimposed negative oedipal conflict.

During the sessions Patient B frequently experienced severe shudders and chills and a fear of physical attack by the analyst. Upon leaving the session he would hurriedly go to the Turkish bath where he would have sexual intercourse. "I was afraid. I nearly ran to the Turkish bath. I feel better when I'm through. I suddenly have a feeling when I'm here or when I'm with other men or when I feel weak that I'm acting like a girl. I'm feminine and defenseless. I'm like my mother. The anal business is the only thing that satisfies me, anal intercourse. I can have an ejaculation the other way but it doesn't satisfy me. I feel it has something to do with being frightened before I go, relieved that the decision is then made to go. I think that's the way I go. I feel somehow I'm going to be *engulfed* and that I may lose my mind. I'm so mixed up. I've got to go. This re-establishes my sexual identity."

The patient, when weak and defenseless, regressed to the undifferentiated phase seeking and fearing engulfment with the loss of himself in the mother. He re-established masculine identification by uniting with the penis of and identifying with the more powerful male and felt able to resist the pull toward mother.

He often had fantasies of his mother's dying or his somehow murdering his father. These murderous fantasies against his father evolved from his negative oedipal orientation to him. "I think fundamentally I'd like to throw something at him and run. I think I'd scream. I can just see him. I was always afraid of him way back in my mind, afraid . . . it is crazy . . . but that he'll find out that I'm a girl. That he suspects it and he will do something awful to me. This occurred to me last night. With men I'm scared that they'll find out I'm a girl. They'll screw me and annihilate me." He engaged in sexual intercourse with men when he felt threatened, to his mind raping them instead of being attacked by them.

During the oedipal period he further denied his penis to avoid destruction and assault by the father and to avoid his incestuous feelings. He sought the protective services of boys by imitating a girl. His aim was to be loved and protected and shielded from his fear. Later on he assumed an active sexual role and penetrated men anally. He became active rather than passively enduring a sexual attack.

In the first two years of analysis the patient was subject to what he called spells of "confusion." These would begin with severe tension headaches in the back of his head, sometimes extending to the front. Occasionally they were one-sided and migrainous in nature. At these times he felt he might "crack up," fragment into a "million pieces." He lost all direction and felt disoriented. Lights could be blindingly bright at these times. The room might shift somewhat and he became frightened. "I feel terribly sick, as if I'm going to crack up. It's a sort of terrible fright and then a compulsion to homosexual activity. . . . Somehow, it's like I'm going to be destroyed or as if I'm going to be attacked. I'm in terrible danger. Shivers and shudders will shake my body and I'll get into bed, pull the covers over my head and curl up like a foetus. It feels like if I don't then go to a homosexual activity . . . I do it for my self-preservation. At that point I'm at my breaking point. If I don't I may go insane. It's not an indulgence at all. I have to do it. I might explode or I'll go crazy. It's as if all time and space are mixed up, as if things are shifted and I am in the deepest, direst trouble."

These attacks might occur when Patient B felt he had mislaid something. He would become increasingly irritated, begin to look everywhere, feel panicky and then develop his "confusion." These extreme reactions to such minor frustrations happened in the general emotional state of insecurity, feelings of weakness, loss of power, threats of loss of the mother, her anger at or disapproval of him, or threats from the external world as a whole. The attacks would be miraculously "cured" by homosexual relations.

His "confusional" episodes had the following characteristics: "I feel primarily apprehensive at first for no specific reason. It takes a lot of forms. Then I feel that I'm unwilling to move . . . I have to move with effort . . . and it sort of frightens me. My mind suddenly gets fatigued. It's as if I'm in a period of block. The first sign that the block is broken is a rush of thoughts and ideas, like water in a main which can't get through, it goes around the edges."

His bodily efforts become uncontrolled. "The idea of something jumping all through my body. It is as if my heart suddenly hits a bit harder. It's as if you're hungry and you suddenly eat food and suddenly you're conscious of blood in your stomach." He felt that he was impelled to act irrationally, "like I might want to kill you and I know you're not going to attack me but I somehow feel this or fear this. I get frightened of myself.

"It's like I walk out of the framework of my face, as if there was a space between my face and there's a mask in front of it. I'm in back of the mask. The mask is the external. It starts out as a disinterest in what's around me and I wish I could go away. A tremendous lack of interest, sort of a split, a break, a distinct impression of withdrawal within my face. The new face, it is blank and unhappy, it is frightened. The feeling of resignation, a bitter resignation. Sometimes I can rejoin the two faces, the mask and the face, and this can click and they become as if I'm in the face. It doesn't actually happen but it's a terribly strong impression. I lose contact with the other face. I feel the two faces are working autonomously. You can snap me back by a direct question or ask me to reply. This last incident occurred when this girl I knew showed too much interest in me and wanted me. It frightened me. I felt as if I wanted to run away. I suspect I'm really playing the part of a man when I act like a man. Then I have to show my hand and I get frightened

and then I want to retreat as if I'm over-extended and then the confusion comes on."

This clinical state was an expression of the affects and sensations
accompanying his regression to the undifferentiated phase. It was
initiated by his inability to deal with conflicts stimulated by the external
environment—in this case the girl's wish to make love to him and to
become better acquainted with him and his desire for and dread of her
doing so. There are in this incident autonomic reactions, visceral and
cardiac, a splitting of the ego, feelings of generalized collapse and
panic, and a beginning loss of identity.

A further description of these sensations, feelings, and affects inci-
dental to or concomitant with the regression to the undifferentiated
phenomena was reported following a girl's rejection of him for another
man. He had been attached to this girl for a number of years, off and
on, and had felt closer to her than any other female. During the analysis
he had been attempting to draw closer to her and overcome some of his
fear. "I had this attack on Saturday. I started writing it down as I felt it.
The urge came on at the end of dinner as she gave me the news of her
engagement. I had a feeling like 'a get out of here' feeling, a feeling of
being trapped. Corollary to this feeling was an antagonism to my
mother as though she were trapping me. Perhaps it was my mother that
I was pushed back toward. I felt terribly nervous, and then a desire to
sleep and then a fast heartbeat. This went into the feeling that I 'deserve'
to go to the Turkish bath. The desire itself does not dissolve the feeling,
however. I went to the bathroom four times, each time I had a small
bowel movement. Concentration became fitful. This feeling disor-
ganizes every other thought. It leaves the compulsion to homosexuality the only answer and outlet. The feeling reminds me of a mean
child that wants its own way.

"It goes all up over my body. It seems to sweep through all my nerve
centers. I feel it everywhere. It could be compared to water rushing
through the rooms of a house. It activates certain things first, like
certain centers, first my stomach, then my head and I don't feel two
things simultaneously. Within an hour or two my hands are trembling.
There's tension in the pit of my stomach, a diarrhea feeling, a terrible
feeling at the base of my spine, a pain. And also, strangely enough, a
feeling of intense genital excitement. It's as if I've been hit at the base of
the spine, too. . . . My headaches then begin and are very intense and
I'm almost in a state of hysterics. If I go out and walk around I can
suddenly feel very depressed and feel aches and pains. I feel so mad, so

disgusted with myself, I'm being so childish. . . . But I can't calm my mind unless I give in to my compulsion. In this confused state it is as if I am under control in a zombie way. I have absolutely no interest in women whatsoever. The sensory sensations I have are the only sexual feelings that I have. Otherwise I am completely dead, I am completely automatic, a robot. My mind is completely blocked. I don't remember a thing that I've thought of."

The patient fled to the Turkish bath that day. "Afterward I felt wonderful, healthy, clear-minded, relaxed, a feeling of security, the way you could imagine a man full of energy would be. I went to the public library and worked for about an hour. I felt very well, concentrated well, then, suddenly my mind began to start draining away again. I started trembling. I started being automatic again. I felt as if I would fall forward. I felt an involuntary thought that I'll kill myself. Then I became balanced somehow, pulled myself together by thinking of you."

To the patient this last episode was a supreme example of the power of the homosexual "compulsion," as he called it. It was so strong that he became quite "robotized." This act of homosexuality was not adorned by any rationalizations or pretense of pleasure-seeking. There clearly was no other way out. This challenge to him by a woman was something that he could not countenance. Other men had it all over him, they always would.

These attacks came on whenever he felt that he would be demeaned by other men or when they were more successful than he, whenever he felt castrated or at the mercy of his mother "who would invade me." Because of the danger in his regressive attempt to merge with mother he was forced by his fear to turn to a homosexual outlet. This was his only solution to the fear of not being a man and his inability to adapt to the adult situation.

After two-and-a-half years in analysis the patient understood the meaning of the regressive phenomena, what stimulated them, the dangers in regression to the undifferentiated phase, and the temporary solution through homosexuality. Such an involuntary solution was seen by him to be so automatic and entrenched that it could not be stopped without its full assimilation into his conscious thinking, feeling and understanding. The regression was obviously touched off by his attempted use of it to seek a closer contact with his mother and retreat to an earlier phase of development. He had unsuccessfully tried to master this phase as an infant and through his early years but never succeeded in making the separation from his mother. While he wished to return to the earlier closeness to the mother he feared the catastrophe should he merge with her. Merging was feared as it evoked a terror of dissolution of self, loss of identity, complete annihilation.

These insights developed after a session which proved decisive for his future treatment. He called the analyst on a Saturday for an emergency appointment and was nearly incoherent on the telephone. He was seen immediately. When he entered the consultation room he was distraught, nearly foaming at the mouth, flushed in face, severely agitated, complaining of an excruciating headache in the back of his head. He alternated between crying and a half-laughter, bitter and childlike, tears were streaming down his face. He was unkempt and would tend to fall from the couch to the floor.

He had just returned from the country. His mother was exceedingly angry at him for wanting to return to the city as he would be away on a business trip and would not see her again for a month. "I felt as if mother were saying that if I left her she'd leave me to Daddy. She compared me to him, saying how thoughtless I was." While in the country the day before he had had a dream that a rabbit had died, whose teeth had been knocked out and were all rotten. He readily equated this to his feelings in his dreams of his own teeth being knocked out. "Mother was exceedingly angry but I still decided to return. I felt apprehensive on the drive back. She had lost her driver's license and asked me to look for it in her dresser." Upon entering the bedroom he opened the drawers of her bureau only to find the lingerie and underwear mixed up as if they were thrown in there. He compared it to the garbage can fantasy he used to have as a child. In this fantasy he was immersed in a garbage can, filled with garbage up to his mouth. If he tried to move he would sink deeper and the garbage would go into his mouth. This had always filled him with disgust and extreme fright. "This was the garbage can, the underwear, being inside her. I began breathing very hard, as if I were there, as if I were inside her. I was breathing very hard and fast like I was going to be sick to my stomach and that I would be compressed and choked and die. I think I'm going to faint now, like I'm going under an anesthetic. The garbage can, that's what I see."

He began to scream and cried uncontrollably. "I've got to get back myself, I'm losing myself. And then before that I lay down on the bed, her bed, and I felt I would be engulfed." At this point, hands clenching spasmodically, he moved his head and rocked back and forth. He choked, sputtered and cried. He said he feels better crying as if he is restoring himself to himself, and continued sobbing saying he felt terrible and recalled that he had experienced something like this before.

He began to roll on the floor, was finally induced to rise, then slumped and collapsed on the couch. "I'm a child, I'm a child. Mommie's coming back to the room. She's got to come back, I think I'm yelling. It's that funny yell, like a child's yell, I think it's rage." While in this state it was, however, quite easy to bring him back to reality although the affect continued. "I had a terrible ear abcess and the pain was like this pain. I remember I used to yell. I'm yelling now. A terrible abcess and the pain wouldn't go away. This happened to me when I was about two, I think. You know, it's almost like you've given me some sodium pentathol and I'm under. I'm just as glad you did. This has been in the back of all things, this state, this is what I'm afraid of, that I'll sink into this. It is Mommie. If only she would come back to me." Now the patient's voice is that of a baby. "If she'd only understand me, protect me." At this point he is pleading and whimpering, his face is contorted, his eyes are staring and wild.

"She must protect me. She said this morning she will leave me to Daddy. Yes, this is what I've been afraid of, that Daddy would kill me and that she would leave me. I kept wanting to turn back to go to her but my mind just became blank occasionally. I said I won't. It's such a private thing. I keep on thinking I was drooling like a baby. Was I drooling? I was never allowed to chew the blanket. My mother saying, 'Don't chew the blanket,' something to do with losing my teeth. Last night I felt some of this, some of her disapproval. I must be under an anesthetic, just as if I were under ether. It's all true what I said, it's like losing myself, like I'm all novacainized. The picture I have is a wish to lie in mother's arms and her loving me and her enfolding me but it scares me. The conflict is I want to love her terribly but we can't because of the sex business. It's a childish thing. I want it so desperately that it links through all this to the fright of the sexual thing. Today I was in acute pain. When I went into the bureau drawers, the childish impulse. . . . As I saw the drawers I felt a terrible impulse to get inside her . . . I think I was *entering her*. I wouldn't ever open her pocketbook or any of her drawers. I actually was acting out the rejoining of her and I couldn't do it. Before I came here I went out to the store and bought some peroxide and I put the peroxide on my hair. Then another conflict began . . . that I shouldn't do that any more. Then I felt terribly depressed. I couldn't change my sex. I thought I'd then go back to lie on her bed and I'd die there, die there like in her arms . . . and I looked at myself in the mirror and I was shaking and I felt, 'Oh, you bitch'."

The patient felt during this scene that he actually became a baby. The scream was the sound he made when he had had his mastoid infection or when he felt afraid of his father. In this session he enacts his fear of abandonment, his being allowed to suffer and his "being given over to Daddy." Out of all this, including his mother's rejection, came an intensification of the wish to be close to her, even to join her and finally merge with her. This grave rise to feelings of massive anxiety as he approached the undifferentiated phase. The wish to merge became the fear of merging, the fear of exploding, fear of dying, fear of personal annihilation. At other times it was noticeable that he developed a sensation of paralysis of his body movements.

The regression was able to be terminated and the patient returned to psychological equilibrium in the present because:

(1) This reliving allowed effective discharge and relief of previously isolated, repressed material.

(2) The verbalization of these affective phenomena allowed the patient to experience them at the level of thought rather than pre-verbal image. Such verbalization allows for their assimilation into conscious thinking and attitude and action.

(3) When the verbalization is followed by interpretation and discussion this reinforces orientation to the present rather than to the past.

(4) The relatedness to the analyst who has shared the reliving allows the patient to undergo the experience once again but without further disruption of reality and contributes to the safe return to present reality.

There was a tendency for the regression to reappear the next day but upon talking briefly with the analyst by telephone the threat of personal dissolution vanished. In actuality his pain and fear of abandonment, the fear of being left to the father, led him to the wish to forcefully merge into the mother as the only way to find security. The wish was a terrifying one as it involved the complete loss of self. It was not that he once experienced this merging that made him continuously ill but that he continued to experience the wish for merging, not at the level of conscious thought but only as a repressed affect, as if it were still a danger. The defensive maneuver was his homosexuality which reassured him against bodily dissolution; was a substitute for reunion with the mother; allowed for the expression, alleviation and discharge of severe aggression aroused by the imperative need to merge. Therefore, after some homosexual outlet the "danger of approaching" the mother in the near future lessened.

Over the succeeding year, Patient B became aware of his castration anxiety, its meaning, the antecedent threat of merging and threat to his personal ego development, his use of masochism both to punish himself for his homosexual wishes and to keep himself weakened and the masochistic sexual slave of his mother. He improved in his work and social relationships.

With the progress made in analysis he began to enjoy the company of a young woman with whom he had his first heterosexual intercourse. She gently coaxed and playfully enticed him to intimacies. He was successful in the sexual act with her, even touching and kissing her breasts, a part of the female body which he formerly could not tolerate thinking about. The relationship, which continued for three or four months, was possible due to the insights he had gained and the absence of his former need for flight from the female. Because of his diminished aggression he was able to accept her marked sexual assertiveness without its invoking in him the retaliatory impulses originally aimed at the mother. Since his fear of merging had decreased he was able to relate sexually to a girl who appeared independent, undemanding and was not possessive.

Eventually she turned against the patient. She had become pregnant but the patient did not feel he was ready to marry and that such a step would be disastrous for himself and for her. He later reported that she had had an abortion.

There ensued a long period in which he felt "soured and bitter" about this experience. He knew, however, that he could now enjoy sexual relationships with women, he could have intercourse without constantly fantasying the image of his mother and felt that he had conquered his fear of incest. He grew progressively away from his mother in many respects although he could be "invaded" by her whenever "down and out." When he felt threatened by her, i.e., the fear of merging, he would stand up for his rights, say to her that he was a man and she should not treat him as a child and on occasion ordered her from his recently acquired apartment.

He discovered that by his masochism he had been playing the passive controller of others: his mother, his analyst, his friends. Through his masochistic passivity he had managed to avoid being the male. He had several relationships with girls and preponderantly heterosexual fantasies although homosexual images would sometimes intrude. He no longer had the fearful periods of "confusion" derived from the regressive pull to the undifferentiated phase.

Patient B had been subject to fresh attacks of his infantile anxiety and preoedipal conflict in full force in a number of instances throughout his analysis. Once when he had unfortunately lost a greatly prized job through no fault of his own and was attempting to make renewed relationships heterosexually he felt considerably weakened and afraid.

This was added to or reinforced by the fact that he had to appear in court having been picked up as a patron in a "homosexual bar."

In the session to be described he re-experienced the original infantile trauma with much of its affective coloration but less intensely than in the session reported earlier. He exercised significant objectivity and remembered the previous states and their meaning. His verbalizations were not simply a repetition of analytic interpretations but entirely his own productions. He was able to pull himself out of the affective state by listening to the analyst's comments and could go in and out of the depth of regression and its intense affectivity, emotions and bodily discharge phenomena.

In this incident he had been awakened by his mother who telephoned and told him to get up and to look for a job. She called him a number of times after that but he did not answer the telephone. The calls seemed quite frantic. The doorbell rang and when he buzzed the latch his mother walked in. Despite his reluctance to see her she immediately put her foot in the door and demanded to be admitted. "She came at me as if she were about to envelop me . . . I felt I would dissolve. . . . She still came on. I said 'Leave me alone.' She said 'You lose your wallets to bums. I don't know where you are. You lose your job.' I felt like I was going out the window . . . as if she had almost caught me with a man. I had to tell her she was not welcome. You know I really want her, I really want to know she is there, but I don't want her *too close* and she knows better than to do what she did and she is so cruel. I think I became stimulated by this fight (the patient shudders). . . . I think I'm going out of my mind. . . . What does she want? What does she want? She wants me. She was like a mad person. She was hateful. She got on the bed . . . oh, oh I'm now so frightened, when I leave here I think I'll be so frightened . . . I'm so vulnerable . . . I don't have a job." The patient squirms and moves his head back and forth. He is flushed and crying. He appears nearly to be drooling.

"It is awful . . . it's this sexual thing, I think . . . it's so awful. She just shouldn't have been there. That's all . . . it was gruesome. I just had a feeling I was going to *swallow my hand*, I felt like masturbating after she left and I also felt I had to kill her if I ever wanted to get married." The patient cries and sobs bitterly.

"Or I also thought I might have to kill myself. It's awfully hard to be a man in a situation like that. She was telling me I wasn't a man and also that I was unfaithful, somehow, by her coming over. (Swallowing of the hand connotes swallowing the mother, swallowing himself or being swallowed. This seems to be clearly the re-establishment of the mother-child unity and threatened disappearance into the undifferentiated phase of development.)

"She's a cruel, destructive, castrating bitch. As we are fighting . . . and why, why, why, I said to her 'Why are you going back to treating me like a four-year-old? Stop it.' And she said, 'I guess I'll just have to kill myself. You're making me so unhappy and maybe the few thousands of dollars you get, maybe that will make you happy, but I know you'll waste it and then you'll kill yourself.' I guess this is the engulfing mother that we've talked about. I truly had the feeling this morning that she was capable of killing me, of being capable of destroying me . . . I had the choice . . . if I started crying and I was just like a baby, she would let up . . . crying . . . crying. If I did that she'd rescue me. But I had to be myself, I had to be a man even though she attacked me. I started to get up and I was going to wear father's suit which he had given me. She said, angrily, 'Don't wear that suit. Don't wear his suit.' This is all the same thing that happened to me as a child: 'Don't be anything like father because he is nothing.' Many years of psychoanalysis did pay off this morning. I've been awful to you in many ways and awfully nutty but I'm very grateful. This is what made me crazy and in the mood I'm in now I probably will get married. That is, I'm damn mad and I want to get rid of her. But the spirits that she let loose are more powerful at times. But right now I can cope with this difficulty. When I said today, 'Mother, you're a castrating bitch,' I still loved her but she still was a castrating bitch. But she was so out of control. She doesn't like me. She's so angry. She wanted me all the way back to the tiny tot. She wants to make me a child. She tries to castrate me and when she does all this and when I felt it I got aroused sexually. Why? Why? I don't think she physically attracts me. Why? I'm so all aroused now as I think of it. I'm so jacked up, I tingle. She's coming at me . . . closer and closer . . . something awful is going to happen and something delicious. My legs are tingling now. I'm almost convulsed, like *throwing myself over into another body* . . . fuck me . . . not in the rear, in the front. This has a terrific discharge in my body, like a convulsion."

To summarize: Patient B was unable to pass through the developmental phase in which he could separate his identity from that of his mother. This defect in development led to later difficulties. Out of the inability to separate and the wish to identify came a threat of identifying and a threat of merging, a threat of being annihilated and of what would happen if he retreated inside the maternal body. The preoedipal fear that crystallized was then added to by the later castration fears of the oedipal period. Passing through the infantile sexual period the patient made use of certain aspects of infantile sexuality which produced the homosexual symptom.

Patient B entered late childhood with an inhibition of self-assertion and aggression and a pronounced female (maternal) identification. There was a strong inhibition of all male sexuality to avoid his fear of merging. He achieved a spurious masculinity, acquired a penis and affection from men, thereby avoiding the dangers connected with mother but still wishing to maintain a close tie to her. In his homosexuality he tried to rid himself of the damaging, destructive urge toward union with mother and attempted to ward off his incorporative needs. When the pressures of adaptation and appropriate masculine role functioning became too pressing in adolescence and adulthood he tended to regress to the less demanding period of maternal closeness.

This period, fraught with its great unconscious dangers, led to an exacerbation of homosexual acting out.

In his homosexuality and feminine orientation there were obvious signs of a severe degree of masochism. The patient in essence sacrificed himself and became the mother through identification. He was rejected by the father as a son and suffered endlessly as a result of this. By becoming his mother he did not need her any more; he had her in himself. A succession of events, which included the humiliating dyeing of his hair, the turning himself into a woman by shaving off his hair and the masochistic fantasies of being an alluring, exotic woman used and loved by men, heightened his masochism. He then wanted done to himself what he felt his father or any powerful, sadistic man could do to his mother: to be impaled, to be cut up, to be subjected to bloody pain and pleasure which he unconsciously imagined to be the fate of women in heterosexual intercourse. In this ultimate self-sacrifice and obeisance he hoped to overcome the lack of paternal love.

The role of the father and mother were acted out simultaneously on his own body. This was the acme of his masochistic fantasy. His concept of sexuality was violence. The violence against him was enjoyed vicariously as well as directly as an expression of his own sadistic aggression against men. The wish for violence of a non-sexual nature hid its sexual character. Many times in adolescence he had been subject to fantasies of cutting his wrists and allowing himself to bleed slowly to death in a hot tub of water. Although this was suffering it was a "delicious" form of pleasure to him. Being in the bathtub, of course, symbolized his reunion with the mother in the quiet, comfort and warmth of her body.

His inviting arrest by homosexual mixing was an expression of his masochism as was his falling on various occasions during homosexual escapades and incurring injuries. Homosexuality was eventually seen by him to be an expression of his masochism and when this was understood he began to "take better care" of himself.

Attributing this patient's condition to preoedipal factors, i.e., the regression to the undifferentiated phase and the fear of merging, does not minimize the importance of the oedipal period and its castration fear. He suffered severe castration anxiety. This was manifested as an irrational fear of children being run over before his eyes, a concern with mutilation, a dread of the sight of injuries, a fear of pointed objects which might penetrate his eyes, and an inability to look at his penis for fear something might have happened to it.

Upon entering the oedipal period he was assailed by many fears related to his "cruel" father, in part a consequence of his allegiance to his mother and his murderous wishes and guilt feelings toward his father and also feared the father's retaliation. This fear of the father was expressed in his negative oedipal complex in which he unconsciously offered himself sexually in place of the mother to the father. At the same time he could be more like his mother, exaggerating and emphasizing his feminine identification, with the hope of thereby gaining safety and protection. Unconsciously he was not only castrated by the father but attained sexual pleasure from him masochistically through substitute male partners. This was in part responsible for his dread of and his desire for anal rape. He successfully fought off consciousness of his dread of anal rape by attacking other men anally and also by transforming them from threatening figures to "loved" figures. The maneuver from passively enduring to actively inflicting was often seen in his dreams. Furthermore, from early childhood the negative oedipal situation made him feel like a girl. Through casting himself in the feminine role he hoped to master the threats of his environment but had to contend with being regarded as a "sissy" by his father as well as by other boys. Later on he felt he could disarm men by getting them to like him and then seducing them.

Patient C

At the age of 25, Patient C had become moderately successful in his artistic vocation, but was severely anxious and troubled for fear that his homosexual behavior would be discovered. Although married for three years he sought treatment because his homosexuality continued despite desperate attempts to terminate it. Most of all he feared discovery by his wife which not only would destroy her feelings for him but he himself could not bear the thought of her being contaminated by the ugliness and misery of his homosexuality. He became unable to work and concentrate, with periods of depression and violent feelings, irritability, extreme moodiness and a tendency to tears. He was impressive in appearance, intelligent, possessing considerable wit and charm, at times jovial and often humorous.

Three years prior to starting analysis he had graduated from a major university and despite his markedly spotty performance in college there were many who considered him of genius endowment. He loved his talented, creative wife and felt she was the only important person in his life. She introduced him to heterosexuality, was patient upon their first attempting intercourse and helped him to gradually overcome his fear of the female genitals and his repugnance toward them. She encouraged and assisted him in achieving erections and functioning adequately.

During the year before entering treatment his heterosexual performance had been unreliable and faltering. Most of the time he had no desire for intercourse unless his wife was fervently passionate and told him that she "needed" his penis and sexual orgasm. Whenever her menstrual period was delayed his potency increased as he felt more masculine because she might "have my baby inside her and that makes me more of a man."

He could not reconcile himself to remaining homosexual but found that despite his inner struggle against it he increasingly frequented public toilets or waited on subway platforms for homosexual contacts. He would wander through subway stations and have two or three contacts a day whenever he felt weak or "unmanned," picking up anyone, deliberately choosing those most unkempt and disheveled. These homosexual excursions took much time from his work and he became depressed, defeated and angry at himself. In the subways he would often look at the man's penis while he masturbated himself because otherwise he would feel "too open" to the other man who might tear off his penis or testicles. On a number of occasions he allowed anal penetration and penetrated others. Fellatio and mutual masturbation had occurred in the past, especially during his teens.

Patient C was an only child, conceived during his father's military leave during World War II. He did not see his father at all for the first two years of his life because the latter was in overseas combat duty. During that time he lived with his mother who was employed intermittently in a minor administrative capacity in an industrial plant.

As a young child, according to his mother, he would lie on his stomach, lift his "heavy head" and drop it sharply, striking the bed. This head-bumping, which still occurred occasionally in adulthood, went on for many years. His head would become sore and he would develop headaches. He later was very ashamed of this activity and continued it only in secrecy.

In childhood he also developed the habit of rocking. He would sit on his bed with his knees under him and make rhythmic motions of the body backward and forward. Between the ages of six to ten he began bed-wetting for a couple of months. "I remember all this kind of activity in terms of violence."

His earliest and most significant memory at age 4 or 5 was an extremely traumatic one. His father, who no longer lived with the child and the mother, visited them. "My father came in one day and apparently they had broken up. The scene I remember occurred in the living room. He may have been drunk or out of control. He had come to ask her for money and she wouldn't give it to him. There was a fight, a huge, huge argument, which got absolutely out of control and he jumped on her and started pulling her hair and I can feel the incredible tension. He's really a kind of introvert and they both get hysterically violent. I see a similarity. He started pulling her hair mercilessly and I stood there frozen. It went on and on and I started screaming and I ran out on the porch and shook and shook and I was screaming at the top of my voice. It was full of the most frightening violence. He was pulling her hair and she was whimpering like a dog. I can remember all the details of the room and I can still feel the screams and then there's a complete blackout."

After this incident the parents were eventually divorced and the patient never again saw his father except for two occasions. The first occurred at the age of seven when with his mother they encountered the father on the street. "Mother abruptly turned me around and we ran for the subway." At the age of 12, "Father called her and he told her he wanted to see me and then she tells me, of course, he never really wanted to see me. She always tells me that. He never cared about me. She told me this for as far back as I can remember. My father was an alcoholic, a sick man . . . I feel so sorry for him. She said she married him out of sympathy. He said that he really wanted to see me and she said she just wanted to protect me and he was a bad influence and he was a drunkard and she got rid of him."

The memory of his parents' fight had an important meaning for Patient C. Whenever he saw any violence he would have a resurgence of powerful emotions. "When I see people fighting I feel all the things I did when my father was fighting my mother . . . a sinking feeling of helplessness and then I thought 'I wish they were hitting me rather than hitting each other.' The feelings are hate, shame, murder and guilt. I guess I needed to be killed by my mother. She's coming by today to see me . . . I hate myself so much, I called my mother and now I won't be able to do anything all day . . . I just hate, hate, hate. I don't remember hating my mother for leaving me but I hate my wife for now wanting to leave me. I feel, however, I've got to make some kind of effort in my life. You know what I'd like to do? I'd like to rock and hum or bang my head and by rocking I hold on. It's a way of controlling, by rocking and humming, preventing myself from hurting myself. I've had the most murderous feelings toward myself and others because of this childhood memory, it seems. If she wants me to die, OK, show me the coffin. I don't have any feelings. I just want to kill someone. You know what I want to do? I want to scream. I want to destroy something, smash my head against the wall. I'm afraid to let go, I'm afraid it would be awfully ugly."

After separation of the parents Patient C was sent to a pre-kinder-garten school for what he termed "other displaced children." He was removed from the school when he developed a mastoid ear infection but the following year was sent to a private school. He lived in that distant community from age six to ten with the maternal grandmother "to convenience my mother." His grandmother was nearly senile and gave him little attention or affection. He was extremely grateful when occasionally his mother would visit but she had an active social life and had become involved with a man whom she subsequently married after her divorce from the patient's father. The mother's suitor hardly ever saw the boy and rarely took him anywhere. Patient C felt lonely and isolated. As a reaction to his feelings of helplessness he would have fantasies of being gigantic and huge. He called this his "Superman Game" in which he could rip trees out of the ground by their trunks and toss them over buildings. There were many such fantasies of omnipotence, hate and power.

He had not seen or heard from his father for whom he yearned and wept. One of his earliest dreams or memories, he could not tell which, was that his father and he were together in the bathroom. The father was urinating and the boy was looking at his father's penis. The father had a pleasant smile on his face. This represented the boy's desire to be loved by the father, to be endowed with masculinity through identification with the father's penis and love and through the father's acceptance of him as his son.

At the age of 11, the boy was returned from private school and came to live with his mother and step-father. He never felt close to either of them. His first homosexual experience occurred at this time when another boy lay on top of him and he suddenly developed a sexual feeling in the genitals and sensations of "love." He recalled intense feelings of aloneness, a sense of being "terribly self-contained and alone, a sense of needing my father and also being very shy and timid. I was in awe of all the world around me and I had a sense of my own oddity, specialness, a sense of difference in an individual way. I felt very much as if I were in a fantasy world of my own—a world of make-believe." This state continued to the second year of high school, playing alone and "like a small child" after school hours.

Once, after an altercation with his mother, he stayed in his room for an entire month and neither his mother nor his step-father attempted to interrupt his self-imposed exile. "I don't feel loved in any way. In my room was myself. I was going to deny them the pleasure of me. I wanted her to love me. I wanted her to be more maternal and she tended to be authoritarian and logical and not terribly affectionate at all. She'd dragged me out of that other environment and given me nothing and now I had nothing here, even in this so-called home."

This period of staying alone in his room followed soon after the second accidental meeting with his father. "My father was carrying a brown package under his arm. I remembered him to be tall and I remembered his face, a very, very shy, gentle, tender face and he impressed me as a very sensitive person with a kind of ashamedness and guilt within him. We shook hands and I was probably frightened. I have since thought I would have liked to have thrown my arms around him."

In many of Patient C's homosexual relations he wished that the man would simply put his arms around him, hold him tight and make him feel secure. This was in direct contrast to a very aggressive sexual move he would make against a male when he was angry and "vicious." These abrupt, violent sexual encounters usually occurred when he was "frantic, fragmented and furious." He felt he would collapse or disintegrate, that he would fly apart at these times and he was only "put together again" when he saw the penis of the man with whom he had sexual contact. In the former instance he was passively enjoying the love of his father; in the latter, he was actively, violently grabbing and forcing love from his partner, the father.

His mother had engaged in a verbal vendetta against his father ever since he could remember. The father was "no good, he never did anything any good, there was nothing good about him."

The patient was beset and troubled by another recurrent memory. At the age of six, when he was about to be sent away to school he recalled that he "drowned the book." The book was entitled *The Little Engine That Could.* His mother had given it to him and then she decided to send him away. "I remember I filled the tub and drowned the book. The color came out red. I hurt her by drowning the book. I can remember doing it. I filled up the tub. I put water in the tub and I put the book in it. I held it down and I ripped it apart while it was in the water. I can remember the bathroom and the basin being higher than me. I could barely see in it. The water turned red and now I often see red and blood in my dreams."

At 16, he was sent to a military academy where he occasionally engaged in homosexual relations. He often was obsessed with an intense feeling of love for a particular type of boy who looked clean-cut, well protected and well cared for. Upon his return from the military school on leave, at the age of 18, his mother found a letter written by a homosexual friend. She became extremely angry and hysterical. She screamed that he was a homosexual and started to attack him physically. The patient suddenly became violent. "I threw her down on the floor and I beat her and beat her just like my father did once. I beat her and there was a minute that I could have killed her but then I looked in her eyes and I saw she was frightened.

"That was just after I felt that the moment of murder might be there and when I saw her frightened I started to cry hysterically and I was sobbing and I said, 'Forgive me, forgive me. You don't love me. You are my mother. Please be my mother.' " His step-father called the police and he was sent to a hospital in a strait-jacket. By then, however, he felt completely calm. He recalled tearfully that he had had many fantasies as a child and even in his teens about how nice it would have been to marry his mother.

The feelings of weakness and inferiority which continually beset him during military school were interspersed with sudden periods in which he felt an intense sense of power and male identity. During these times he was elated. There was a kind of "exultant power." His voice was full, his faculties sharpened, he was fulfilled, happy, and had a sense of dignity and importance. "I felt like a god and the full brilliance of my mind came into play. I would get a lot of love this way because others admired my strength and I felt I made many friends."

During his four years in college he did exceptionally well while euphoric—but not in the contrary state, during depressions and when in "need of a man," and twice attempted suicide. Once he felt rejected by a schoolmate who did not come to see him when he said he would. The patient was drunk, cut his wrist lightly so that a drop of blood would come and he could then be discovered bleeding by his neglectful friend. In the other instance, while drinking, he became jealous of a homosexual partner's interest in another boy. "I was jealous. I couldn't stand it any more. I started to leave the room and the other boy wouldn't let me. I ran and threw myself through the second floor window." He broke the glass, cut himself severely and was rendered unconscious. "I strangely enjoyed the whole experience, jumping through the window."

The theme of jumping through windows or into space frequently appears in the dreams, fantasies or acting out of homosexual patients.

Behind this lies a rebirth fantasy: death (a return to the mother), rebirth and achieving a new life.

He was unable to establish any relationship to his step-father and his dreams indicated fear of him, a suspicion that the new father did not want to have anything to do with him and would like to see him dead. This dream also represents his wish to disarm the step-father by masochistic sexual submission to him (the anticipated oncoming trolley symbolizing the penis).

Dream: "My step-father had just come out of the Army. We are in a small town. A boy threw my hat underneath the trolley car. My step-father had me down on the track trying to find it and I'm lying across the track."

Continually and pervasively troubled by the traumatic memory of the assault by his father upon his mother he experienced an insistently recurrent *dream:*

"I was on a plain, a plateau, and it stretches for miles and miles with splotches of cactus and grass. It was a nightmare. This whole dream seems death. The landscape means death. Lots of sand and I'm standing there on the plain and there is before me a hard prickly nightmare plant, ugly looking. In the middle of this a little sandy area. There is a mother chicken and little chickens and the mother chicken's head is cut off and her feathers plucked out and she's bleeding blood out of her neck and in spurts. (The spurts reminded him of sperm and the chicken with the head cut off reminded him of the time when he was four or five and watching chickens being beheaded in a butcher shop.) There was blood all over the place and the little chickens running along and the feathers all plucked out. That's the real horrid part, soggy with blood, matted, and it's disgusting. It's all so unhappy and the mother was dying."

The plucking of the chickens refers to the hair of his mother being pulled out by the father. The patient wished her dead for many years but he knew he could not bear to lose her.

The injuries to his mother could also be visited upon himself as in the following *dream:*

"It took place in a subway toilet. Lots of people there. A policeman there, too, and a man is standing in front of a urinal with his penis out and someone had slashed it with a knife or pin and I got frightened but morbidly fascinated. The color, the poetic redness, was very fiery and very beautiful, a sort of vermillion. Yes, I think of the pin being stuck in him or a knife, like blood running out of Christ's hands."

Having recounted this dream he expressed a sudden impulse to show the analyst his penis and then he suddenly felt like crying. He felt childish. He felt angry and aggressive toward homosexual partners' penises and at times angry at his own. He had had fleeting thoughts of cutting his penis, hurting himself, slashing his wrists. He felt the same angry resentment toward his mother's breasts which he recalled having seen occasionally when he was living at home. They were the penis that was denied him. It was the penis which he was angry about and searched for. The presence of the policeman in his dream is his superego defense against committing these sadomasochistic acts.

Patient C felt most masculine after relations with a man and secondly after he had masturbated. He was then able to have intercourse with his wife with much more ease, his masculinity having been reinforced. However, he continually felt that his wife might at any time become unfaithful to him and frequently dreamt that she was flirting with another man and he would lose her. In these dreams her behavior was completely opposite of what it was in reality, wild and acting giggly, cold at heart and cruel. She showed none of her sensitivity and gentleness and her concern for him. These dreams of jealousy and deception represented his own wishes to possess the other man vicariously. They also served as punishment for his homosexuality. At times, there was a frank wish, openly expressed, of homosexual desire for a man which transcended the love feelings for his wife, along with jealous competitiveness toward his wife. This clearly related to his being torn between his father and his mother, his unconscious oedipal wishes for her and his fear of her. Turning toward the male (father) meant gaining masculinity, women (mother) offering only cruelty, deprivation and deception.

He often consciously wished that he were a girl because "boys like girls. I like boys because they are gruff and funny. As a girl I think about being sentimental and how I would be loved. I remember my mother used to put her tongue in my mouth when she kissed me. I feared that. I used to hear my mother and my step-father having sex and she was crying. She was weak and horrible and I got terribly upset. She sounded like she hated it but she really liked it and I think at times I've been jealous."

He had profound fears of homosexuality and these were represented in dreams as the fear of being bitten by poisonous snakes. At these times he would cry out for his wife and ask her to save him.

During the analytic transference he experienced feelings of warmth and love clearly traceable to the search for his father. "I'm also afraid of you and I become nasty to you and violent and extremely critical. I feel I could tear you apart with my tongue because I would love to love you as if you were my father and I would like you to love me back and I'd like to be held like a baby and comforted and I'd like you to take me into the bathroom and give me a bath and hold me and love me and I know you won't and you can't. I'm afraid to give you this love. I'm scared of being rejected by you and ultimately it involves sex and I'm afraid of the rejection. I'm afraid you'll say, 'You're mad. You're a homosexual.' And I want to kiss you and it upsets me."

Alternating with his love feelings the patient had tremendous destructive urges toward men. "I want to kill a man in battle, perhaps, and then to have intercourse with the dead or dying or murdered. I'm helpless and you see I'm crying (he is sobbing hysterically). It would be nice if the man were crying, too, and we'd cry together. I would bite off his penis. I'm just so violent and it's of a sexual nature, too. A lot of love and kisses. His arms, chest, his lips. I'd want him to be helpless and immobile. Why would I want that? I think it's because my father's dead, I think . . . although I don't know where he is. He's dead for me, in a sense. I would like to be able to act out on him all the things I wanted from my father, that is, the being loved part. He's always away or dead. Also if he were dead or dying or unconscious I could do all these things without his knowing it. Perhaps maybe he then would have no choice but to love me. And its about the only way I could get a normal man and he couldn't hurt me or laugh at me or hurt me in some way." The lifelong search for his father was filled with a limitless poignancy and despair.

During analysis the patient became aware that in his homosexual relations he was both angry at his father and yet searching to find him and love him. There was a fusion of maternal and paternal images; whenever he sucked a man's penis he was also having the good and giving maternal figure substituted for by a man. He expressed his aggression by forcibly seizing the penis and became whole again through identification with the male partner. He realized that he was "sick," sick with desire and longing for parental love and affection. "This morning when I went into the subway nothing happened. I couldn't do it . . . (he cries and whimpers). It's getting harder and harder to do anything homosexual. I've tried asking myself how I felt and I felt rotten. I think I just want to be held in my father's arms or to hold my father's hand as I walk down the street. Perhaps someone strong next to me. I'm so ashamed. Oh, I don't hate him at all. I hate her but I don't hate him. But they both hate me. One left me and one never paid attention to me. (He starts a hysterical, high-pitched laughter.) He should have pulled her hair out and pulled her legs out and shoved them down her throat. He should have killed her and taken me with him.

"I can see his head balding if I imagine him. I don't like the way he looks. He looks like me and I'd like to look like him. I wonder what his hands look like, what his chest looks like. I wonder what it would be like to put my hands on his chest or to be kissed. I'm getting dizzy now. I feel as if I'm floating away. He had nice blue eyes. I think she killed him. She made him drink. She cut his penis off the way she has tried to cut mine off. I think the reason he left her was that if he didn't he would have killed her. I'll kill her now. (He cries and sobs.) He loved me. I kept thinking I ought to see my mother this week but I guess it's because I'm lonely."

Patient C was in analysis for approximately two years. He showed considerable improvement and a beginning ability to refrain to some degree from homosexual relations except when he was "pressed to the limit" by external circumstances such as visits from his mother, her attacks against him or feelings that his wife had become unfaithful or was about to be. The wife decided to enter analysis and their financial difficulties increased. It was her money that he had been using for treatment. He could not continue to use her money as she needed it and he reluctantly terminated therapy.

In the last few months of analysis he had become increasingly able to detach himself from his mother and her demands. For weeks he had no need to see her and when he did he "stood up to her like a man" and did not "become a child."

Patient C, like Patients A and B, showed severe regressive phenomena related to the preoedipal period. In free association, especially at times of exceptional stress, his voice would change and he would become angry, bitter, snarling. "As I'm talking I feel my hands getting bigger now. The fingers are clasped like there's a penis in a hole. In my dream I was thinking the man with my wife is faceless, the one who gets her, who goes away with her, there is no detail in his face. It seems to me that he is laughing at me, that he knows something about me, that he has taken my wife away from me and he doesn't have a face or identity and somehow I get pleasure out of her deceiving me. I feel like a little boy . . . a little boy . . . I'm sinking, sinking, my whole body's going down, almost as though I'm shriveling up. I feel like I couldn't get up, like I'm embedded in this couch and tons of weight are on me and as I was about to cry a second ago I felt a relief feeling as if by your interrupting me that you are going to say some thing to make it clear and all this would go away now and I'd come back somehow. And I feel now like I am being rolled on a ship. I have nausea. My hands have gotten very cold. I'm swinging now. I love and hate all men. I like to beat them. I got very upset as I said that. It's as if I'm at the bottom of a hole.

The opening is way up and it's very dank and warm and wet and my head is out, however, it seems at times. My penis is covered and I'm lying flat."

The regressive phenomena appeard on numerous occasions when the patient felt the need to be closer to his mother, when he was overwhelmed by her, or when he felt weak and hopeless. When regression became too intense he was asked to sit up for most of the session. Any question of whether this was a true fixation to the preoedipal period or represented a regression from the oedipal conflict was readily resolved. The phenomena appeared again and in similar forms to the other cases cited. The change in bodily size and shape, the loss of sense of identity, the feeling of sinking, the loss of orientation and the outright fantasy or near hallucination of being inside the mother's womb were unmistakably preoedipal in origin.

Unfortunately, Patient C could not complete treatment. He returned to the analyst once in a while to report his progress. His wife divorced him and although suffering intensely from this loss he simultaneously "felt good about it," saying he "could not offer that lovely, intelligent, attractive and creative girl any chance for happiness."

He continued to communicate with the analyst for four years after terminating treatment and most recently reported that he was living with a somewhat older woman with whom he regularly had intercourse. He felt fond of her as she was a rather gentle and maternal person.

His homosexual activities seldom recurred. He had enough insight, he said, to realize that he could not find either his father or his mother "in these deluded acts of self-destruction." Whenever he felt homosexual inclinations he attempted to have heterosexual intercourse and much of the energy of his residual homosexual wishes was discharged in this way. At times he missed his former wife intensely but disciplined himself not to think about her excessively. He felt content with his circumstances and expressed the hope of eventually marrying the woman with whom he was living. His artistic endeavors had continued and he had produced several finished works although he had masochistically withheld them from public display.

Chapter XIII

FEMALE HOMOSEXUALITY (Part 1)

Female Sexual Development

In 1933, Freud[87] depicted female sexuality as that "mysterious and dark continent." A girl's development is more complex and somewhat slower than the boy's. When the stimulation of the anal phase recedes the sexual energy does not find an object for outlet through the body of the girl as easily as it does through the body of the boy due to the anatomical difference. This sexual energy has been referred to as the diffuse narcissistic libido which later becomes directed toward the genital region. Freud's thesis as to the primary sexual development in the female, described in "The Psychology of Women," was that the genitals of the girl, except for the clitoris, remain undiscovered and without sensation until puberty. Therefore, the girl's sensations have to do with curiosity as regards the genitals of the opposite sex which she compares with her own, and her first affect as regards the genitals originates in the realization that she has no penis. Only later does she discover the clitoris as a substitute. As a result of this a comparison ensues. This leads to a sense of inferiority which motivates "the intense biologically determined wish to have a penis, the familiar 'penis envy'."[9] Penis envy is at the center of the female castration complex. By the female castration complex we mean that the female finds herself "lacking," as if having been mutilated or damaged in her genital region.

Since the girl's dependent needs are satisfied by the mother, what motivates her to turn toward the father? According to Freud, penis envy mobilizes the tendency to incorporate the penis, to hold on to it and to possess it. This concept attributes a primary ambivalent motivation to her heterosexuality.

In the normal course of the maturational process the feminine sexual anlage directs the libido toward the male sex. This leads to an instinctual conflict, that is, the girl has a desire for her father's love and this is in direct conflict with losing the gratification of her dependent needs from her mother. One result of this is a prolongation of the preoedipal phase in the girl. Another is that she feels guilty because of her oedipal desires and an emotional upheaval is produced. This upheaval may lead her to favor her dependent needs and she may regress to a dependent situation with her mother. The result is a concurrent, diffuse erotization of the body and an increase in her pregenital autoerotic behavior. At the same time she may resort to genital stimulation in masturbation and new conflicts may result. Through such repetitive processes the girl finally develops the oedipus complex.

The oedipal conflict for the girl represents two conflicting instinctual tendencies: (a) the wish to be in mother's place and to be loved by the father; (b) the wish to be the child and be loved by the mother. (This is in direct contrast to the boy who wishes to be in the father's place and be loved by the mother.) As regards the first wish, the competition with the mother carries with it the fear of punishment and the fear of losing mother's love. Therefore, this may produce a stop signal and the girl regresses to the infantile but safe dependency relationship with the mother.

As regards the wish "to be the child," girls find that it is "safe" to be with mother. To accomplish this the girl strives for an *identification* with the father or with a brother. Such identification makes her safe against her heterosexual wishes and lovable to the mother as she assumes her father and brother are. This results in an intensification of penis envy or a fixation of development on an infantile level. It is interesting to note that there are qualitatively different directions in the female development and the postoedipal development in the girl continues in one of the two ways. The quantitative difference in the fixations accounts for the individual differences in women as regards the degree of pathological character formation.

Beyond the direct manifestations of sexual impulses, there are psychosexual activities characteristic of a given period which reveal not only the sexual tendencies but also the ego defenses against them. They indicate the psychodynamic processes by which the oedipus complex is finally repressed and resolved in the female. These consist of (a) sexual curiosity; (b) infantile sexual theories which actually help to deny the significance of the genitals; (c) denial itself; (d) a sadistic conception of sexuality which changes the meaning of sexuality. However, this last intensifies the fear of the girl's own sexual impulses and may produce massive inhibitions or an increase in the identification with the opposite sex.[8]

In the girl's identification with the opposite sex she repeats the pattern of her dependence on the mother yet the resultant female castration complex may interfere with the further oedipal sexual development.

The fear of the male (father's penis) tends to increase the intensification of the girl's incorporative tendencies. This is in essence an identification with the aggressor. The little girl's fascination with the penis and the ensuing active curiosity and manifestations of heterosexual tendencies have as their goal the *possession* of the penis. Penis envy as a defense against the female sexual tendencies dominates the outcome of the oedipus complex.

One notes in passing that bisexuality is a primary quality of the biological anlage. Its manifestations may be discerned in the variations of the child's tendency for identification. But it takes the struggle of the oedipus phase to reveal the quantitative differences between male and female tendencies.

At puberty arising sexual needs again localize the earlier castration fear and produce fears of the envied male organ. A flight from the feminine sexual role, as the sexual maturational process proceeds, then takes place. Ultimately the libido tension finally succeeds in overcoming the fear of being hurt and the sexual act becomes possible. Crucial to this outcome is that the girl proceed in adolescence from an attachment to mother to an identification with mother and later to a wish to have a baby like the mother.*

During adolescence the female, as does the male, utilizes repression to a large extent in her sexual development together with sublimation and expansion of interests, fascination for abstract problems and a heightening of creative imagination. In time, these ego defenses yield partially to the sexual impulses with an ensuing vacillation between aseticism and sexual expression so typical of adolescence.

Development of Homosexuality

Many overt female homosexuals experience little conscious guilt although suffer intensely from a deep sense of inferiority. This sense of inferiority may also tend to keep the homosexuality hidden from others in contrast to the male who may flaunt his homosexuality. Often homosexual women settle for companionate relationships with their female partners and seem to have little orgastic desire. This is in contrast to other homosexual women who feel it is the orgastic pleasure which is most important.

---

* R. de Saussure once stated to the author that it is important in the late oedipal phase for the father to present his daughter with a baby doll as a gift and in that fashion through symbolic efficacy help promote her *identification* with the female other than an infantile attachment to the mother.

In female homosexuality there can be a form of identification, *resonance identification*,[170] in which prepuberty or adolescent girls may identify with the sexuality and erotogeneity of an older female whom they know enjoys intercourse with men. By so doing they bolster up their beginning femininity thus "sharing the guilt" in sexual encounters with these females, thereby increasing their own capacity for erotic feeling.

Women can also identify with males, in effect saying to mother she has nothing to fear from their sexual wishes toward the father as they themselves wish only to be male. They therefore escape the retaliatory aggression of the mother toward them.

Some homosexual women, after having identified themselves with the father, then choose girls as love objects who represent themselves and love them as they wished they could have been loved by the father.

Female homosexuals may assume a very masculine manner toward men reflecting their virility traits, wishing to acquire these characteristics as their own. For they believe they can be loved by the father only if they have a penis, convinced that the father once denigrated and demeaned them for this lack.

Obligatory female homosexuality, as in the male, is always reparative in function. A partner of the same sex is the only individual who can offer pleasurable sexual satisfaction. In addition, the organs of the female are desired while those of the male are abhorred and feared. Women so afflicted may receive the penis with vaginismus or vaginal anesthesia. If the tendency toward orgastic desire with persons of the same sex is strongly repressed there may be complete or almost total unawareness of homosexual desires and wishes.

The female homosexual patient usually does not seek psychoanalytic treatment because of her homosexuality. She may have been moved to enter therapy due to pressure from her family or depression over the loss of a love partner. Or, as we have seen before, homosexuality may be only a partial expression of an underlying neurosis or psychosis which, at the time of beginning treatment, may have been temporarily warded off through homosexual outlets.[172]

Primarily it is usually the feelings of depression and anxiety arising out of rejection by another woman which impels her to therapeutic consultation. If she can overcome her reticence to confide in a man she may display intense envy of the penis by hostility toward the male analyst. Often she suffers from suicidal ideas and murderous fantasies toward her mother, both arising from preoedipal unconscious wishes and dreads. The aggressive murderous hatred occurs simultaneously with a desire to merge with the mother. As in the male, this is the nuclear conflict.

Sexual excitement in most homosexual women has been bound up with maternal prohibition and there are the most intense aggressive impulses toward the mother on a conscious level. These aggressive impulses are resisted and, as a reaction to them, unconscious guilt toward the mother is generated. Hate impulses are then transformed into a masochistic libidinal attitude which disguises her hateful feelings, diminishes her guilt and punishes her through suffering. She punishes the mother as well by unconsciously dramatizing her self-defeat and reproaches against her.

The homosexual libidinal relationship, basically masochistic, may temporarily ward off severe anxiety and hostility with concomitant florid neurotic symptoms. The mother-substitute (homosexual partner) momentarily pays off the infantile grievances by providing sexual satisfaction.

Most overtly homosexual women will in treatment acknowledge the mother-child relationship which they have with the love object. Sexual satisfaction is usually obtained from a close embrace, mutual sucking of the nipples and genitals, anal practices and mutual cunnilingus. There is quadruple role-casting for both partners: one now playing the male and the other the female; one now playing the mother and the other the child.

Homosexuals are particularly engrossed in and satisfied by the *sameness* of the sexual responses which they have together. Male-female contacts, on the other hand, are characterized by *alternation*.[170]

The schizophrenic patient involved in homosexual activity may be consciously aware that her sexual impulses are specifically directed toward her mother or siblings. In analysis it becomes quickly apparent that in sexual experiences occurring between homosexual females the homosexual is able to transform the hate of the mother into love at the same time that she is being given the mother's (partner's) breast and thus obtains what she once felt deprived and frightened of as a child. Invariably present is an intense conflict over masturbation which began early in childhood. In the homosexual act "mother" is sanctioning masturbation through a sharing of the guilt mechanism.

The homosexual woman is in flight from the man. The source of this flight is her childhood feeling of guilt toward her mother, the fear of merging with her and the fear of disappointment and rejection at the hands of her father if she dared to turn to him for love and support.

If she expected that her father would fulfill her infantile sexual wishes there is a masochistic danger present, too. Or she may feel that her father would refuse her and then she would suffer the danger of narcissistic injury. The end result is to turn to the earlier love object again—the mother—more ardently than before. However, she cannot return to the real mother due to her fear of merging and being engulfed. "The economic advantage of this new turning to the ersatz mother lies in the release of the feeling of guilt but it seems to me that its most important accomplishment lies in the protection from a threatened loss of object: 'If my father won't have me and my self-respect is so undermined, who will love me if not my mother?' "[35]

Preoedipal fears of being poisoned and devoured by the mother lead to giving up in utter failure when confronted by the later conflicts of the oedipal period.[132] Flight to the poisonous mother is resorted to in an attempt to gain her love and protection, alleviate feelings of murderous aggression toward her and to protect oneself against the assumed murderous impulses of the mother. These fears of poisoning and being devoured relate to the earliest anxiety of the infant and these disturbances are closely related to psychosis. Therefore these patients, characterized by such primitiveness, demand the utmost of effort and concentrated attention on the part of the treating psychoanalyst.

Homosexual women, deprived of their love object, very often become suicidal. They interpret this loss as a threat to survival, a total abandonment and develop anxieties of total extinction, that is, aphanisis.[119] (The male homosexual has a marked proclivity to become suicidal whenever he is rejected by a man who represents his own "ideal narcissistic image.")

In homosexual women there are intense desires for revenge and aggression. This impulse to assault links first with revenge ideas for betrayal by the father, especially where another child has been born. It has also strong penis-envy components mixed with highly sadistic oral wishes. The oedipus-revenge correlation is even clearer in varieties of behavior which stop short of avoidance of men. These homosexual women get along fairly easily with less virile, presumably impotent types of men. This is not simply due to their being less dangerous but they offer less temptation to the patient's sadism. Oedipus-revenge ideas exist in all women so that it seems possible that such revenge impulses normally reinforce violation anxiety and .the two together produce a strong drive to detachment from the father but it is a drive which may very easily become too strong and neurotically bind one to the father. Behind the more obvious oedipus determinant of the violation and revenge ideas there is a wealth of tangled fantasies of the primal scene leading through all the pregenital phases apparently to the womb.[26,27]

Certain guiding threads can be distinguished, i.e., trains of masochistic and sadistic ideas relating to both parents. One set of masochistic thoughts expresses the fear that intecourse would prove a repetition of injury already experienced at the mother's hands. This injury has a vivid phallic version but, equally, definite fecal and nipple connotations. It often goes back to the deprivation of weaning and, as castration, it was a punishment for masturbation. Another set of masochistic ideas deals more with the internal life injuries of the Kleinian type[132]: disembowelment and feminine impotence. *It is these masochistic ideas which make the heterosexual position untenable* (my italics). In these cases, however, homosexuality is not a way out completely because even sexual acts with a female partner would awaken severe sadistic impulses.

Interwoven with the masochistic fantasies the highly aggressive ones are connected with the primal scene father, the penis and the mother's body. "One often finds self-sufficient fantasies which are genital, fantasies of hermaphroditism, dreams of self-violation, babies and lovers made in the lavatory appear in dreams as fecal characters. These are definitely archaic-oral fantasies. There are fantasies also of oral intercourse and oral parturition. . . . Genital ideas are not lacking . . . but the impression gains ground that in spite of evidence of regression we are here up against an *original pregenital core* (my italics) which has a vital connection with the later genital failure and especially with the accentuation of aggression which bulks so largely in it. These fantasies center around introjected nipple-penis objects; there is a sense of oscillation between external and internal dangers."[27] In short, there is accentuation of primal oral sadism which did not always lead to homosexuality but to flight from homosexuality and all sexuality.[26]

Is the accentuation of sadism from the primal scene or is there congenital predisposition? Is it perhaps due to early weaning or that the primal scene was experienced during the period of acute oral frustration and in conjunction with it? In all homosexual women identification with the father is marked since any approach to femininity is heavily banned. A striking feature of these identifications is that they are all "maimed."[119] The ego is always a castrated father or a barren, shattered mother and its conduct of life is correspondingly crippled. This nevertheless has a definite economic advantage as it protects the homosexual woman from gratification of id and superego sadism although at great expense to the ego.

Certain women manifest their homosexuality only after marriage. They are often of the cyclothymic type, frequently quite successful in their careers. There are common features in their reaction to marriage, that is, they suffer from an excessive guilt due not only to the incest meaning which intercourse has for them but even more because of the stimulation of their sadism in the sexual act. Violation-revenge impulses are highly developed; however, their attitude toward sexual relations is nevertheless contradictory. At the same time that they are demanding revenge for childhood "injuries" they are often also expressing disappointment if they are not hurt enough in heterosexual relations. Real intercourse does not satisfy their primal scene expectations or satisfy their need for punishment. Feeling guilt-ridden their superego threatens them with severe bodily punishment after marriage.

"The husband in these cases may often represent the tender, sexual father, safe enough to marry but not brutal or sensual enough to be satisfying."[26] In this type of homosexual woman we see the same characteristics as described by Deutsch where sexual sensation depends upon the fulfillment of masochistic conditions. These women necessarily have to choose between finding "bliss in suffering or peace in renunciation."

Ambivalence is continually reinforced by the lack of satisfaction in intercourse and often activated by "faulty technique" on the part of the husband. Because of pleasure prohibition and the "cannibalistic cathexis" of the vagina, treatment must proceed with great care. Pregnancy, delivery and motherhood mean continuation of guilt and ambivalence toward the self and child.

Being married provokes masculine trends already present and penis envy takes the form of rivalry with the husband. There is a conviction that the penis ought to have been the wife's based on the fantasy that the mother had deliberately given the infant's nipple-penis to the father. The failure of the marriage is the signal for the activation of unconscious (latent) homosexual attitudes.

Such patients are exceedingly sensitive to being financially dependent which they regard as a mark of inferiority. Behind this they feel guilt for their inordinate wish to be completely sustained by the husband as this derives from their insatiable need for supplies from the mother. Prior to marriage they "may enjoy all the advantages of a man's life plus certain prerequisites belonging to womanhood without the disadvantages of either."[26] Masochism in these women may assert itself but they are usually not ill and they lead an aim-inhibited life with aspects of both homosexuality and heterosexuality. Furthermore, if such a woman is obliged to give up her career in marriage this loss of an outlet may play an important part in precipitating severe neurotic symptoms with or without overt homosexuality.

There is abundant evidence in these cases of reanimation of pre-oedipal phases by regression. Primary disturbances of oral development are also among the most vital and important factors in the later emergence of these genital difficulties. Woman's primary masculinity must be coordinated with feminine impulses or else it may very easily become exaggerated as a means of defense against femininity.

There can be established a division of homosexual women between several clinical types:

(1) Those who may often retain their interest in men but set their hearts on being accepted by men as one of themselves. To this group belongs the familiar type of women who often complain of the unfairness of women's lot and their unjust and ill treatment by men.

(2) A second group consists of women who have little or no interest in men but whose libido centers on women. In analysis one discovers that this interest in women is a vicarious way of enjoying femininity; they are employing other women to exhibit femininity for them.

(3) This group obtains gratification of feminine desires providing that the penis is replaced by the tongue or finger and that the partner using this organ is a woman. Though clinically they may appear completely homosexual, they are nearer the normal than either of the previous two types. In all three groups an identification with the father is present. This identification serves the function of keeping feminine wishes in repression. This type does not wish for a penis for gratification; she already "has one," and certainly desires no one else's.

(4) A fourth type may arise more directly from the fact that female homosexuality may derive from a warped bisexuality conditioned by the idea of castration and penis envy. Therefore, a girl identifies with her father in order to give a child to the mother. In these cases homosexual fixations correspond to the patient's projections. A woman may, therefore, project her femininity onto the mother and then on to other women who continue to represent the mother. The homosexual woman may see herself mirrored in other women who have a high degree of feminine narcissism. In effect this woman has projected her femininity onto others and enjoys an identification with *herself*. Also she often has

projected this femininity only onto women who are known by her to make men suffer and refuse them satisfaction. With them she has an "ideal" partner.

In all homosexual women there is an intense unconscious aggressive murderous hatred against the mother and reproachful feelings toward the father.

(5) Since homosexual women play a "mother and child" relationship to the exclusion of the intruding father, one sees homosexual women who identify themselves with the active mother. They are, therefore, drawn to very young girls although they do not actively attempt to seduce them.

(6) Others, as seen in the previously mentioned type (5), continue to act the child they once were and are chiefly attracted to older maternal protective women toward whom they act passively. However, on occasion, both active and passive attitudes are evident. In these cases the clitoris is the executive organ of pleasure; the presence of a penis or penis-like substitute is abhorred and no masculine clothing is worn at any time by either individual.

(7) Another type of homosexual woman identifies herself with the primary *active mother* who cares for the child and has also identified herself *with the father*. In actuality the father followed the mother in objects to be loved by the girl in her development. The women with this *double identification*—one superimposed upon the other—show more clitoridal fantasies than the groups previously described. They may wear masculine clothing, including ties, etc., and strive to act the man in relation to the beloved woman. Some find it extremely difficult to admit to any passivity or wishes to be caressed themselves.

(8) The most difficult of all women to treat psychoanalytically are those who pass from loving mother to the father as their love object. They cannot appreciate any love object so beneath them as to lack a phallus. They cling tenaciously to the idea of an unconscious fictive phallus and although they may have heterosexual intercourse are ambivalent in the extreme in their relationships to their male partners and experience great pleasure in being admired, sought after and loved by women.

(9) Extreme femininity may also be connected with female homosexuality. This is due to a special configuration of the castration complex. For example, an active homosexual may have identified herself with her father and may then choose young girls as love objects to serve as ideal representatives of her own person. Masculine-appearing

homosexual women may then behave toward feminine-appearing homosexual women as they wished to have been treated by their fathers.[24,119,170]

Patient D

Patient D entered psychoanalytic therapy at the age of 24 with complaints of moderate depression and feelings of self-depreciation. She was an attractive young woman with a figure of average proportions and a bright, winning personality. For the past six months she had begun to feel intensely drawn toward a girl and "wanted a caressing thing with her."

The patient had not worked for several months and felt "lost, unable to function and with no direction. I want to love somebody and I want them to love me. No one will love me because I'm nothing." She was attracted to women but at the same time felt that she liked men. She was "not a part of this world, not coping and achieving like others," and urgently desired success. A few days before deciding to start treatment she had felt "terribly affectionate" toward a girl who hugged her. On occasion, when her anxiety became intense, she felt a state of "no relatedness, dizziness, and something like "unreality."

She had become increasingly concerned over the number of affairs she had had with men during the past three or four years.

When Patient D was born her father wanted a boy, even a name for the wanted son having been chosen. Her mother was planning to separate from her father but her pregnancy with Patient D intervened. "Mother wore the pants in the family," was in fact the matriarch dominating the home. There was a sister four years older and at the age of six another sister was born. She pictured her childhood as consisting of a martyred mother and a rejecting father. One of her earliest memories was of crying over her lost galoshes and nobody wanting to help her.

At around age two and a half she recalled watching her father urinate and would hold his penis while he was doing so up to the age of four. At this time she was subjected to a severe traumatic experience. The father suddenly turned upon her when she attempted this act, shouting: "Leave me alone, you slob." This memory had persisted and influenced the course of her entire life. She was extremely hurt, crestfallen and guilty over having done something "dirty."

After this she gave up trying to hug and kiss her father or get close to her mother. She experienced a keen sense of loneliness and deprivation. Nightmares of falling from high places and obsessional and compulsive acts such as having to count all the tiles in the bathroom developed.

At five she was a problem eater and would occasionally vomit upon being forced to eat. She recalled her mother as continually saying, "You'll be sorry when I'm gone." At about the same time she developed crushes on girls and a horror of insects.

The age of six was especially significant for her. She remembered being thrilled when a girl of 18 approached her lovingly. "She was just lovely. I really felt like a boy and that she wanted me as a boy." She also recalled being kissed by a girl of 10, which pleased her. However, this did not prevent her, at the age of 8 or 9, from having crushes on boys in her class. She would "beam" when an older boy paid attention to her.

During the same year her older sister almost drowned while the patient watched her sink into the water. "I saw her going down and just stood there." She felt guilty for watching her floundering. Also at this age her younger sister was born and recalled her father's great disappointment that he still did not have a boy. She complained bitterly that the father "paid very little attention to us." Shortly after the birth of the third sister the mother left the home temporarily. The patient felt abandoned, rejected and "terror-struck. She really did leave us."

At seven she recalled how ugly she felt: "I had buck teeth, a very long neck, dental braces. I felt unwanted and unlovable." She remembered an incident in which her father, angry that she had not moved from the living room floor where she was lying, suddenly kicked her in the head. She had harbored a profound resentment toward him for this over the years. At age eight she recalled an aggressive attack on her older sister. She struck her sister full force with a baseball bat and the sister was ill for a number of days and the patient was remorseful. In the same year her father had a "semi-nervous breakdown." She remembered his crying, head between his hands, and moving agitatedly around the room. This produced severe feelings of anxiety and helplessness in her. He was prone to depressions and would constantly complain "there is nothing to live for." Negativism permeated her own life; she repeatedly commented to the analyst that "no good will come from other people or from the world and no happiness can ever come from men."

At the age of nine she was subjected to two traumatic events. Her appendix ruptured and she required extended hospitalization. She then suffered a fractured skull having fallen from a bicycle. At the age of ten, when in the fourth grade of school, the class was divided and she was separated from her favorite teacher (the good mother); she had no appetite and lost twenty pounds. In the fifth grade she was very unhappy. "I had a miserable teacher, very unloving. She would yell all the time at the students and had a very bad temper." The patient did not want to go to school and would complain of stomach cramps and headaches, cry and get sick to her stomach. Before this change in teachers she was, indeed, the teacher's pet.

Occasionally she was taken to ballgames by her father who tended to treat her more like a boy than a girl. "I was a good baseball player and even boxed with boys." At the age of 12, at the time of her somewhat late pubescence, she stopped playing with boys and spent a lot of time by herself. She began to develop headaches due to what she now saw as anger. Whenever she observed someone who she thought was "great," a female movie star or an attractive, confident-looking woman on the street and knew she could never meet them she became depressed.

By thirteen, when she had developed a feminine figure, she was unable to take her clothes off in front of her sisters and would undress only in private, believing herself to be gawky, uncomely and unattractive. She loved to be with older people. Upon entering high school she felt severe inhibitions in getting up in front of others. She had nightmares about her teeth being crooked and ugly and about having a long nose and long, skinny neck. Up to the age of sixteen, she recalled, she "would have given anything to be a boy" and it was an amazing revelation at this time "that I was becoming attractive."

At eighteen her older sister was hospitalized because of a suicidal attempt and subsequently recovered within a year. Patient D had to accept the fact that "I was becoming physically attractive. I don't think I wanted to be a boy any more."

At 21, she engaged in her first sexual intercourse only to develop "strange pains" in her stomach within a week which she now attributed to guilt. She began to experience an intense preoccupation about being loved and accepted by prominent women of the stage or screen and vowed that this "will be my field of endeavor and work for life." She undertook relentless pursuit of contacts with well known women in the theatrical world which led indirectly to homosexual involvement.

In the setting of a pronounced feeling of rejection by a male lover, a man whom she had hoped to marry, she became involved in a homosexual relationship with a somewhat older and rather "glamorous" woman. This was the patient's only sustained homosexual relationship. It lasted for a year-and-a-half and she felt it both "terrified and gratified" her.

Thus, the rejection by the male had led her into a profound regression and a search for good maternal love. The maternal supplies available from her homosexual partner were "vital" to her. The partner was wealthy, popular and insistent. Despite the patient's protestations that she be allowed to continue her heterosexual life concurrently, the partner managed to isolate her.

Patient D enjoyed most of all the feeling of being held like a child, sucking her partner's breasts and being gently soothed. Introduction of the partner's finger (fictive penis) into the vagina with orgasm and mutual cunnilingus left her somewhat depressed and repelled. The partner's paranoid jealousy and inability to tolerate any contact with men on the part of the patient forced a separation and ultimate break. The patient suffered feelings of loneliness and despair. There was a resurgence of her anger toward men; while she condemned them as "immature and weak, unable to offer fulfillment," she still raged at their lack of interest in marrying her. In actuality, she consistently chose men who were unsuitable or unavailable for marriage. For example, prior to her homosexual affair, she had lived with a married man, the father of three children, for over two years.

From her female partner she had received much help in her work and became quite successful both professionally and financially. Thus it seemed that only through women could one be gratified, taken care of, protected and loved. Her partner would continually reassure her of her deep concern for the patient and her wish that she be happy. Here was "a dream come true" but with the important feature that it was provided by a female which she found almost impossible to completely accept. Vaginal penetration by the finger or tongue of the partner was both enjoyed and abhorred. Upon awakening in the morning and finding herself entwined with the body of a female she felt anxious and depressed but welcomed the protection, solace and concern as well as orgasm.

Following one brief separation from her partner she re-entered therapy, complaining of severe loss of weight, intense stomach cramps, excruciating headaches and anxiety whenever she attempted to live apart from the partner. The only relief from her anxiety were the analytic sessions and her work. Her interest in her partner was obviously to enjoy the good maternal supplies and protection of the female (mother). Her oral needs could thereby be gratified.

During breaks with her partner she had begun to have successful orgastic experiences with men but continued to chose men who were unsuitable for marriage. She complained that there were no desirable men around to marry and she had no interest in marrying in any case as a man would only treat her like her father had and as her mother had been treated. She did not trust men and their promises. The anguish she doled out to her female partner through her recurrently expressed intention to "break it off" she "felt doubly" herself. She wished she could somehow enjoy a friendly maternal protective relationship with her female partner without a sexual component. This was not possible and during separations she desperately craved contact with the partner whom she had left.

In the transference she resented the analyst's not becoming the "good" mother and father to her and supplying to her all the needed satisfactions and gratifications for which she yearned, denied to her by both parents. These needs, met by her homosexual partner, had the impossible price of a sexual "transformation" which she was unable to make, feeling repelled by playing an anatomical role contrary to reality. Her motive in entering analysis was her renewed determination to find a male who offered enough protection, strength and love for her to marry. She had at first hand learned that "homosexuality was futile."

At the beginning of treatment Patient D's resistance consisted initially of feeling wronged, of blaming the analyst and of suffering. She wanted to evade all psychodynamic material which she found disturbing and whenever pressed to reveal her feelings she would state she "felt nothing." She repeatedly asserted that the analyst wanted to "put things in my mind." She would try to taunt the analyst by saying that "I know what you want me to say but I just won't give it to you." She felt that no one had ever really cared about her and the analyst certainly would not so why should she expose her intimate thoughts and feelings. She acted as if he were the depriving father who wanted to seduce her into holding his penis but who would, in the end, reject and debase her and make her feel ashamed.

She demonstrated immense oral cravings for love with a fear of expressing this imperative need. In the unconscious she imagined herself as a very aggressive, unattractive, destructive and "smelly" object. She "gave off smells" and was filled with bad things within her. She had deep feelings of guilt for her aggression toward both her mother and father. "If I show my evilness everyone will abandon me." She was angrily insistent that everyone give her love and take care of her. She wanted to yell and scream her hatred of her mother. This aggression was turned against the self in dreams and made her feel bad as if she were "a piece of smeared feces." Most of all she feared that there would be "no response" from either parent were she to show her affection and love. This fear was projected onto all important figures in her life. She felt that in her anger "I will lose my mind and explode" and certainly as a result she would not be able to enter the good mother's body and be accepted by her.

The nucleus of her fears was the repressed emotion centered around her oral deprivation, aggression on the part of the bad mother and herself, and anxiety over the possibility of merging with the bad mother. She feared abandonment by mother which was consciously experienced as a fear of starvation and lack of protection. As a child she constantly imagined that the mother would leave her; as a result the wish to merge with the mother was reinforced. This frightened her as it would mean her own destruction, loss of ego and being subjected to a life in which she was "nothing" but a piece of her mother's body which even could be expelled like a piece of excrement.

There was no support to be expected from father, no help, no reassurance, no protection, no feeding and no love. During the oedipal period she was subjected to severe rejection and shame and guilt over her sexual curiosity and feelings toward him which he had himself provoked. Only in becoming a boy could she find salvation. She tried to do this up to her pubescence, playing baseball, going to ball games with her father, but nevertheless feeling that he basically disliked her and did not want her. Since she could not achieve his love even though she tried to please him by acting like a boy she instead began to seek love from other girls. In this way she gained the identity of the beloved woman and thereby was orally gratified. It was the re-emergence of these tendencies during her late teens and early adulthood and the conflicts which they produced which led her to seek psychoanalytic treatment. Whenever she tried to feel like and be a woman she developed anxiety and fears that she would only be abandoned and hurt.

In the male position she actively endowed herself with a penis and tried to find protection and love and pride in herself. Her wish to be a boy and have security had "survival value"; in the feminine role she could anticipate only rejection and loss. To be a female was to be subjected to intense anxiety expressed in dreams as castration, attacks by women, fears of death and being feces. As a female she was bad and guilty for to be a girl was a sign of unworthiness, unlovability and vulnerability. Only through being a male would she have security. To be a girl also exposed her to tremendous aggression toward her mother. She often commented that "I am afraid to let out the hate toward my mother's very ineptitude, self-concern and lack of love for her children."

Whenever feminine wishes were stimulated during the course of analysis she attempted to deny her warm and heterosexual feelings and would be upset by them. She tried to deny her positive feelings for the analyst by imagined abuse and accused the analyst of bad treatment. For example, she would often complain that "you did not treat me right" as she still had her symptoms and he had not provided her with a man. She indirectly blamed the analysis for her frustration and continually expressed a chronic pessimism as to its outcome.

Patient D's attempt in childhood to remain feminine became too dangerous; she feared mother would attack her for this and she would retaliate with murderous impulses. She was forced into a masculine identification with sensations of bodily change and wishes for a penis. She would subjugate herself by being a man, give up her feminine desires and live with a woman. During her active homosexual episodes "I would allow myself to be walked all over in order to get love," to diminish her rage and guilt and rid herself of abandonment anxiety. To her it was the choice of the lesser evil. The homosexuality revolved around two factors: (1) fear of merging with a depriving, destructive and abandoning mother and the murderous hatred behind it; (2) disappointment at the hands of the father.

She was compelled to deny her biological identity and even at an early age had displaced the penis to the breast and imagined she possessed a penis. Her aim was to forcibly extract from women their femininity, love, affection, narcissistic and oral supplies. She had an unconscious rage at men as the father originally rejected her and she felt she would always be rejected. Her preferred sexual activity with men was fellatio, except when the man proved "much more powerful" than she. Then she could have vaginal intercourse with orgasm on occasion. By sucking the penis (breast) she was incorporating it and being "filled up."

Patient D vacillated between severe depreciation and overvaluation of the self. "One of the things I felt about myself is that there is nothing I cannot do if I want to but I have severe inhibitions. That's the way I feel about my work. If I get down to the point of doing it I will be great. I want to express myself." During the course of the analysis, the patient became prominent in her professional field with proportionately high financial rewards. Even this, however, was not sufficient gratification to quiet her anxiety and feelings of deprivation.

She felt that she could not wear sweaters or any clothing which hugged her body closely and required loose fitting garments to conceal her feminine figure. Since age 18, she had not known how to deal with her increasingly attractive appearance. She was pleased but at the same time upset with the full development of her breasts and tended to be critical of them and resented them as she wanted her male identification. The presence of breasts would make it more difficult to acquire the feminine love she so urgently desired; masculine love could be only disappointing and depressing.

This attitude changed as the analysis progressed. She continually chose men whom she knew were afraid of women and who were no threat to her. Whenever a relationship with a man grew emotionally intimate she would destroy it with the rationalization that "He will see my dullness." When attracted to a man she usually felt elated but it did not last. Despite her self-accusation of dullness she had always felt creative. "Other people have a base from which they operate—a big thing which they have—I don't have anything that I really love to do and I have no one to say to me, 'Boy, you're good'."

When she first had intercourse she felt it was "great." She was not in love with the man or did she want to marry him and within a week developed the strange stomach pains and fears of having a cancer of the genital system. Both reactions disappeared within a short time. Following the first relationship she had intercourse with a number of men which exacerbated her guilt. Although the attention given her by men was stimulating and exciting, it produced more confusion for her. She was "stuck with" her interest in becoming a man herself and obtaining from women maternal affection and care.

A year prior to starting analysis she met a "Lesbian with whom I had a big physical thing. It made me furious and excited, too. I usually fantasied kissing the breasts of this girl but at the same time she would be me. If I wasn't with men I usually would think about women and their breasts and sucking them. If I have an attraction to a man I cannot eat if I've seen him only a few times and have no security with him." The problem of eating was intimately connected with her feelings of gratification and worth. Whenever deprived, food was bad and made her nauseous just as love from women was bad and love from men was not forthcoming.

She constantly wondered why she could not show affection. "My father was not a demonstrative person and he stopped us from being demonstrative and mother had nothing to offer at all. Why can't I show affection? I get terribly affectionate when I'm out, especially with a girl. I feel uncomfortable even with a fellow. I'm so conscious of it, I'm conscious that I'm doing something that it was taboo to do, feel these things for girls. My father would often say to me, from the age of three or four, 'Leave me alone.' "

Immediately preceding entry into analysis she had the feeling that she was "walking as if in a dream, everything seemed so strange." She was dizzy and felt very depressed, "I just couldn't relate to anyone. There was no relatedness and I hadn't talked to anybody for weeks." In actuality, she was overwhelmed by her wishes for homosexual relations and concerned about the direction her life was taking. "The day before I came to you I wasn't noticing a thing. I was completely removed from everything. I had terrible guilt feelings about my family, about my mother. I met a girl to whom I had declared my undying love last winter and she had said to me, 'You're a phony' because I wouldn't go through with it."

The incident with her father had been a consistently painful memory but was recounted only after a year-and-a-half of analysis. Before age 5, especially at two or three, she recalled with great affective release that she used to watch her father urinate and "I used to ask to hold his penis and he let me. This must have gone on for about a year and then suddenly I asked if I could and started to and he said, 'Oh, leave me alone, you slob.'" She was "extremely hurt and insulted" and her "face felt very warm. . . . You know my father was really a very modest man." After that there was "the no-kissing thing" with her father. She felt "like a slob . . . I felt like I wanted to do something dirty and I wanted to be a boy definitely. I would go out and sell papers and things like that." She connected this incident to her inability to give to anyone since that time. She was stingy about food and money. She did not feed herself and was "a skinny maverick. I'm always so conscious of what it's costing me and I'm always getting by on the base minimum in life."

Her dreams indicated strong wishes to possess a penis. *Dream:* "I had strange warts on my stomach and they began to grow like on a stem. I was upset when I saw them and my father said, 'Why don't you cut the stems?' I said, 'No, it would hurt.' To cut off the stem it would hurt me." The meaning of this dream was obvious to the patient. She would not give up her masculinity because she could not trust men and would only suffer at their hands were she to become feminine.

Another *dream* refers to her oral needs and the deprivation which provoked them: "A little girl is 'going down' on me. I don't know who—it was either my niece or a little girl in a show I had seen. We had been joking with each other in real life. I was being pursued by this child. I knew that's what she wanted to do to me and I didn't want her to. I didn't want her to suck me but I seemed to remember someone encouraging me to do it. Finally I let her and I became very excited by it. I tried to get away and she kept pursuing me. I used to find that very, very exciting with men—finally it was so exciting I'd have to have intercourse right away." It seemed to her that the penis must be a breast. She was trying to take femininity from women in her wishes to suck their breasts. "I thought maybe this kid tried to take my femininity. I seemed to be the woman and this little girl last night, when I looked very feminine and I got a lot of admiring looks at the theatre, was also then interested in me because I was good, attractive, charming and lovely. In the dream there was a lot of fluid coming out from me, like it was milk, and the little girl was sucking it. Perhaps I was the little girl." Her homosexual oral incorporative wishes were desires to suck and be filled up by the maternal milk displaced onto a little child rather than onto her mother from whom she felt she could get nothing.

A typical *dream* is the following: "Ladies with blond moustaches, homosexuals hugging and kissing each other on the train, and I'm hugging and kissing my younger sister and mother is nodding approval. I'm thinking 'I haven't done this in years' but I feel very funny. I am then eating fruit salad sensuously and sitting down with two Puerto Ricans who own the place and who I had assumed were poor slobs wanted to put the bill on the house after friendly conversation. I was buttering up to a girl, not making it too well. I was insincere. A stiff piece of fruit is in my mouth and I am mortified." Here she demonstrated her oral desires, her feelings that mother would approve of her becoming obeisant to her but at the same time her inability to accept the role of making love to a woman. She wanted to stop but could not. Men, on the other hand, were simply foreigners, lowly in caste, who really wanted things "on the house" and who did not want to give to women.

She urgently desired in most of her dreams to become the female but could not produce proof that she was, indeed, female, wanted, admired and loved. *Dream:* "The proof to my mother that I was a female was to show then that I had my diploma. It's in a tan leather cover with another document. My mother tells me to find it. I begin searching the house and they're nudging me and I can't find anything. Suddenly I remember I took it to my apartment where it belongs. The other document is a birth certificate. They're mine and I want them with me. Daddy is mad at me. I go home to find it but I cannot." One noted her feeling that the father did not want a daughter or for her to have earned her diploma thereby becoming a wanted, admired and valuable person. From the dream and the associations it was evident that the deprivations in the dream are a form of retaliation and vengeance against the father. She hurt herself in order to hurt him and thereby showed him what he had done to her by not accepting her as a girl in childhood.

Her ambivalent feelings were dramatized in a subsequent *dream:* "My oldest sister is eating next to my father. I am across from them. Her food drips on his leg. He is very annoyed and states 'Why are you such a slob?' as he wipes food off his knee very thoroughly. I feel for her as her eyes fill up with tears. She cries and tells him off, 'What's so important about your lousy clothes? Is it so important that you should hurt my feelings?' I'm with her as she keeps on and I look at Daddy who feels very bad and then I'm with him." Obviously she projects onto her sister the very incident (a screen memory) which occurred in her own early childhood when she touched her father's penis and he reprimanded her. Here the timeless indestructibility of the unconscious and the proof of infantile sexuality are again manifest: the dream revealed to her that her father actually experienced an ejaculation (food) when she had handled his penis. His guilt had led him to blame her for his sexual excitement. By calling her a "slob," he had attempted to deny his ejaculation, projected his guilt on her and she now understood the traumatic incident correctly and realized it was he who was the "slob." The source of her deep and abiding bitterness against him was this unfair and hypocritical condemnation.

The patient who had been unable to proceed through the separation-individuation phase of development successfully had utterly lacked the support, reassurance, protection and strength of her father. Furthermore, she had been forced into a masculine identification in the earliest period of life and was not acceptable to the family as a female member of it. Her mother, upon whom she depended for oral gratification, was denying and depriving. This fact intensified her oral cravings and her desire to be close and never separated from her. Any attempt to move away from the dependency toward her mother was experienced as grave anxiety both from the fear of retaliation and the fear of her own aggression toward her mother. She had to substitute teachers, older girl friends and other females for love and affection. Certainly her father was in a most ineffectual and weak position. He reacted to her with severe aggression, kicking her in the head, deploring her femininity, openly wishing for a boy, becoming depressed and severely rejected, and shaming her for her sexual interest in him during the oedipal phase. She could only regress toward mother, and in her mind mother was filled with malevolence, inadequacy and martyrdom and therefore she chose other women (good mothers). All signs of femininity, including the wearing of feminine clothing, development of her breasts, menstruation, were greeted with antagonism by the patient. She felt these would lead to her further devaluation and demeanment. She urgently desired femininity but she felt that femininity was "full of shit" and men were also "full of shit."

During the analysis these factors were present in the transference relationship. On occasion she felt she did not like the analyst at all and would sometimes imagine that he was taking advantage by making fun of her behind her back. One was not in control of anything and he was making use of her the way her father had—by not enjoying her sexually or by allowing her to enjoy him.

Patient D's main interest in life was to prove that men would only disappoint her, degrade her and make it impossible for her to find happiness as a woman. The analysis itself would prove to her by its failure that no hope could be offered by men and she could achieve satisfaction, support and gratification of dependency needs only through women.

From women she wanted food and love, milk, breasts, but in her dreams women turned into frightening animals that would attack her. Both the fantasy of being loved by women and the fantasy of being loved by men were threatening. If in a dream she felt loved by women she would soon find herself "being attacked by them, by a cat, angry and mad, tearing me apart." In her dreams of men she wished to attack the penis, at first to play with it but then to strike at it or to appropriate it for herself. She dreamt of castration and death at the hands of her mother if she dared to become a woman. When deprived by both male and female lovers, she dreamt of loss of food, starvation and emptiness. She vacillated between intense feelings of love for women and a wish to be close to their breasts and equally intense feelings for a man who would satisfy and protect her.

The following *dream* typifies her strong penis envy: "I was washing a little boy, about two or three. I was giving him a bath. He was fighting. I think he had a grown-up face. I was scrubbing his back very hard. He was relaxed. I massaged his back and shoulders. There was a sexual connection. I shouldn't be doing this. I also thought I wanted to wash his penis but I didn't dare. I was very curious to see if he had an erection. I looked down. There was a penis there and it was not attached. I thought 'Now they're going to know what I've done.' Then it didn't look like a penis, it was something else."

Whenever she felt she had no one, neither man nor woman, she had unconscious fears of "being attacked by a woman and being eaten by her, becoming feces, being abused or an intense fear of death." This fear consisted of her swirling into a large whirlpool-like abyss in which she would be engulfed. It was quiet and dependent and loving in a way but at the same time most frightening. She felt that it was a fear of merging with her mother, of becoming one with her, but becoming dissolved, impotent, unable to function, incompetent and a "nothing" (regression to the amorphous undifferentiated phase).

She believed she could be protected from her homosexual drive by the love of a strong man (father). *Dream:* "I was grown-up. I was with a man, an elderly man but not my father, maybe a boy friend. I was looking for a place to spend a vacation. I said 'Why not the place I used to go when I was a child?' I wanted to go back (the patient cries and sobs). Back where we used to go when my father would come up during the summer for two weeks, a big, round-front car, swimming. I don't know what set me off. I am very happy. It reminds me of all the wonderful things he could have given me, if he only could have loved me. I just wanted him, to throw myself at him, and he would grab and hug and kiss me. It's the first time I've thought of that in years. I'm so happy to be back there. I'm just dying to go back there sometime and see it again.

"I'm crawling in the dream. I'm just like a little child. I'm crawling toward my father. Isn't it funny I can't walk on the ground, just on a sort of plank. Then a terrible fright. Mother and a man in an adjoining room. I thought mother might walk in when I'm hugging my father and ask 'What is this all about?' Oh, fuck her. I want father to explain to mother that I wasn't doing anything. In the dream I was dying to get back to the place where my father hugged me nice and firm. I think the man was you, the man with gray hair, helping me across. I guess helping me to heterosexuality. He was telling me to stand up and walk across and I wasn't afraid of falling off but I just wanted to stay on the plank that I was on. A round lawn and a hole in it. It's all like a vagina. Somehow it has something to do with the boy-girl thing. This is not intellectual. I think perhaps it's a rebirth, coming out of the vagina, and you're finally joined with a man. I must have been very happy there when I was a child."

Chapter XIV

FEMALE HOMOSEXUALITY (Part 2)

Patient E

SIMILAR TO male homosexuals, female homosexuals have nuclear conflicts belonging to the earliest period of life which force them into choosing partners of the same sex for ego survival. The female homosexual, unable to pass successfully through the separation-individuation phase of early childhood, has suffered maturational (psychological) failures and thereby incurred severe ego deficiencies.

Patient E might well be placed in the group of homosexual women who identify themselves with the female love object, not with men. The external object relationship to women is very imperfect, merely representing her own femininity through identification. Her aim is to vicariously enjoy the gratification of femininity at the hands of the unseen man (the father). This particular group has little or no interest in men and their libido centers exclusively on women, employing other women to exhibit their femininity. One notes here the correspondence to the male homosexual who identifies himself with the maleness of the partner.

The patient was in her mid-thirties when she first entered analysis. She complained of anxiety, fears of loss of her girl friend, migraine headaches, depression and phobias concerning food contamination. Her symptomatology appeared very severe and diagnostically she belonged in the paranoid group rather than the neurotic. Throughout her analysis she excelled in a demanding position in the field of economic research which required ability of a high order. She underwent psychoanalytic treatment for four years and since then has returned for periodic visits.

During the course of treatment, heterosexual interest had been observed and one time—approximately the third year of treatment—she felt strong affectionate interest in a male college associate with whom she had a social acquaintance. This was not reciprocated and, rejected, she continued her former relationship with her female partner. She remains homosexual, having lived with the same woman for a decade. In actuality little sexual contact or enjoyment has been experienced, the union being essentially that of a companionate pair. The companionate nature of the relationship was riddled with strife between these two women, filled with envy, hostility, and jealousy.

The patient had been overtly homosexual since the age of 19, and had lived with approximately seven partners, ranging in length of time from one to two years, except for her present extended liaison.

Early in life she was told that her mother's milk had disagreed with her and that she had frequently vomited in infancy. From birth to two years of age she suffered from an excema over the entire surface of her body. At approximately 12 months she had "worms," for which she was given anti-helminthic medication which produced considerable chronic abdominal pain. She sucked her thumb up to the age of six and was cured only after mother put "bitter medicine" on her thumb. She still remembers this as having caused "a queer feeling in my head."

She reported a screen memory, between the ages of two and three, of a violent flood which she felt was an actual first memory. Her father was knocked down, the house inundated and she recalled the clouds "dipping down" and her cowering in the attic. Around the age of three she felt very close to her father and believed that her mother was "jealous."

Also between two and three she developed a fear of feathers. Her mother, in order to prevent her from venturing from the top floor to the lower floor of the home, piled feathers at the head of the stairs; this would terrify the child. At the age of five a brother was born toward whom she developed considerable hostility. Between four and five she remembered that she was frequently constipated and forced to drink castor oil. She then developed obsessional thoughts concerning the death of her mother. These continued up to age 11: "If I step on a crack I'll break my mother's back."

Between four and five she still felt very close to her father and considered her mother "a terrible creature." For example, "Mother would pour boiling hot water on a spider when she saw one on the porch." At age six the patient could recall actually hating her mother and wanting to kill her. She had fantasies of putting glass in her mother's orange juice in the morning so that mother would die.

At five, a severe tomboy, she often had fantasies that she was not really a member of her family but belonged to some other family. She hated her little brother as her mother always seemed to take his part. "I felt I could actually kill him." At seven, another brother was born whom she liked and dominated. At the age of nine she was aware that she was extremely attracted to a girl of approximately the same age and, in an episode of teasing, took a piece of chocolate away from her, ran away and ate it. She suddenly felt severe guilt and could not stand to be seen.

From eight to age 12, there seemed to be a reversal from an overt fear that she might kill her mother; she began instead to dread that her mother would kill her. On one occasion at about this time she fell off the roof of the garage, was knocked unconscious and suffered several broken bones. This was in expiation for her chronic aggressive fantasies toward her mother.

At age nine a tonsil operation was performed and she was sure she would not survive the surgery. Around that time she had recurrent dreams of a bear chasing her. She now felt that this bear was her mother who hated her and wanted to murder her. Another recurrent dream was of standing on the tips of her toes and being "swished down a long passageway like a penis."

Between 11 and 12 she was repelled by her mother's body and could not stand the sight of it. She had a very vague recollection of swallowing iodine at about age 14, feeling "terrible and angry at my mother." At 13, upon first menstruating, she developed a horror and fear of death and consciously wished to be a boy. During high school she was a good student but felt "awkward and different." She became very interested in religion. Another girl, two years older than she, told her she was a "homosexual." She felt very relieved and close to this girl and later developed a guilty feeling toward her.

When she was 16 her father, who had suffered a business reverse, was drinking excessively and there was frequent parental discord. At 18, she entered college and for the first time felt a degree of pleasure and security within herself. She had no crush on anyone during her first year away from home and felt "happy." It was at 19 that she had her first homosexual affair. She felt terror that she would be "engulfed by the passion" of her homosexual partner during orgasm.

Following this there ensued a series of affairs with other girls. She left college just before she would have received her degree. At the time she claimed to have "lost interest" in completing her courses but came to recognize in treatment this self-defeating act was due to guilt for the unconscious murderous hatred of her mother and siblings. After leaving college she met the partner with whom she has continued to live to the present time.

During the father's military service in World War II, when Patient E was in her mid-twenties, they corresponded frequently. She was startled, overwhelmed and guilty by the evidence of loving feelings in her father's letters. She also felt unaccountably "frightened" by these tender and affectionate messages.

By age 27, completely immersed in her homosexual way of life, she was often frightened at the possibility that previous homosexual partners might, somehow, seek retaliation against her. A year later she began to have difficulty with her present partner, fearing that the girl would leave her, and this would make her "terribly upset." This was, in actuality, a reflection of her own ambivalence in the relationship.

Whenever another girl kissed her passionately the patient would have sudden feelings of panic, terror and guilt. This reaction was due to her unconscious fear of the oral destructiveness of both the other girl and herself.

In her late twenties she felt threatened by the political factionalism which developed in her place of employment and as a result of being singled out by the owners as a trouble-maker. She developed feelings of bodily weakness, a severe degree of apprehension, a rash erupted over her entire body and she was hospitalized with a diagnosis of erythema-multiforma, an illness with a potentially fatal outcome. When all somatic therapies failed she was seen by the attending psychiatrist at the hospital and with daily psychotherapy recovered in four weeks.

Patient E had always been jealous of her partner except in the very early years of their relationship. Signs of love and tenderness would temporarily quiet her jealous fears. Her partner had said that if the patient were ever unfaithful to her she would "somehow get even." At age 34, for the first time in her adult life, she had a conscious fear of being poisoned although this had been a preoccupation during childhood. The poisoning, she thought, would be brought about by her partner. At this point she entered psychoanalysis.

It was strikingly evident that the patient's deepest conflicts consisted of oral incorporation fears of the poisonous bad maternal object. She both feared incorporating the mother and merging with her. Significantly in her early history she had been told that although breast-fed she did "not get much milk" and in infancy lost weight, "screaming all the time." At the age of one year she overturned a hot water kettle and most of the skin of her hands was severely burned. This injury required prolonged painful treatment and mechanical restraint which undoubtedly increased her sense of deprivation.

Out of the incorporation-destruction fears came fantasies of being poisoned by the mother and the patient developed one of the most upsetting ideas of her life: "A vague thought of a knife and wanting to kill my mother" and also lying in bed and thinking "I will be killed. Up to the time I was 13, whenever my mother would punish me I often thought she intended to kill me. I sort of had a feeling that the sausage patties in the pantry—I thought of them as being poisoned and ready. I've always felt that my mother didn't love me and she really wanted to kill me. The only person who was really nice to me was my grand-mother, my father's mother. When my first brother was born I loathed him. He was awfully mean. I think I actually could have killed him if I could have found a way. He was always the baby and I was always left out."

The fear of incorporation is well illustrated in a late childhood ex-perience. "This girl . . . I felt attracted to her. I felt I loved her very madly. I asked her one day to take my lunch to school. I was teasing her. The girl had little squares of chocolate. I grabbed one and ran and she couldn't really catch me. When she came close to me I popped the chocolate into my mouth. I felt guilty. I felt like a thief. I couldn't stand to be around her after that."

As a consequence of the patient's oral destructive urges she de-veloped a profound sense of guilt. This was in direct correspondence to the degree of her oral sadism. From hating and wishing to destroy the mother (homosexual partner) she instead wished to fondle, be desired by and love her as a reaction formation and defense.

The childhood event described above was representative of this patient's inhibitions against taking enjoyment for herself, including sexual or other pleasures in life. "The chocolate . . . how horrible I felt . . . absolutely obsessed with guilt. I had taken the chocolate to tease her. Ever since then I've been allergic to it." Since then she had also been afraid of taking oral medication under any circumstances until late in the analysis.

Patient E's father was a rather unhappy, withdrawn person who, apart from the one reversal during his daughter's adolescence, had been a successful businessman. He was very fond of the patient but as a child she rejected him because of her unconscious guilt. This was due to her fear of retaliation from the mother, a cold, unsympathetic woman, subject to episodes of acute depression.

The mechanism of homosexuality did not afford the patient more than a marginal degree of comfort and gratification because of the strength of the oral sadism inherent in it, fear of the incorporated object (the mother) and its destructive effect upon her. Very often her fear was projected and she developed expectations of her partner's retaliation and aggression. While severely inhibited and constrained sexually, the patient felt extreme rage when she was not satisfied sexually on those infrequent occasions when she desired sexual relations and attempted to initiate them. "My feelings of love are so strong, at these times, more than they should be, so intense. I feel that I may be raping the girl. I feel that if I moved toward her and she said, 'No,' I think I'd have to stop and think what to do. I think I might frighten her. I have a feeling I would rip her vagina with a knife or kill her or beat her up "

The patient suffered equally from the most intense feelings of inferiority. "A feeling that I'm no damn good and that I never was . . . that people have laughed at me all my life and they know I'm homosexual and they never have accepted me. . . . I'm afraid of kissing any of these girls. When I start to kiss them I'm terrified and when I kiss them I sometimes suddenly grow cold. I guess I'm afraid of feeling too much, a feeling of great fright. It's not a fear of being rejected; it's a wave of vulnerability. I'm afraid of the woman, I guess, and isn't that strange that I should be, when I'm homosexual."

These feelings reveal that the patient was afraid of her own oral aggressive desires toward the mother which, carried too far because of her oral sadism, involved the destruction of the mother, fusion or merging with her, loss of identity. Because of these inhibitions all sexual partners moved away from her as the relationship continued. Her jealousy and aggression then increased and migraine headaches would occur. They would come on especially whenever she was jealous, frightened, feared the loss of her partner and wished to attack and destroy. Any attempts to become sexually intimate with other women also terrified her. "I'm afraid of my own feelings, I guess. I'm afraid they may not like me and then what might I not do?"

Patient E's dreams revealed many of the essential trends which regularly appear in female homosexuality. In one *dream* she is trying to have intercourse with another girl, not her long-time partner. As she put her hand on the girl's vagina her father walked by. "I woke up with a great desire for this sexual affair but I am terribly frightened at what I have done to my father." The desire for revenge against the father's "not loving enough" was present in Freud's study of a homosexual girl.

Another *dream* revealed her fear of orgasm, her intense jealousy, recurrent anxiety of impending breakup with her partner and resulting murderous rage: "It's a summer resort, I was looking for X. No one would say where she was. She heard I was looking for her. She was having an affair with somebody else. Would I sign a paper and release her for this? I said I would but first I wanted to talk to her. After all, we'd been together for many years. I had almost decided then that she must come back to me and then I woke up."

There was a second part to this dream: "I felt very excited when I got X in bed with me. Then all of a sudden I didn't feel anything any more. I had difficulty in reaching an orgasm." The third part: "She and I were going to a movie and walking around to find a seat. It was very precarious as we were in the balcony. She slid down, it seems, five or six stories. As she slid down there was a loud crash. I went down there and I found her dead. The sound as she hit was like a terrible crash. It reminded me of falling off the garage which I did as a child . . . the horrible feeling as she fell away . . . nothing now to do. She would fall in the street and be killed. I couldn't reach her. I couldn't grab her. She was gone. It was death. I couldn't see her body as she fell between a couple of cars. I wonder if that's why I can't do anything . . . if I'm so afraid that I'll bring about this terrible punishment to her."

Here we see that Patient E's ambivalence about experiencing any satisfaction with her partner, her wishes to give her up and at the same time to keep her, lead to her feeling that if the partner (mother) desires to love and satisfy someone else the punishment is death.

On occasion the patient desired women other than her partner, X: "I fell terribly in love with Y. It was almost as if I didn't have any control. I felt perfectly horrible about feeling this way for someone, almost physically sick, kind of like she was cold, however, and I had to make her warm. If she's cold I can't stand it. I must make her warm. These people ought to be warm, as though they feel something, like it's their duty. Also you could make them feel more than anybody else could (an obvious reference to her mother). However, when this happens and they don't get warm I get scared. Somehow, I feel that if they don't get warm I might hurt them."

Another *dream* revealed her fear of the poisonous substances from the mother which will attack and destroy her as she incorporated or is incorporated in (fear of fusion with) the body of the mother. "There was a bath in the kitchen and water running into it. It was very dark brown water. I was waiting for it to clear up, then I turned it off. The water had seeped out of the tub and come out of the bottom and had come out of the two drains instead of one and there was something about a roast that X was cooking, a roast that was supposed to be sliced by me, and I realized that it was very hot and that it shouldn't be sliced the way I was slicing it, and then I wondered whether X had cooked it in this terrible water." The patient's associations concerned the water of a cistern in a town in which she had lived as a child. It also reminded her of the color of her grandmother's face when she was dead. Someone had lifted her up to see it as as child and she had been horrified by the terrible color.

Some dreams reflected her guilt over her homosexual relations with her partner. "The dream occurred after some sort of sexual relationship yesterday when I felt so bad. However, after it was over I wanted to call home . . . X and I on an elevated thing, a car, I think, going downhill. Then we stopped in a washroom. She washed her hands. All of a sudden a reddish mold growing all over my hands. I started ripping it off. It was feathery-like. It's all right if I can rip it all off. A big thick layer and X had it on, too. I ripped it off the hands. Something about fire and something burning underneath."

The female homosexual must love the attacking, hostile mother but fears the poisonous substances that will come from the mother's body; therefore, she faces an extremely dangerous love object as shown in the following *dream:*

"I was in a rather civilized place. There were parks and trees. I went in this bathroom which was long and narrow and was washing something in the sink. I put on some rubber gloves, skin-color, so that my hands wouldn't become contaminated or get wet. I realized they were my mother's rubber gloves and that I didn't know what they had been used for. She might have used them for something poisonous and I would get it on me. The water was running over in the sink and people outside heard it and opened the door to see who was in there. I hid in the corner so they couldn't see me. This happened twice. Finally I found the stopper and pulled it out so the water could run out. I pulled off the gloves, held them up and was appalled at having used them."

Because of the danger of aphanisis upon loss of the love object, homosexual women show tremendous aggression toward the partner. This aggression, of course, arises from the preoedipal period and is heightened by the oepidal conflict.

This *dream* occurred after suspecting her partner of an infidelity: "I was living with X in a large house with other people. I came home from work one evening and noticed that she and Z had been throwing each other fond glances. Z asked if we were going to have a salad and I said that I didn't think it would be necessary because we had plenty of other vegetables. I noticed that there was cellophane curled up in the dishes of food and had been cooked with them. I asked who had done that and Z laughed and said she guessed either she or X.

"This made me angry since they were so unconcerned. I took Z into another room and pulled down the blinds. Then she said that I shouldn't treat X that way, the way I did. I realized that she loved X. I got so violently angry that I started fighting her. Then I threw her out of the room and I pulled X in and started fighting her. I hit her and was crying and acting like an insane person yet I couldn't help myself. I kept realizing the way I was acting could only drive someone away from me, yet I couldn't stop. I threw her around the room and the next minute I would act more rational and try to reason with her.

"I realized I was just bringing all this out in the open instead of keeping it under cover and trying to make X love and respect me. I finally asked her what she intended to do and she just smiled at me and said 'Have a place of my own by next summer.' She was exuberant and I was a miserable wreck. I told her that I had spent so much money in analysis in order for us to have a better life. She said 'You can't have a life on only foundations of an old life,' and I said you had to tear everything down to the bare foundations in order to build a new life, that I loved her and that I wanted to build a new life with her. I knew she still intended to leave me for Z."

Other dreams frequently referred to certain themes: themes of castration, penis envy, the conception of enjoying a fictive penis; poisoning dreams, dreams of becoming insane and losing control and destroying the mother; dreams of penis identification.

In the third year of analysis Patient E began to develop heterosexual desires. She also expressed heterosexual desire toward the analyst which caused her to become embarrassed and have guilty fears toward her partner. Typically, she had guilty dreams about her father.

In the fourth year of analysis her father became seriously ill and she experienced intense feelings of love and sorrow for him. These were the first genuine positive feelings she could remember ever having had for him which were completely acceptable to her. She had never permitted any appropriate physical closeness between her father and herself but realized now how much she wished she had had such contacts with him. She felt that she deeply loved her father but had completely repressed it. Subsequently her dreams consisted of yearnings for love from men but she felt "it was probably too late to find a suitable man." She was deriving very little pleasure from her homosexual partnership but she still occasionally felt a "female love" for a newly met woman. She could imagine meeting a man who might be quite suitable for her, a consideration that would formerly have been terrifying to her and entirely disagreeable.

This case is representative of female homosexuality in which the basic disorder occurred in the earliest period of infancy. The conflicts revolve around the most primitive aggressive, destructive and incorporative urges of the infant toward the mother and the resultant defenses against them.

The anxieties associated with these patients resemble those seen in psychosis. This type of homosexuality is frequently present in clinical practice as the patients enter therapy for the concomitant and ongoing symptomatology and not usually because of a desire to change to heterosexuality. The issue of their homosexuality is a critical one and attempts to change or challenge their homosexual state should proceed with great caution as there is marked possibility of provoking severe paranoid, phobic and hypochondriacal anxieties.

With this patient the fear of destruction by the female is clearly seen to be a fear of poisoning and incorporation. The fear of merging is represented as a fear of contamination and death at the hands of the woman. Because of her fear of her projected sadism there is a compensatory death wish for the destruction of her homosexual love object.

Patient F

Patient F was a 19-year-old college student who entered psychoanalytic treatment following a period of hospitalization after attempting suicide by slashing her wrists. This was a second attempt after release from a sanitarium where she had received electroshock treatment occasioned by a prior suicide attempt using tranquilizers and aspirin. After the first attempt she had received psychotherapy but her condition remained unaltered. During psychotherapy she had been silent and uncommunicative, hostile and scornful of any efforts to help her.

After the second suicide attempt psychoanalytic treatment was begun. The patient, an attractive, cultured, intelligent girl, was condescending in manner toward everyone including the analyst. Her father was extremely wealthy as were other family members, a factor which was subtly insinuated by her into most of her therapeutic sessions. From this wealth she derived power and strength to do, as she said, "whatever I please," especially in her sexual life. She felt herself quite "above the crowd" and special by virtue of her intellectual cultivation and artistic temperament.

Patient F's intellectual ability was, indeed, appreciable but her achievements were non-existent at this point. Much to her annoyance and disappointment she had had to attend a college which she regarded as beneath her. She was particularly unhappy about this as a slightly older cousin, with whom she compared herself, enjoyed an enviable academic success at a more renowned school as well as great social success with an elite group of men and women. The patient suffered from intense shyness in relation to men and would develop acute anxiety upon entering a room where there were new men to be met.

Two and a half years before her first suicidal attempt she had traveled abroad with her uncle and her cousin, whom she both envied and resented. Throughout the three-month tour, when they were guests of prominent residents of the foreign countries they visited, she felt lacking in poise and grace compared to the other girl, feeling herself humiliated and demeaned.

Patient F had a sister four years younger to whom she paid little attention and treated as if she were a small child. There was, on the other hand, an intense rivalry with this younger sibling who received more than she did of the limited affections of a rather cold and passive father who lived on inherited wealth. The mother, from all accounts, appeared to be a psychotic or prepsychotic individual who, during the patient's childhood, would often threaten her daughters with knives. The patient felt her mother was "inferior." She had little affection for her and had actively taunted, teased and been hostile to her for many years. The father was described by the patient as calm and reserved, displaying little emotion; she gave a perfect picture of the cautious, prominent, but passive, patrician of their rural upper-class community.

The patient first announced her difficulties at school by informing her parents on the telephone that she was "a homosexual" and was going to live her life any way she pleased. As a matter of fact this was harder to accomplish than she had originally anticipated. She found herself becoming the "dupe" of numerous homosexual girls on the campus and "I was unable to dominate or control them in any way." She suffered from feelings of being left out if a girl made love to her and then rejected her. After being scornfully abandoned by one of her "conquests," her anger mounted for six months prior to her first suicidal attempt. She underwent a severe depression (threat of aphanisis) with impulses to cut her wrists or take sleeping pills. She felt no desire to do anything, "to make anything of myself." She wanted women "not because I like them but so I would have them and have them care for me. I don't really care about them anyway nor do I care for mother. I like women more than men, mostly because I'm not afraid of women." This statement was made during a rare moment of candor as Patient F was intent throughout the early phases of treatment on demasculinizing the analyst, showing him he had no strength in the situation and could "not possibly make me into a heterosexual."

Shortly after starting analysis the patient defiantly began a homosexual relationship with a woman ten or fifteen years older than herself, a friend of the family, who was known by the patient to be a homosexual. The patient preferred to be the active one in the relationship, to make her masculine-like partner achieve orgasm through her caresses and through her manual manipulation of the partner's vagina. In this strong masculine role she felt in possession of a penis which pleased her. On occasion she had to submit to the same activities but this was not nearly as gratifying.

She felt intense dislike of men, would curse their penis, and deride the analyst. Her major intention in life was to show that all men were weak, ineffectual and like her father who had not protected her from the cruel, psychotic, sadistic mother of her childhood. In essence she was asserting that she was a man and therefore did not need a man.

On a couple of occasions she attempted heterosexual intercourse expressly to show the analyst that she was not impressed by it and did not feel much for the man or for the situation. She would passively submit to heterosexual intercourse and then laugh about it to the analyst insisting that there was nothing to being heterosexual; she could be either but preferred the love of her woman partners and herself being the man. She came to sessions dressed as a man, wearing slacks and without any semblance of femininity. She would have her hair cut in a style that made her look quite masculine.

Beneath this facade the patient suffered severe anguish due to: (1) her intense feelings of inferiority as a female; (2) her lack of acceptance of a feminine identification which, to her, meant an active identification with the psychotic or prepsychotic hateful mother; (3) angry, resentful feelings toward the father for not having loved her enough as a child and protected her from the depradations of her mother.

The immediate precipitating cause of her homosexual behavior developed out of her intense feelings of envy and rivalry toward the more successful, attractive and powerful girl cousin. This produced feelings of shame, self-diminution, and lack of self-esteem. Underlying all this were lifelong wishes to excel over everyone, possess a phallus and not be subjected to what she imagined would only be humiliation and lack of love at the hands of men. By controlling women she no longer needed men; she could acquire all the love she wanted; and obtain relief from her severe aggression toward her mother. Her homosexuality was the choice of the lesser evil, preferable to facing her deep conviction that she would fail heterosexually. Her sense of underlying inferiority, her frustration in trying to gain and hold the love of women during college together with her unconscious conflict over accepting the homosexual position produced an agitated depression which culminated in attempted suicide.

Her suicidal feelings substantially disappeared during treatment. Despite a homosexual relationship with the family friend and her insistence that she was interested only in women, she simultaneously harbored unexpressed heterosexual wishes. There were erotic transference feelings toward the analyst whom she wished to make the perfect heterosexual partner, that is, the loving, caring father.

In addition to her preoedipal conflict she suffered an intense oedipal conflict from which she regressed to the earlier fixation. Such regression brought her closer to mother and she experienced feelings of doom. This is why the presence of a "good" maternal substitute in the person of her female partner was so reassuring. These doom feelings were signalled by tremendous "void-like" emotional states in which she felt she would be engulfed into a whirlpool of disgust and destruction by getting so close to her mother. She feared her mother's breasts, her very presence, finding them "strangely malevolent" in every way. She had experienced these sensations as far back as she could remember.

The following *dream* reflected her heterosexual yearnings and the conflicts which they engendered. "A father was having intercourse with a daughter. It was more or less forced on her but not in the sense of rape. She put up with it and tried to forget it and she couldn't do anything about it." Her associations were when the father or any man came close to her she sometimes wished she could cut off their penis, not in actuality but certainly in fantasy. The sex act in her dream was performed in the usual way, once or twice, and then "the man asked if he could just hold his penis there for a while and I could do nothing about it. I was on my stomach, like a child, it seemed.

"I recall one time when my mother was away, around the time I was 11. I was fairly young and I was a little bit shorter than father since I have always been quite tall and I was a little jealous of my sister when I grew up. We used to take showers with Daddy and around age 11 I said, 'OK, I'll take a shower with them.' Then I suddenly remembered and I realized I was too old for that. I try to pretend that father doesn't have a penis and I don't like the idea of his having one because that makes him like the other older men and there's the possibility that I might think of it and be disgusted.

"The one-time college friend of my father would come to see me and I had a crush on him at about 11. He used to carry me on his shoulders and I remember thinking that I had to hold myself away from his neck because I couldn't stand the idea of someone touching me there. He used to hug me very tightly, almost as tight as he could, and I used to get a sexual thrill out of that. I've made myself try to forget all these kinds of things. I remember thinking that when they were in bed together, mother and father, that there was something between his legs and I could feel it there between mine. I was afraid of the possibility that it might bother me and I tried to put it out of my mind. When I was in college the first year there was a persistent desire to have a penis inside me. I really wanted it. I didn't want to give myself up to a man, however, at the same time."

This dream illuminated the oedipal conflict, her fear of her father's penis and her wishes to have intercourse with him. She was jealous of the favored place of her younger sister who had not yet reached puberty and could still enjoy intimacies with the father that she was now denied. Growing up meant getting rid of any fantasies which concerned her father and other men. It became quite clear that she then developed a severe envy and hostility toward the penis which would threaten her. She wished for love but could not have it.

It would seem that in college, following the crisis of her severe rivalry with her cousin, reactivating the previous conflict with the sister for paternal affection, she "switched to homosexuality" as a temporary measure, at least as it seemed to her, so that she would not worry about the possibility of being tied up with any man (father). "I wouldn't have to worry about the time when he would no longer be able to love me." She was unable to make the transference from her father to other men and as a result turned to homosexuality as a partial relief. It was also in part revenge, a retaliatory move against the father who was unable to give her a strong feeling of femininity and acceptance of it. She characterized him as completely devoid of sexual interests, saying that "He and mother have hardly ever had sexual intercourse."

Patient F was a severely repressed individual whose sexuality had sought expression but for unconscious reasons had been unable to find a suitable object. Her incestuous wishes toward the father as revealed in the last dream produced more conflict and she regressed to her pre-oedipal fixation to the mother with the substituted older female partner. In her homosexual activities she wished to be the man, the proud possessor of a phallus and thereby avoid the cataclysmic destruction in union with the mother and the threatened and terrifying identification with her. She ardently detested and despised the mother; she sustained murderous feelings toward her which she knew, of course, she could not act upon in reality. Her depression was a mixture of the most intense rage and loss. This rage was directed toward numerous factors: her mother, her disastrous and damaging upbringing in early youth and her lack of any personality traits with which she could buttress her femininity; the coldness, ineffectuality and lack of acceptance of her sexuality by her father; the failure of the girls at college to physically love her and allow themselves to be controlled by her.

Impulsive to an intense degree, Patient F attempted suicide on two occasions and felt a severe hostility toward all therapists. Following the "successful" relationship to her older woman partner she abruptly withdrew from the analysis. She would return to see the analyst at six-month intervals for the next two years to discuss current environmental problems. She was leading an active homosexual life with her partner and had not resumed college. She no longer suffered from depression although at times she felt considerable anxiety as she could not entirely accept her homosexual role, especially when her partner took over the active masculine role and asked her to remain passive.

Because of the patient's need to thwart her progress, the treatment ended before the potential for heterosexual adaptation could be realized. However, her suicidal acting out was eliminated as was the deep depression which had precipitated it. Her defensive self-aggrandizement would not permit her to face the infantile incestuous longings for her father and she desired to show the analyst (father) that she had no further need of him. She said she felt well and happy and would be able to manage her life herself.

Section Four

THERAPY

Chapter XV

SELECTION OF PATIENTS, MODIFICATION OF TECHNIQUE AND TURNING POINTS

IN 1905, Freud wrote that the only possibility of helping homosexual patients was by commanding a suppression of their symptoms through hypnotic suggestion.[63] By 1910, he believed that psychoanalysis itself was applicable to the treatment of perversions, including homosexuality,[66] but later expressed caution about the possibility of complete cure.[75] His criterion of cure was not only a detachment of the cathexis from the homosexual object but the ability to cathect the opposite sex. Freud recognized that it was especially difficult to analyze an individual while he is at "peace" with his perversion; a combination of neuroses and perversion, according to him, presented a hopeful therapeutic possibility.

In 1950, Anna Freud[59] lectured in New York on the recent advances in treatment of homosexuals, stating that many of her patients lost their inversion as a result of analysis. This occurred even in those who proclaimed their wish to remain homosexual when entering treatment, having come only to obtain relief from their neurotic symptoms.

An early analyst-author, Boehm,[21] concluded that homosexuals leave treatment at the time when heterosexual tendencies begin to emerge along with hatred and castrating wishes directed against the analyst-father. It became the consensus over the years that homosexuals could be treated most like phobics. However, this presented considerable difficulty including the probability of premature termination of treatment and the production of excessive anxiety The major difficulty in treating homosexuality has been the misconception that this disorder was of hereditary origin, the patient commonly believing that he "was born that way."

It is widely agreed that to achieve therapeutic success it is necessary to interpret to the patient his fear of castration; his fear of oral dependence; his disgust with the opposite sex; and his fear of his own destructiveness and sadism. But the interpretation that most achieves a relaxation of his resistance is the attempt to acquire masculinity through identification with the partner and his penis in the homosexual act. After this interpretation is worked through the patient may be able to function heterosexually, going through a strong narcissistic-phallic phase, women serving only the grandeur of his penis. The unconscious fearful fantasy of homosexuals that they would dissolve in a woman at the height of the sexual act is another crucial interpretation in all treatment of male homosexuality.

Numerous authors have reported a significant proportion of successful outcome in the psychoanalytic treatment of homosexual patients.[5,15,18,19,32,37,87,145,152,169] An unpublished and informal report in 1956 of the Central Fact Gathering Committee of the American Psychoanalytic Association was one of the first surveys to compile results of treatment. It showed that out of 56 cases of homosexuality undergoing psychoanalytic therapy by members of the Association, 8 in the completed group (which totaled 32) were described as cured; 13 as improved; 1, unimproved. This constituted one-third of all cases reported. Of the group which did not complete treatment (a total of 34), 16 were described as improved; 10 as unimproved; 3 as untreatable; 5 as transferred. In all reported cures, follow-up communications indicated assumption of full heterosexual role and functioning.

In 1962, Bieber[18] and his co-workers presented a systematic study of 106 male homosexuals. Their results do much to clarify the progress in therapeutic knowledge and effectiveness. Out of the 106 homosexuals who undertook psychoanalysis, 29 (27 per cent) became exclusively heterosexual.

The structure of homosexuality consists of neurotic conflicts involving both anal and genital stages of sexual development and the oedipal phase. These are superimposed on a substratum of preoedipal nuclear conflict. The vicissitudes of the preoedipal conflict pass through the later developmental periods and complicate, add to and give a particular configuration to the later conflict. All oedipal conflict has an admixture of the preoedipal danger. Therefore psychoanalysis is the treatment of choice for this disorder. Both preoedipal and oedipal anxieties can be relieved through the revival of infantile memories and traumatic states and the reintegration of the individual achieved. Treatment of preoedipal damage requires in addition to the uncovering techniques of psychoanalysis, educational and retraining measures, more intensive supportive interventions and modifications in the handling of transference, resistance and regression.

The Contributions of Fenichel and Glover

Up to 1945, the psychoanalytic therapy of perversions, including homosexuality, was summarized by Fenichel[47]:

(1) One factor absent in the neuroses complicates the problem in perversions. In the latter the symptoms at least promise to be pleasant and

treatment not only threatens to rekindle the very conflicts the patient have evaded by means of his illness but it also threatened to destroy the only sexual pleasure the patient knows. The possibility of normal sexual pleasure is to him most remote.

(2) The prognosis depends upon the extent to which the determination to get well is present or to what extent this determination can be awakened. A trial analysis will have as its main task the evaluation of the will to recover.

(3) Some patients ask that psychoanalysis rid them of their neurosis but wish to preserve their perversion. The very nature of analysis makes this impossible.

(4) The analysis of perversions is, on the whole, no more difficult than that of "pregenitally determined neuroses." Several authors have pointed out that the prognosis for psychoanalytic treatment of homosexuals is better than generally assumed. Certain modifications in technique become necessary analogous to those suggested by Freud[73] for hysteria, the normal sexual situation representing the phobically avoided situation, the seeking of which the analyst may suggest at a certain point during treatment.

(5) The need for reassurance expressed in perversions is frequently due to an intensified narcissistic need, the capacity for "reassuring denials" to an instability of the function of reality testing. In consequence, there are many patients who show in their transference behavior as well as in their general demeanor in life a narcissistic character disturbance or who may even present an almost psychotic picture.[157] In such cases psychoanalytic treatment meets the same difficulties as in the attending character disturbances of psychoses.

Edward Glover, in his book, *The Roots of Crime*,[101] devotes considerable attention to the problem of therapy of male homosexuality:

In 1953 the Portman Clinic Survey in England reported the following conclusion: "Psychotherapy appears to be unsuccessful in only a small number of patients of any age in whom a long habit is combined with psychopathic traits, heavy drinking or lack of desire to change."

Glover divided the degrees of improvement into three categories:

(a) Cure, i.e., abolition of conscious homosexual impulse and development of full extension of heterosexual impulse.

(b) Much improved, i.e., the abolition of conscious homosexual impulse without development of full extension of heterosexual impulse.

(c) Improved, i.e., increases ego integration and capacity to control the homosexual impulse.

In conducting focal treatment (brief therapy aimed at the relief of the homosexual symptom), Glover states that the following must be carefully kept in mind: the degree of social anxiety which prevails, particularly among patients seen in private. This social anxiety, however, is based on a projected form of unconscious guilt. The penal attitude of society enables the patient to project concealed superego reactions on to society or to the law.

Glover feels that it is at this point that the therapist must decide whether to pursue the problem through the regular and prolonged course of analysis or whether he will be satisfied with a focal relief. If he adopts the latter course, he will soon find that having uncovered some of the guilt, he will then strike against a core of sexual anxiety, and, in particular, on the multifarious manifestations of the castration complex. Here will be the point that the history of the individual familial relations, traumas, frustrations, disappointments, jealousies, etc., will come to the surface or should be brought to the surface.

Also, it is necessary to demonstrate the defensive aspects of the homosexual situation, for only by uncovering the positive aspects of his original relation to women (mother, sister) and demonstrating the anxieties or guilts (real or fantasied) associated with the hostile aspects of these early relations can a path be cleared for the return of heterosexual libido.

As regards psychoanalytic treatment of male homosexuality, Glover offers vitally useful points of information.

(a) There is a generalization that given appropriate selection of cases the ultimate success (or failure) or the psychoanalysis of male homosexuality lies in the thoroughness or inadequacy with which the analyst explores the unconscious libidinal phases of the negative oedipus complex and the reactive aggression with which these are associated. The effect on ego and superego structure of those identifications and introjections that are laid down during both positive and negative phases of the oedipus complex must also be fully analyzed.

(b) That the technique of psychoanalysis proper precludes a focal attack on symptom formations or other psychopathological manifestations is well known. It is therefore not possible to direct analytic attention to any one phase of mental development to the exclusion or neglect of other material. This can be attempted only in the cases of short focal treatment. In any case the requirements of psychoanalysis cannot be satisfied by libido analysis only, or for that matter by the analysis of the unconscious hostility and aggression that run in series with libidinal development. Glover remarks that if the course of psychoanalysis can be said to be directed at all, it is directed by the vicissitudes of anxiety and guilt and by the defense maneuvers (resistances) which these affects engender. Effective interpretation of resistances may in this sense be said to guide the analysis, but effective interpretation is regulated at all times by *ad hoc* considerations, *not* by preconceptions of the symptom structure.

(c) The second generalization is quite obvious: this is arrived at on the strength of the clinical observation that despite the priority of homosexual object choice, homosexual psychic organizations comprise a wide range of component impulse. There is consequently a wide scope for regression to various contributing fixation points. It follows that there can be no standard course in the progress of analyses of homosexual cases considered as a group. In this respect the analysis of homosexuals differs from the analysis of most transference neuroses, where fixation points are more clearly localized at definite ego levels.

Analysis must finally concentrate at the same levels associated with the formation of hysterical and obsessional states, viz., the genital level. To this extent it is still true that the homosexual perversion is the negative of a neurosis, to vary Freud's dictum,[63] according to Glover. But this concentration at the genital level of the patient's development cannot be successful so long as the pregenital regressions are not fully ventilated. Some hint as to the pregenital regressions can be obtained from study of the fantasy systems and actual sexual practices. Behind these conscious fantasy systems and manifest practices, however, lie more primitive unconscious systems the analysis of which is essential to the loosening of defensive regression.

(d) It is at this point that some of the most intractable resistances are to be found, more particularly since these early unconscious sexual fantasies if powerfully enough charged are capable of disturbing the patient's reality sense to a degree that if persistent would give rise to pre-psychotic reactions.

(e) The factor which serves to tide the patient over such crises is *the degree of transference rapport*. As fixation points in homosexuality vary, so do the transference manifestations vary. Reactions corresponding to hysterical, obsessional, depressive and paranoidal transferences can be observed in different types. On the whole, the obsessional type of transference seems to be the most commonly encountered.

There are some transitional forms in which obsessional reactions and perverse sexuality seem to overlap, e.g., the patient converts his associations into a running obsessional commentary on his manifest homosexual reactions and often on his anti-feminist disposition. By so doing he blocks the approach to his underlying hostility to men and attraction to women. Unless this situation is dealt with by effective interpretation the analysis is liable to end either in stalemate or in the acquisition of control only.

(f) Furthermore, as regards transference, the reactions are the obsessional type and very rarely reach the hothouse intensity observed in the hysteric or even in the fulminating crises of the psychotic type. Manifest erotic transferences are rarely observed and seldom exceed the compulsive expression of fantasy or, at the most, exhibitionism.

In the early stages of analysis there are, of course, many indications of spontaneous transference some of which can be recognized as essentially *maternal* in origin. There exists in particular a passive receptive attitude to interpretation which alternates with disappointment when this is not forthcoming. But as is only to be expected from the first, open expressions of active analytic rapport take the form of father transferences in which the positive element at first predominates.

It is essential, however, to uncover the *negative elements* of the father transference; only when these have been fully ventilated is it possible for the deeper mother transferences, both positive and negative, to appear.

Most analytic failures in the sense that the patient retains his homosexual system even if only in a less marked form are due to the failure to uncover and analyze these potential mother transferences, which at first are almost exclusively saturated with pregenital sadistic fantasy. With the successful overcoming of these deeper regressive phases the prospects of a successful outcome are greatly improved. As a rule the first sign of fundamental improvement is the appearance of anxieties which would ordinarily set up neurotic defenses. These differ from the earlier manifestations of social anxiety which are encountered at the beginning of the analysis of most homosexuals. These deeper anxieties gradually give place to guilt reactions and it is at this point that super-ego analysis can be made effective. This calls for persistent ventilation of the projection systems by means of which the patient covers his guilt. During this period the patient may manifest a number of transitory symptom formations of a conversion type and his inhibitions in work and in social contact may be exacerbated.

Once these have been worked through the way is open to analyze the genital kernal of his oedipus complex which the homosexual has used every unconscious mechanism to conceal.

It is safe to say that under present conditions of selection success in treatment depends upon the following factors: (a) The effectiveness with which the purely psychological disposition to homosexual object choice can be uncovered. (b) The degree in which current ego difficulties and frustrations can be offset. (c) The degree of transference rapport that can be established or, in the case of the psychoanalytic technique, analyzed.

The first of these factors depends on the amount of primary gain secured through the perversion; the second, on the amount of secondary gain obtained in current life; and the third on the degree of potential accessibility of each case. As in all other forms of treatment of mental disorder, the third factor is by far the most important.[101]

The Selection of Patients

In this writer's experience, the selection of patients with homosexual symptomatology is no different from the selection of all patients for psychoanalytic therapy. The two major considerations are the presence of a feeling of guilt on the part of the patient for the unconscious wishes experienced under the guise of homosexuality and that psychoanalytic treatment must be voluntarily undertaken.

The absence of conscious guilt does not mean that the patient does not suffer guilt but instead is experienced by him as a need for punishment and self-damaging behavior. *Unconscious guilt will always be disclosed.* His conscious guilt prompts him to seek treatment sooner and makes him more cooperative in the therapeutic endeavor. It is attributed by the patient to behavior contrary to the morals of our society. The presence of unconscious guilt, arising from infantile fears and wishes, lifts the problem out of its externalized context into an internal conflict. Once seen as an internal conflict the patient is at last on the path toward resolution of his homosexuality and no longer can view himself as the victim of society's attitudes and judgments.

Even if the patient is influenced by others to seek help, one invariably finds the presence of a desire to alleviate his suffering often hidden by a number of rationalizations and a maze of defensive attitudes.

All homosexual acts constitute a masochistic-sadistic transaction between the homosexual and his partner which serves as a defense against regression to early points of fixation (undifferentiated phase). The psychotic, because of his lack of integrative capacity due to his thinking disorder, as well as the psychopathic patient, because of the failure in the restraining mechanism of conscience and his inability to forego immediate gratification (poor impulse control), are the most difficult to treat. They require changes in technique dependent on the structure of the concomitant psychopathology. It is conceivable that in some schizophrenics, homosexual behavior may represent a floundering and chaotic attempt to establish even the most elementary of human contacts, an attempt to "try anything" in order to feel relatedness to another person.

Therapeutic accessibility is promoted by the presence of guilt. Conscious guilt feelings, however, are not the major consideration. Most important is the capacity to experience unconscious guilt. It is mainly the unconscious part of the superego which produces guilt feelings of sufficient intensity to place powerful demands on the ego thus aiding the therapy. Often conscious guilt can be mitigated or rationalized or "paid off" through deliberate or superficial expiatory moves. For instance, such a move may consist of beginning treatment as a self-punitive and face-saving device.

Ideally homosexual patients should voluntarily seek treatment and not under duress from parents or other authority figures for they are beset by a savage, unconscious hatred against their parents—a hatred that is in direct proportion to their wild self-damaging tendencies which their aggressive homosexuality camouflages.

Special Problems

All homosexuals suffer from a sense of inferiority and guilt over their disability due to their infantile fears which have isolated them from the social-sexual relationships of a majority of the population. This remains constantly a deep-rooted source of shame, humiliation and discontent. Semi-automatic and conscious repair of this damage to self-esteem, both consciously and unconsciously, are strived for. As a consequence of these maneuvers the patient may present a facade of pseudo-confidence and self-aggrandizement. He may do everything in his power to convince himself and the therapist of the validity of his face-saving rationalizations.

It is absolutely necessary that the analysis provides the homosexual patient with an opportunity to admit the extent of his desolation. A somewhat lengthy interval will be required, of course, before the appearance of unconscious material which reveals aspects of himself which he abhors and wishes to change. It is important to discourage him from a masochistic display of his homosexuality to spare him added guilt and shame with increased isolation. This only continues his previous path of incurring punishment and inviting "martyrdom." The patient must begin to suspect that what he says and does as regards his homosexual behavior really makes no sense; only then will he become curious about the unconscious factors responsible for his irrational behavior.

His real intent is to prove that homosexuality is as "rational" as heterosexuality. It is obvious that as long as he remains committed to the idea that his interest in men represents the expression of an inherent biological choice the benefits of therapeutic help are limited. An early interpretation should point up that in part his lack of sexual interest in women is due to fear of them rather than the absence of heterosexual desires. Often he will then begin to reappraise his "commitment to homosexuality" and question his grave reluctance to make the acquaintance of women beyond the narrow and preconceived fashion which has so far characterized any contact with them. This redirects his anxiety from his fears around homosexuality to his fears of the female and reopens a long avoided avenue fraught with anachronistic danger of both preoedipal and oedipal periods as related to the mother.

The course of treatment may take many directions, either on a consistent basis of gradual progress with no dramatic and sudden change of sexual practices or intermittently undergo a series of reversals and detours. Three patterns most frequently seen at the beginning of psychoanalytic therapy are:

(1) The patient who has been engaged in homosexual behavior for many years prior to entering therapy.

(2) The patient who has already restrained himself from such behavior, although formerly engaged in it, prior to entering therapy or does so shortly after.

(3) The patient who has experienced strong impulses toward such behavior and is driven to seek help because his control is weakening. Analysis may from the beginning enable him to refrain from acting out these impulses. Conversely, once certain that the analyst will not condemn him for being unable to cope further with the impulses—constituting a life-or-death struggle—and will retain him as a patient worthy of every consideration, he may then engage in such behavior, the alternative being suicide or psychosis for some patients.

The patient must not be permitted to utilize his self-deceptive rationalizations as a threat to terminating treatment. He cannot be permitted to belabor the doctor with arguments that the latter is biased against homosexuality and interested only in its eradication. The homosexual's confrontation of the analyst with arguments that certain famous men were or are homosexuals can be disposed of by pointing out that such achievement did not ensue because of their homosexuality but because of their abilities.

The patient should be helped to see that he tries to rely on infantile omnipotence to save him from an assortment of humiliations and fears. Not only does he try to feel superior but he also tries to appear as all-powerful, sometimes to megalomanic proportions. He casts himself in the role of being super-attractive, in fact irresistible to others. Underneath this bravado is an unremitting fear of external punishment because of the disapproval, parental and social, to which he is vulnerable as a homosexual. Even more he fears internal punishment. Part of his unconscious mind resents the solution of homosexuality and continues to produce conflict; the unconscious part of his superego objects to the basically aggressive meaning of the homosexual act.

Homosexuals seem to approve of their choice of love object because they are unconsciously afraid of being unable to change it. The realization that his fear of women is a mask hiding his hatred and aggression toward them is a vital insight for the patient. These feelings can then be traced back to the oral stage and derived from his fear of the maternal breast.

Unlike obsessional neuroses, phobias and hysterical symptomatology, homosexuality represents a varied constellation of symptoms which are manifestations of both preoedipal and oedipal phase conflicts with the nuclear conflict originating in the preoedipal phase. While the patient's productions are likely to be limited during the earlier stages of therapy to material centering around the oedipal conflicts, both positive and negative, it is most important to bear in mind that they represent accretions to the difficulties originating in the preoedipal phase. They therefore reflect aspects of the unresolved primitive excessive anxieties and aggressions so prominently a part of the earliest psychic functioning. For example, a homosexual's (oedipal) love for his mother is fused with the most disturbing aggressive incorporative affect. The analysis of phallic and anal material is necessary but only supplemental to the analysis of the oral stage and its antecedents.

Homosexuality requires full-scale, thoroughgoing analysis of all phases of development. This is not meant to convey that symptomatic improvement may not be achieved early in therapy. Symptomatic cures, usually transient in nature, in which a patient previously engaged exclusively in homosexual acts is able to participate in heterosexual intercourse, may be due to his overcoming phobic avoidance of the female genitals because of the reduction of his incestuous (oedipal) fear of his mother. However, he still remains homosexual motivationally and to regard this change as anything more than partial and probably temporary is completely misleading.

Ferenczi[50] was the first to emphasize the fact that homosexuality constitutes a symptomatic formation—a prophylactic device: "Homosexuality gains its significance from the content of the unconscious fantasy which is realized in the perversion." Lorand[145] is of the same opinion and emphasizes the importance in analyzing this fantasy in great detail. A minute examination of the practice and its fantasy proves, of course, to be an acting out of drives, infantile and polymorphously perverse in character, concomitant anxieties and guilt feelings. Anna Freud suggests that "The basis for classification of homosexuality should not be the overt practice carried out with a partner but the fantasy which accompanied the act. . . ."[58]

Ferenczi[50] described the fundamental difference between the "active" and "passive" type of homosexual. In his opinion, the passive type does not seek treatment; the active type is more aware of and disturbed by the abnormality and tries to change it. He considered the active type to be a "typical obsessional neurotic," one whose homosexuality is a "compulsion." He described therapeutic success on a transference basis in such cases but felt that the slightest conflict would cause a relapse and real analysis had then to begin.

To this author there is no difference between the active and passive type of homosexual as both experience vicariously the actions of the partner. It is, of course, essential that the unconscious meaning of the fantasy during homosexual intercourse be completely understood along with its multiple substitutions, displacements and symbolizations which help make the symptom at least partially acceptable to the ego. The more primitive the unconscious fantasy the nearer we are to the source of the original anxiety. The analysis of the symptom gives the analyst information as to the preoedipal anxieties and facilitates their elucidation and working through.

In practice what one attempts to do is to mobilize the patient's feelings and fantasies which accompany his sexual contacts and masturbation. We direct the patient's interest to a minute investigation of all that he aims at in his perversion and in his acting out. Many of his fantasies will be found to originate around incorporating or being incorporated and an intense interest in the breasts of the mother. In the male homosexual, therefore, we will see that there was once a very strong attachment to the first heterosexual object, the mother. He must re-experience and understand the early frustrations, intimidations and fixations, give up his attachment to his mother and transfer his libidinal interest to other women. Before this aim could reach fruition all developmental phases would have to be investigated including his identification with the father (analyst) in the transference. Analysis of the homosexual patient is global, a total analysis of the personality at all stages.

Rosenfeld's studies[159] on paranoia and homosexuality are of great significance because they explore the type of homosexuality which seems to be the most difficult to cure. It can be traced back to the paranoid anxieties which have occurred in the earliest period of life. Castration to these patients which is implicit in homosexuality was willingly accepted in order to ward off the danger of being killed or annihilated. Homosexuality appears here as a specific defense where the persecutor is appeased by homosexual intercourse. On the other hand, another kind of complication may occur. This is described by Anna Freud in a brief communication.[58] She stressed the projection of the good and potent penis onto the other man, in certain types of homosexuals. However, she related this only to the phallic phase.

It is important in therapy to trace the basis of this projection mechanism which lies in the early oral-sadistic impulses of forcing the self into another object. For example, it can be clearly established that the impulse of forcing oneself into the mother, which belongs to the earliest phases of infancy, is strongly evident in patients and had been reinforced later by regression and certain related factors, namely, by the overpowering attitude of the patient's mother who may have ruled the patient's life completely and who had virtually forced her ideas into him. This could include the forcing of food which continued even after the child would vomit.

These impulses are then partially transferred onto the father at an early age and constitute the most important fixation point, both of homosexuality and of paranoia. At the same time they are responsible for the use a patient makes of the projection mechanism. Clinically, the homosexual fantasies, paranoid attitude and preoccupation gradually begin to disappear only after the entire structure of the mother-child relationship is fully understood and worked through in the transference when the desire and need to project have considerably diminished.

Modifications of Technique

In the history of psychoanalysis every advance and insight have been closely followed by an advance in technique; conversely, every technical rule has been considered valid only when solidly founded on a specific piece of analytic theory. It has been shown that deviations from classic technique become necessary to meet deviations in a patient's ego structure and that technical experimentation in this respect may lead to new insight into abnormality in the structure. This has been stated by numerous psychoanalytic authors, especially Anna Freud.[61] However, modifications of technique should be firmly based on the structure of the particular condition and rooted firmly in the theory of the disorder. Alterations cannot be carried out arbitrarily or without sufficient cause.

The analyst's position must be examined from the sides of the ego and id (resistance and transference) variations, respectively. This has been done in schizophrenia where patients' narcissistic withdrawal makes them nearly inaccessible; with paranoid patients where the transference may not remain within controllable limits; with delinquents where the destructive quality of id urges poses serious problems. Variations in technique become necessary whenever the aspects of a case lead us to expect manifestations of transference or resistance which exceed in force or malignancy the extent with which we are able to cope effectively. At the beginning of analysis, before we have insight into the structure of the condition, it is impossible to predict how the patient will respond. There is no guarantee that two homosexual patients or any two individuals with the same symptomatology will react similarly to the same technical procedure.

Let us take, for example, the traditional rule of asking a patient to stop any activity in which he derives pleasure by self-damaging action. This is based on the idea that there is little chance of successfully treating any disturbance which approximates "addiction" while the gratifying aspects of it are allowed full scope. Applying this rule to two homosexual patients provides a basis for comparison. In Patient J an attempt to prohibit his homosexual activity will move him to outbreaks of hostility and anxiety which threaten the continuation or the effectiveness of the analysis. To insist upon it would be a grave technical error. In Patient K, although he experiences intense anxiety, such prohibition results in decreased frequency and duration of homosexual episodes, the analysis penetrates deeper and heterosexuality may more readily be achieved. In the latter case, cutting down on homosexual practices will be seen to play a beneficial part. It would seem that identical symptomatology is here based on somewhat different psychopathology and it is the latter, not the former, which decides how a case should be dealt with from a technical point of view. In Patient J the outburst of homosexual practices serves to reduce the anxiety which was aroused by active, aggressive masculine urges. Passive advances to male partners served as reassurance in lessening anxiety.

It will be possible for the patient who wishes to be constrained and protected during treatment to reduce homosexual practices because of the transference; a new attachment, that to the analyst, has taken place. The analyst would then be in the role of protecting him against the dangerous destructive impulses. When the analyst fills this role in the patient's imagination the patient does without the male partner. This implies, of course, that the analyst be available to the patient at all times without fail and interruption of the analysis cannot be tolerated for long.

In Patient K the perverse activity may serve a completely different purpose. Men often become homosexual due to having invested other men with the attributes of their own phallic masculinity. They cannot then bear to be without these other male figures, ideal either in the bodily or mental sense, and pursue them unremittingly. By urging a patient of this type to restrict his homosexual practices, one urges him to commit self-castration. What then ensues is an immense resistance and hostility to the analyst when the restrictive edict is imposed. This type of management is not applicable to this kind of case. Interpretation of the origins of the patient's projection of masculinity has to come first and enable him to assume his own phallic properties; thus, he is no longer dependent for his masculine identity on the homosexual partner. Male partners will begin to lose their importance and the patient will be better able to do without them.

To summarize this issue: the question of prohibiting homosexual activity should be decided on the basis of its unconscious meaning to the patient. Outbursts of hostility and anxiety may threaten continuance of therapy if the therapist prohibits activities which the patient considers necessary for his survival. Prohibition, if it induces or connotes an active self-castration, is not recommended. On the other hand, if the patient has an adequate identification with the analyst and there is little danger of feelings of self-castration, prohibition may be attempted in the manner of the technical handling of phobic patients.

Other modifications in technique have been suggested by several authors such as Lorand,[145] Clyne[169] and Anna Freud.[58,61]

Control of the depth of regression in order to offset its utilization as resistance in the transference relationship is another modification. The depth of regression will reveal important psychodynamic material but the patient's degree of anxiety must be manageable. His tendency to regression to the earliest paranoid anxieties must constantly be watched and dealt with immediately. One can readily see here that the modification must take into account the structure of the pathology and is based upon it. A further modification is the management of severe dependency wishes. Often these patients have intense oral conflicts and as long as their orality is fulfilled they do not rise to a higher level of integration. Dependency strivings should be adequately controlled inasmuch as our goal is to achieve a higher level of integration. Prolonged oral regression is not advisable.[169]

An additional modification is the use of extra-analytic transferences. Bacon[5,169] has observed that the homosexual must be induced to set up a "triangular relationship once again." One of the great difficulties has been that the homosexual can never love a person of one sex and simultaneously a person of the other sex. He must always be "taking sides." If he feels love for his mother then he cannot love his analyst (father) or feel any warmth toward him. If he feels close to the analyst he will have nothing to do with his mother or any other female, despising and hating her. Elucidation of this material helps to resolve the oedipal conflict.

It must be stressed to the patient that the resolution of his problems will ultimately have to take place outside the analyst's office. At the same time the depth and intensity of his regression in the transference must be reduced in order to enable him to carry out this very interaction with the environment. To accomplish this the sessions may be intermittent or decreased in frequency in order to diminish regression and to direct the patient's attention toward the external world, especially when there is not excessive castration anxiety present or exceedingly intense aggressive feelings. A therapist may make interventions into the analytic work by discussing aspects of the patient's career, friendships, social and cultural pursuits.

The modification of decreasing sessions and suggesting interruptions in therapy is dependent upon the current motivational state of the patient. During intervals of severe aggression the sessions should be increased so that aggressive discharges with their concomitant psychic material can be ventilated rather than suppressed or acted out. Behind this aggression is a deep need for love which the analyst neither condemns nor criticizes. The running away from extra-analytic problems into a regression with identification with the "good" mother and becoming an infant must be constantly interpreted. The continuing identification with the analyst increases the patient's strength and he finds that his aggression does not kill the analyst (father), nor does it destroy the mother or himself.

Special Aspects in the Treatment of Female Homosexuality

The female homosexual, even more than the male homosexual, suffers from intense feelings of inferiority and self-depreciation which may be completely unconscious and result in a proportionately intense reaction-formation of superiority and self-aggrandizement. Therefore, her initial hostility toward the therapist may be quite powerful and the analyst must be prepared for this from the start, not allowing it to impair or disrupt the beginning therapeutic alliance.

This hostility also has another source, the feelings of rejection and banishment by the father. Much of the transference revolves around this basic fear, resentment and vengeful attitude arising from the experience of having been forsaken by the father. In these cases the father could not allow his daughter to exhibit her feminine wishes in the oedipal situation with tolerance, acceptance and love.

The female homosexual will enact in the transference her relationship to the father much more vividly than the male homosexual and, upon finding she is not rejected, will put the analyst to the test by attempting to act out directly with him her reawakened oedipal wishes, a totally unreal test as she realizes the analyst cannot gratify them. Such acting out can become a crucial making or breaking point for the therapy if the analyst does not interpret the meaning of her erotic and dependency demands before they have attained an unsustainable peak of intensity. If not interpreted early enough the patient can then claim a new humiliation at the hands of the analyst (father) when these demands are not met by him. Very seldom are such importunate demands for direct libidinal gratification made of the analyst by the male homosexual patient.

The female's primary identification with the mother does not necessarily change her basic anatomic identification and capacity for heterosexual functioning. Therefore, oedipal material should be analyzed immediately and quite often. With the resolution of her aggressive and incestuous feelings toward the father, heterosexual relations may be brought about sooner than can be anticipated in the male homosexual patient whose primary identification with the mother has inevitably impaired such capacity.

The female homosexual does not have to undergo, as does the male, a change in gender identification. Of course, her primary identification with a hateful sadistic mother and her fears of incorporation and merging with the mother must be analyzed in order to bring lasting improvement or cure.

Many homosexual women with a marginal heterosexual adjustment and functioning suddenly become openly homosexual as a result of their disappointment in transversing crucial phases of life—menstruation, first intercourse, marriage, motherhood—situations in which they may experience once again a feeling of rejection and abandonment by the male (father). The overtly homosexual woman may be restored to heterosexual functioning by the direct analysis of these precipitating events. This symptomatic relief serves the patient's purpose and she does not seek further analytic therapy at that time.

It would be erroneous to assume that homosexual women do not experience the intense anxiety of their male counterparts. It is precisely the female who, upon losing her female partner, experiences anxiety of total extinction, namely aphanisis. This condition is usually the reason for entering analysis because of its implications for suicide. Aphanisis can also occur if there is a premature attempt on the part of the patient during therapy to separate from her partner. Thus prohibitions as to continued homosexual behavior not only must follow the same principles as prescribed for the male, depending upon the individual structural dynamics, but the dangers of massive anxiety leading to panic and suicide are very great and must be worked through as thoroughly as possible when separation is contemplated.

Turning Points

In all homosexual cases there is an insatiable yearning for the father which the patient may have suppressed or repressed for years. As elucidated in Chapter VI on the preoedipal origin of homosexuality, the damage is done in the earliest mother-child relationship. Thus it would not have been possible to completely prevent this fixation through any maneuvers on the father's part after the fact of the child's failure to pass through the separation-individuation phase successfully. Nonetheless, had a strong and active paternal relationship intervened, the force of the later homosexuality might have been considerably modified in expression or diminished in intensity.

This yearning is a plaintive cry for the father whom the patient unconsciously feels to be his only source of help in his fight against the phenomenon of engulfment and merging with the mother. The importance of the father to the child's psychological development cannot be overestimated. To the boy he is the model for masculine identification, giving him a feeling of security in relation to the environment. For the girl it is the father's love which creates a model for heterosexual love in adulthood.

Studies of male homosexual patients have so emphasized the role of the crushing, domineering mother and of the hostile poisoning mother in female homosexuality that it is essential to balance the picture by emphasizing the importance of the father's contribution to the psycho-sexual development of the child.

During psychoanalytic treatment, in this writer's experience, it is imperative that the analysis be conducted along the lines of providing a suitable father substitute. Thus, the deficiency can be somewhat attenuated and a modification of the deep-seated yearning for the father achieved.

All homosexuals deeply fear the knowledge that their homosexual behavior constitutes an erotized defense against a threatening maso-chistic state and in some cases the most severe masochistic state of the undifferentiated phase fusion. A concentrated attack on this aspect of the problem must be made.

The patient's turning to heterosexual relationships often coincides with a strong positive transference. In the positive transference the patient is able to identify himself with the good father and thus achieve in the transference what he has been unsuccessfully trying to achieve in homosexual relationships, namely, to get possession of the good father's penis and become free of his enslavement to the mother. If at the same time, during the positive transference, the patient becomes aware that he has been attacking his partner in homosexual relationships and that the partner is really the mother figure, via the breast-penis equasion, he may start to give up homosexual relations. Then through an identifica-tion with the good father he can feel stronger and new possibilities in life appear.

During this phase the first heterosexual relationships occur. He may well prove himself to be potent almost immediately only to find that it is the insides of the woman which he then fears. However, one must be sure that he no longer feels that closeness to a woman may lead to his being engulfed, imprisoned or swallowed up. Still subject to such fear he may revert to homosexual relationships corresponding with an acutely negative transference. The therapist then may be seen as a bad father figure. Once more the patient may look for homosexual relation-ships hoping to acquire the penis from his homosexual partner. How-ever, the patient very often already is unable to return to homosexual relations as he previously knew them even if not yet entirely free from preoedipal anxiety.

Homosexual contacts become less frequent compared with the past and, at the same time, lose the degree of imperativeness which formerly characterized them, an indication that the patient is no longer so anxiety-ridden. His awareness of his feelings has become much greater and he is more potentially capable of object love. It is promising if a patient shows corresponding progress in his work. If this occurs together with an interest in women there will also simultaneously occur more interest in and respect for his internal psychic life.

Another turning point may be the diminution of mild to moderate persecutory feelings which may have remained somewhat on the periphery of his consciousness throughout the analysis. His homosexuality has been a constant source of anxiety, requiring that he repress his hatred of male rivals and substitute "love" of them in its place. He has to become aware that his main competition is with men; love and comfort are to be found with women. He no longer needs to forcibly repress all his aggressive and self-assertive urges in competition with male figures.

BIBLIOGRAPHY

1. Abraham, K.: Manifestation of the Female Castration Complex. In *Selected Papers on Psychoanalysis*. London: L. and V. Woolf, 1948, pp. 338-369. (Hogarth Press).

2. Alexander, F.: The Neurotic Character (1927). *Int. J. Psychoanal.*, 11:292-311, 1930.

3. Alexander, F.: A Note to the Theory of Perversions. In *Perversions: Psychodynamics and Therapy*, ed. Lorand, S. and Balint, M. New York: Random House, 1956.

4. Arlow, J. A.: Psychodynamics and Treatment of Perversions (Panel Report). *Bull. Amer. Psychoanal. Assn.*, 8:315-327, 1952. Also Perversions: Theoretical and Therapeutic Aspects (Panel Report). *J. Amer. Psychoanal. Assn.*, 2:336-345, 1954.

5. Bacon, C. L.: A Developmental Theory of Female Homosexuality. In *Perversions: Psychodynamics and Therapy*, ed. Lorand, S. and Balint, M. New York: Random House, 1956.

6. Bak, R.: See Arlow (Panel Report), 1954.

7. Bak, R.: Aggression and Perversion. In *Perversions: Psychodynamics and Therapy*, ed. Lorand, S. and Balint, M. New York: Random House, 1956.

8. Barahal, H. S.: Female Transvestitism and Homosexuality. *Psychiat. Quar.*, 27:390-438, 1953.

9. Benedek, T.: *Psychosexual Functions in Women*. New York: Ronald Press, 1952.

10. Bergler, E. and Eidelberg, L.: The Breast Complex in Men. *Int. Z. Psychanal.*, 19:547-583, 1933.

11. Bergler, E.: The Respective Importance of Reality and Phantasy in the Genesis of Female Homosexuality. *J. Crim. Psychopath.*, 5:27-48, 1943.

12. Bergler, E.: Eight Prerequisites for Psychoanalytic Treatment of Homosexuality. *Psychoanal. Rev.*, 31:253-286, 1944.

13. Bergler, E.: *Counterfeit Sex*. New York: Grune and Stratton, 1951.

14. Bergler, E. and Kroger, W.: *Kinsey's Myth of Female Sexuality: The Medical Facts*. New York: Grune and Stratton, 1954.

15. Bergler, E.: *Homosexuality: Disease or Way of Life:* New York: Hill & Wang, 1956.

16. Bergler, E.: *1000 Homosexuals: Conspiracy of Silence on Curing and Deglamorizing Homosexuality*. Paterson, N. J.: Pageant Books, 1959.

17. Bibring, G. L.: On An Oral Component in Masculine Inversion. *Int. Z. Psychoanal.*, 25:124-130, 1940.

18. Bieber, I. et al.: *Homosexuality*. New York: Basic Books, 1962.

19. Bieber, T.: On Treating Male Homosexuals. *Arch. of Gen. Psychiat.*, 16:60-63, 1967.

20. Blos, P.: *On Adolescence*. New York: Free Press, 1961.

21. Boehm, F.: Homosexuality and Oedipus Complex. *Int. Z. Psychoanal.*, 12:66-79, 1926.

22. Boehm, F.: The Femininity Complex in Men. *Int. J. Psychoanal.*, 11:444-469, 1930.

23. Boehm, F.: Über zwei Typen von männlichen Homosexuellen. *Int. Z, Psychoanal.*, 19:499-506, 1933.

24. Bonaparte, M.: *Female Sexuality.* New York: International Universities Press, 1953.

25. Bonaparte, M., Freud, A. and Kris, E.: *The Origins of Psycho-Analysis: Letters of Wilhelm Fliess.* (Tr. E. Mosbacher and J. Strachey.) New York: Basic Books, 1954.

26. Brierley, M.: Some Problems of Integration in Women. *Int. J. Psychoanal.* 13:433-448, 1932.

27. Brierley, M.: Specific Determinants in Feminine Development. *Int. J. Psychoanal.*, 17:163-180, 1935.

28. Brill, A. A.: Homoerotism and Paranoia. *Amer. J. Psychiat.*, 13:957-974, 1934.

29. Bychowski, G.: The Ego of Homosexuals. *Int. J. Psychoanal.*, 26:114-127, 1945.

30. Bychowski, G.: The Structure of Homosexual Acting Act. *Psychoanal Quar.*, 23:48-61, 1954.

31. Bychowski, G.: The Ego and the Introjects. *Psychoanal. Quar.*, 25:11-36, 1956.

32. Bychowski, G.: Homosexuality and Psychosis. In *Perversions: Psychodynamics and Therapy.* ed. Lorand, S. and Balint, M. New York: Random House, 1956.

33. Deutsch, H.: *Psychoanalyse der Weiblichen Sexualfunktionen.* Vienna: Int. Psychoanal. Verlag, 1925.

34. Deutsch, H.: Female Sexuality (Also: Homosexuality in Women). *Int. J. Psychoanal.*, 14:34-56, 1932.

35. Deutsch, H.: On Female Homosexuality. *Psychoanal. Quar.*, 1:484-510, 1932.

36. Deutsch, H.: Motherhood and Sexuality. *Psychoanal. Quar.*, 2:476-488, 1933.

37. Deutsch, H.: *The Psychology of Women.* New York: Grune and Stratton, 1944, Vol. I, II.

38. Eidelberg, L.: Analysis of a Case of a Male Homosexual. In *Perversions: Psychodynamics and Therapy,* ed. Lorand, S. and Balint, M. New York: Random House, 1956, pp. 279-289.

39. Eissler, K. R.: Notes on Problems of Technique in the Psychoanalytic Treatment of Adolescence: With Some Remarks on Perversions. *Psychoanalytic Study of the Child*, 13:223-254. New York: International Universities Press, 1958.

40. Ellis, A.: The Sexual Psychology of Human Hermaphrodites. *Psychosomatic Med.*, 7:108-125, 1945.

41. Ellis, H.: Sexual Inversion in Women. *Alienist & Neur.*, 16:141-158, 1895.

42. Ellis, H.: *Studies in the Psychology of Sex* (1905). New York: Random House, 1940, Vol. I, II.

43. Fairbairn, W. R. D.: A Note on the Origin of Male Homosexuality. *British J. Med. Psychology*, 37:31-32, 1964.

44. Fenichel, O.: The Pregenital Antecedents of the Oedipus Complex (1930). *Collected Papers*, 1:181-204. New York: W. W. Norton, 1953.

45. Fenichel, O.: The Psychology of Transvestitism (1930). *Collected Papers*, 1:167-180. New York: W. W. Norton, 1953.

46. Fenichel, O.: Further Light on the Preoedipal Phase in Girls (1934). *Collected Papers*, 1:241-289. New York: W. W. Norton, 1953.

47. Fenichel, O.: *The Psychoanalytic Theory of Neurosis*. New York: W. W. Norton, 1945, pp. 340-343.

48. Ferenczi, S.: More About Homosexuality (1909). *Final Contributions to the Problems and Methods of Psychoanalysis*. New York: Basic Books, 1955, pp. 168-174.

49. Ferenczi, S.: *Contributions to Psychoanalysis*. Boston: Badger, 1916.

50. Ferenczi, S.: The Nosology of Male Homosexuality (Homoerotism) (1914). *Contributions to Psychoanalysis*. New York: Robert Brunner, 1950, pp. 296-318.

51. Ferenczi, S.: *Further Contributions to the Theory and Technique of Psychoanalysis*. London: Hogarth Press, 1950.

52. Ferenczi, S.: *Final Contributions to the Theory and Techniques of Psychoanalysis*. London: Hogarth Press, 1955.

53. Fleischmann, O.: Comments on the "Choice of Homosexuality" in Males. In Theoretical and Clinical Aspects of Overt Male Homosexuality (Panel Report). *J. Amer. Psychoanal. Assn.*, 8:552-566, 1960.

54. Fliess, R.: *The Psychoanalytic Reader*. New York: International Universities Press, 1950.

55. Ford, C. S. and Beach, F. A.: *Patterns of Sexual Behavior*. New York: Harper-Hoeber, Inc., 1951.

56. Freeman, T.: Clinical and Theoretical Observations on Male Homosexuality. *Int. J. Psychoanal.*, 36:335-347, 1955.

57. Freiberg, S. H.: Homosexual Conflicts in Adolescence. In: *Adolescents: The Psychoanalytic Approach to Problems in Therapy*, ed. Lorand, S. and Schneer, H. I. New York: Harper Bros., 1962.

58. Freud, A.: Some Clinical Remarks Concerning the Treatment of Cases of Male Homosexuality (summary of presentation before the International Psychoanalytical Congress, Zurich, 1949). *Int. J. Psychoanal.*, 30:195, 1949.

59. Freud, A.: Homosexuality. *Bull. Amer. Psychoanal. Assn.*, 7:117-118, 1951.

60. Freud, A.: Studies in Passivity. Lecture to the Detroit Psychoanalytic Society at Western Reserve Medical School, Cleveland, October 25, 1952 (unpublished).

61. Freud, A.: Problems of Technique in Adult Analyis. *Bull. Phila. Assn. Psychoanal.*, 4:44-70, 1954.

62. Freud, A.: Adolescence. *Psychoanalytic Study of the Child*, 13:255-278. New York: International Universities Press, 1958.

63. Freud, S.: Three Essays on the Theory of Sexuality (1905). *Std. Ed.*, 7:125-245. London Hogarth Press, 1953.

64. Freud, S.: Psychical (or Mental) Treatment (1905). *Std. Ed.*, 7:283-305. London: Hogarth Press, 1953.

65. Freud, S.: Hysterical Fantasies and Their Relation to Bisexuality (1908). *Std. Ed.*, 9:155-167. London: Hogarth Press, 1959.

66. Freud, S.: Leonardo da Vinci and a Memory of His Childhood (1910). *Std. Ed.*, 11:59-137. London: Hogarth Press, 1957.

67. Freud, S.: Psychoanalytic Notes on an Autobiographical Account of a Case of Paranoia (Dementia Paranoides) (1911). *Std. Ed.*, 12:3-82. London: Hogarth Press, 1958.

68. Freud, S.: The Disposition to Obsessional Neurosis (1913). *Std. Ed.*, 12:311-327. London: Hogarth Press, 1958.

69. Freud, S.: On Narcissism: An Introduction (1914). *Std. Ed.*, 14:67-105. London: Hogarth Press, 1957.

70. Freud, S.: *A General Introduction to Psychoanalysis* (1917). New York: Garden City Publishing Co., 1943.

71. Freud, S.: The Taboo of Virginity (Contributions to the Psychology of Love III) (1918). *Std. Ed.*, 11:191-209. London: Hogarth Press, 1957.

72. Freud, S.: From the History of an Infantile Neurosis (1918). *Std. Ed.*, 17:3-104. London: Hogarth Press, 1955.

73. Freud, S.: Lines of Advance in Psychoanalytic Therapy (1919). *Std. Ed.*, 17:159-168. London: Hogarth Press, 1955.

74. Freud, S.: A Child Is Being Beaten (1919). *Std. Ed.*, 17:175-204. London: Hogarth Press, 1955.

75. Freud, S.: Psychogenesis of a Case of Homosexuality in a Woman (1920). *Std. Ed.*, 18:145-175. London: Hogarth Press, 1955.

76. Freud, S.: *General Introductory Lectures* (1920). New York: Garden City Publishing Co., 1943.

77. Freud, S.: Group Psychology and the Analysis of the Ego (1921). *Std. Ed.*, 18:67-134. London: Hogarth Press, 1955.

78. Freud, S.: Some Neurotic Mechanisms in Jealousy, Paranoia and Homosexuality (1922). *Std. Ed.*, 18:221-235. London: Hogarth Press, 1955.

79. Freud, S.: The Infantile Genital Organization: An Interpolation into the Theory of Sexuality (1923). *Std. Ed.*, 19:141-147. London: Hogarth Press, 1961.

80. Freud, S.: The Ego and the Id (1923). *Std. Ed.*, 19:3-63. London: Hogarth Press, 1961.

81. Freud, S.: The Passing of the Oedipus Complex (1924). *Collected Papers*, 2:269-277. London: Hogarth Press, 1946.

82. Freud, S.: The Economic Problem of Masochism (1924). *Std. Ed.*, 19:157-173. London: Hogarth Press, 1961.

83. Freud, S.: Negation (1925). *Std. Ed.*, 19:235-243. London: Hogarth Press, 1961.

84. Freud, S.: Some Psychical Consequences of the Anatomical Distinction Between the Sexes (1925). *Std. Ed.*, 19:243-261. London: Hogarth Press, 1961.

85. Freud, S.: Fetishism (1927). *Collected Papers*, 5:198-204. London: Hogarth Press, 1950.

86. Freud, S.: Female Sexuality (1931). *Std. Ed.*, 21:223-247. London: Hogarth Press, 1961.

87. Freud, S.: The Psychology of Women. *New Introductory Lectures on Psycho-Analysis*. New York: W. W. Norton, 1933.

88. Freud, S.: Letter to a Grateful Mother (1935). *Int. J. Psychoanal.*, 32:331, 1951.

89. Freud, S.: *Collected Papers 1893-1938*. London: Hogarth Press, 1950.

90. Freud, S.: *An Outline of Psychoanalysis* (1940). *Std. Ed.*, 23:144-205. London: Hogarth Press, 1964.

91. Freud, S.: *Sigmund Freud's Letters: The Origins of Psychoanalysis*. New York: Basic Books, 1954.

92. Geleerd, E. R.: Some Aspects of Psychoanalytic Technique in Adolescence. *Psychoanalytic Study of the Child*, 12:263-283. New York: International Universities Press, 1957.

93. Gershman, H.: Psychopathology of Compulsive Homosexuality. *Amer. J. Psychoanal.*, 17:58-77, 1957.

94. Gillespie, W. H.: Notes on the Analysis of Sexual Perversions. *Int. J. Psychoanal.*, 33:397-402, 1952.

95. Gillespie, W. H.: The General Theory of Sexual Perversion. *Int. J. Psychoanal.*, 37:396-403, 1956.

96. Gillespie, W. H.: The Structure and Aetiology of Sexual Perversion. In *Perversions: Psychodynamics and Therapy*, ed. Lorand, S. and Balint, M. New York: Random House, 1956.

97. Glass, S. J. et al.: Sex Hormone Studies in Male Homosexuality. *Endocrinology*, 26:590-594, 1940.

98. Glover, E.: Notes on Oral Character Formation. *Int. J. Psychoanal.*, 6:131-154, 1925.

99. Glover, E.: The Relation of Perversion Formation to the Development of Reality Sense. *Int. J. Psychoanal.*, 14:486-504, 1933.

100. Glover, E.: *Psychoanalysis*. London: Staples Press, 1939.

101. Glover, E.: *The Roots of Crime: Selected Papers on Psychoanalysis*. London: The Imago Publishing Co., Ltd., Vol. 2, 1960.

102. Grauer, D.: Homosexuality and the Paranoid Psychoses as Related to the Concept of Narcissism. *Psychoanal. Quar.*, 24:516-526, 1955.

103. Greenacre, P.: Pregenital Patterning. *Int. J. Psychoanal.*, 33:410-415, 1952.

104. Group for the Advancement of Psychiatry: *Sex and the College Student*. New York: GAP Publications, Report No. 60, 1965.

105. Harley, M.: Some Observations on the Relationship Between Genitality and Structural Development at Adolescence. *J. Amer. Psychoanal. Assn.*, 9:434-460, 1961.

106. Hartmann, H., Kris, E., and Loewenstein, R. M.: Comments on the Formation of Psychic Structure. In *Papers on Psychoanalytic Psychology*. New York: International Universities Press, 1964.

107. Heimann, P.: A Contribution to the Re-evaluation of the Oedipus Complex—the Early Stages. In *New Directions in Psychoanalysis*, ed. Klein, M., Heimann, P., Money-Kyrle, J. New York: Basic Books, 1955.

108. Henry, G. W.: Psychogenic and Constitutional Factors in Homosexuality. *Psychiat. Quar.*, 8: 243-264, 1934.

109. Henry, G. W.: Psychogenic Factors in Overt Homosexuality. *Amer. J. Psychiat.*, 93:889-908, 1937.

110. Henry, G. W.: The Homosexual Delinquent. *Mental Hygiene*, 25:420:442, 1941.

111. Henry, G. W.: *Sex Variants: A Study of Homosexual Patterns*. New York: Hoeber, 1941.

112. Hirschfeld, M.: Forms of Relationships of Homosexual Men and Women. *Geshlect Gesund*, 8:11-12, 1914.

113. Hirschfeld, M.: *Sexual Pathology*. New York: Emerson Books, 1940. (Originally published in German 1916-1921.)

114. Hirschfeld, M.: *Sexual Anomalies and Perversions*. London: Encyclopedia Press, 1938; revised edition 1953.

115. Horney, K.: The Flight from Womanhood. *Int. J. Psychoanal.*, 7:324-339, 1925.

116. Jacobson, E.: *The Self and the Object World*. New York: International Universities Press, 1964.

117. Jones, E.: *Papers on Psychoanalysis* (1912). London: Ballière, Tindall & Cox, 1948 (5th edition).

118. Jones, E.: *Essays in Applied Psychoanalysis*. London, Vienna: International Psychoanalytic Press, 1923.

119. Jones, E.: Early Development of Female Homosexuality. *Int. J. Psychoanal.*, 8:459-472, 1927.

120. Jones, E.: The Phallic Phase. *Int. J. Psychoanal.*, 14:1-33, 1933.

121. Joseph, E. D.: *Beating Fantasies: Regressive Ego Phenomena in Psychoanalysis*. The Kris Study Group of the New York Psychoanalytic Institute, Monograph I. New York: International Universities Press, 1965.

122. Jung, C.: *Psychology of the Unconscious*. New York: Moffet, Yard, 1916.

123. Kallman, F. J.: Comparative Twin Studies of the Genetic Aspects of Male Homosexuality. *J. Nerv. & Mental Diseases*, 115:283-298, 1952.

124. Kardiner, A.: *The Individual and His Society: The Psychodynamics of Primitive Social Organization*. New York: Columbia University Press, 1939.

125. Kardiner, A.: *Sex and Morality*. Indianapolis: Bobbs-Merrill, 1954.

126. Kinsey, A. et al.: *Sexual Behavior in the Human Male*. Philadelphia: W. B. Saunders Co., 1948.

127. Klaif, F. S. and Davis, C. A.: Homosexuality and Paranoid Schizophrenia. *Amer. J. Psychiat.*, 116:12, 1960.

128. Klaif, F. S.: Homosexuality and Paranoid Schizophrenia. *Arch. Gen. Psychiat.*, 4:84-90, 1961.

129. Klein, H. R. and Horwitz, W. A.: Psychosexual Factors in the Paranoid Phenomena. *Amer. J. Psychiat.*, 105:9, 1949.

130. Klein, M.: Notes on Some Schizoid Mechanisms. In *Developments in Psycho-Analysis*, ed. Klein, M., Heimann, P., Isaacs, S., Riviere, J. London: Hogarth Press, 1952.

131. Klein, M., Heimann, P., Isaacs, S. and Riviere, J.: *Developments in Psycho-Analysis*. London: Hogarth Press, 1952.

132. Klein, M.: *The Psychoanalysis of Children*. London: Hogarth Press, 1954.

133. Kolb, L. C. and Johnson, A. M.: Etiology and Therapy of Overt Homosexuality. *Psychoanal. Quar.*, 24:506-515, 1955.

134. Krafft-Ebing, R. von: Neue Studien auf dem Gebiete der Homosexualitat. *Jb. F. Sex. Zwisch.*, 3:1-36, 1901.

135. Krafft-Ebing, R. von: *Psychopathia Sexualis* with special reference to the antipathic sexual instinct (1906). Brooklyn, N. Y.: Physicians and Surgeons Book Co., 1922.

136. Krafft-Ebing, R. von: *Psychopathia Sexualis*. Stuttgart: Ferdinand Enke, 1924.

137. Krich, A. M.: *The Homosexuals*. New York: Citadel Press, 1958.

138. Lampl-de Groot, J.: Problems of Femininity. *Psychoanal. Quar.*, 2:489-518, 1933.

139. Lichtenstein, H.: Identity and Sexuality. *J. Amer. Psychoanal. Assn.*, 9:179-260, 1961.

140. Litin, E., Giffin, M., and Johnson, A.: Parental Influence in Unusual Sexual Behavior in Children. *Psychoanal. Quar.*, 25:37-55, 1956.

141. Loewenstein, R. M.: Phallic Passivity in Men. *Int. J. Psychoanal.*, 16:334-340, 1935.

142. Loewenstein, R. M.: A Contribution to the Psychoanalytic Theory of Masochism. *J. Amer. Psychoanal. Assn.*, 5:197-231, 1957.

143. Lorand, S.: Fetishism in *Statu Nascendi*. *Int. J. Psychoanal.*, 11:419-427, 1930.

144. Lorand, S. and Balint, M.: *Perversions: Psychodynamics and Therapy*. New York: Random House, 1956.

145. Lorand, S.: The Therapy of Perversions. In *Perversions: Psychodynamics and Therapy*, ed. Lorand, S. and Balint, M. New York: Random House, 1956, pp. 290-307.

146. Lorand, S. and Schneer, H. I.: *Adolescents: The Psychoanalytic Approach to Problems in Therapy*. New York: Harper Bros., 1962.

147. Mahler, M. S. and Gosliner, B. J.: On Symbiotic Child Psychosis: Genetic, Dynamic and Restitutive Aspects. *Psychoanalytic Study of the Child*, 10:195-211. New York: International Universities Press, 1955.

148. Mantegazza, P.: *Sexual Relations of Mankind*. New York: Anthropological Press, 1932.

149. Marmor, J.: *Sexual Inversion*. New York: Basic Books, 1965.

150. Menninger, K.: See Arlow (Panel Report), 1954.

151. Miller, M. L.: The Relation Between Submission and Aggression in Male Homosexuality. In *Perversions: Psychodynamics and Therapy*, ed. Lorand, S. and Balint, M. New York: Random House, 1956.

152. Nacht, S., Diatkine, R. and Favreau, J.: The Ego in Perverse Relationships. *Int. J. Psychoanal.*, 37:404-413, 1956.

153. Nunberg, H.: Homosexuality, Magic and Aggression. *Int. J. Psychoanal.*, 19:1-16, 1938.

154. Nunberg, H.: Circumcision and Problems of Bisexuality. *Int. J. Psychoanal.*, 28:145-179, 1947.

155. Oraison, M.: *Illusions and Anxiety*. New York: Macmillan, 1953.

156. Payne, S. M.: Some Observations on the Ego Development of the Fetishist. *Int. J. Psychoanal.*, 20:161-170, 1939.

157. Rado, S.: The Fear of Castration in Women. *Psychoanal. Quar.*, 2:425-475, 1933.

158. Rado, S.: An Adaptational View of Sexual Behavior. In *Psychosexual Development in Health and Disease*, ed. Hoch, P. H. and Zubin, J. New York: Grune & Stratton, 1949.

159. Rosenfeld, H. A.: Remarks on the Relation of Male Homosexuality to Paranoia, Paranoid Anxiety and Narcissism. *Int. J. Psychoanal.*, 30:36-47, 1949. (Also in *Psychotic States*. New York: International Universities Press, 1965.)

160. Sachs, H.: On the Genesis of Sexual Perversions. *Int. Z. Psychoanal.*, 172-182, 1923. (Tr. Hella Freud Bernays, 1964; New York Psychoanalytic Institute Library.)

161. Sadger, J.: *Zur Aetiologie der conträren Sexualempfindungen*. Med. Klinik, 1909.

162. Sadger, J.: Sexual Perversions. *Jb. f. Psychoanal.*, 6:296-313, 1914.

163. Sadger, J.: Neue Forschungen zur Homosexualität. Berliner Klinik, Fev., 1915.

164. Saussure, R. de: Homosexual Fixations in Neurotic Women. *Rev. Franc. Psychanal.*, 3:50-91, 1929. (Tr. Hella Freud Bernays, 1961; New York Psychoanalytic Institute Library.)

165. Sherman, M. and Sherman, T.: The Factor of Parental Attachment in Homosexuality. *Psychoanal. Rev.*, 13:32-37, 1926.

166. Silber, A.: Object Choice in a Case of Male Homosexuality. *Psychoanal. Quar.*, 3:497-504, 1961.

167. Socarides, C. W.: The Function of Moral Masochism: With Special Reference to the Defense Processes. *Int. J. Psychoanal.*, 39:1-11, 1958.

168. Socarides, C. W.: The Development of a Fetishistic Perversion: the Contribution of Preoedipal Phase Conflict. *J. Amer. Psychoanal. Assn.*, 8: 281-311, 1960.

169. Socarides, C. W.: Theoretical and Clinical Aspects of Overt Male Homosexuality (Panel Report). *J. Amer. Psychoanal. Assn.*, 8:552-566, 1960.

170. Socarides, C. W.: Theoretical and Clinical Aspects of Overt Female Homosexuality (Panel Report). *J. Amer. Psychoanal. Assn.*, 10:579-592, 1962.

171. Socarides, C. W.: The Historical Development of Theoretical and Clinical Concepts of Overt Female Homosexuality. *J. Amer. Psychoanal. Assn.*, 11:386-414, 1963.

172. Socarides, C. W.: Female Homosexuality. In *Sexual Behavior and the Law*, ed. Slovenko, R. Springfield, Ill.: Chas. C Thomas, 1965.

173. Socarides, C. W.: A Provisional Theory of Etiology in Male Homosexuality: A Case of Preoedipal Origin. *Int. J. Psychoanal.*, 49, Part I, 1968.

174. Spitz, R. A.: *A Genetic Field Theory of Ego Formation*. New York: International Universities Press, 1959.

175. Storr, A.: *Sexual Deviation*. Baltimore: Penguin Books, 1964.

176. Thorner, H. A.: Notes on a Case of Male Homosexuality. *Int. J. Psychoanal.*, 30:31-35, 1949.

177. Weiss, E.: *The Principles of Psychodynamics*. New York: Grune and Stratton, 1950.

178. Weiss, E.: *The Structure and Dynamics of the Human Mind*. New York: Grune and Stratton, 1960.

179. Wiedeman, G. H.: Survey of Psychoanalytic Literature on Overt Male Homosexuality. *J. Amer. Psychoanal. Assn.*, 10:386-409, 1962.

INDEX

INDEX

239